Mechanics

INTERNATIONAL SERIES IN PURE AND APPLIED PHYSICS

Leonard I. Schiff, *Consulting Editor*

The late F. K. Richtmyer was Consulting Editor of the series from its inception in 1929 to his death in 1939. Lee A. DuBridge was Consulting Editor from 1939 to 1946; and G. P. Harnwell from 1947 to 1954.

Mechanics

by JOHN C. SLATER, Ph. D.

Professor of Physics
Massachusetts Institute of Technology

and NATHANIEL H. FRANK, Sc. D.

Professor of Physics
Massachusetts Institute of Technology

NEW YORK AND LONDON

McGRAW-HILL BOOK COMPANY, INC.

1947

MECHANICS

PREFACE

The present book is the first of several volumes which are intended to replace the *Introduction to Theoretical Physics* written by the same authors in 1933. By separating the material on mechanics, on electromagnetism, and on the quantum theory, we believe that it is possible to give a somewhat better rounded treatment of each of these fields, which will be more useful to the teacher and the student. At the same time, we have tried to preserve, and even to extend, the general unity of treatment which we believed so important when the earlier book was published. We have a conviction that the teaching of theoretical physics in a number of separate courses, as in mechanics, electromagnetic theory, potential theory, thermodynamics, and modern physics, tends to keep a student from seeing the unity of physics, and from appreciating the importance of applying principles developed for one branch of science to the problems of another. In the present volume, we have tried constantly to emphasize not only those topics important to mechanics itself, but also those which make the study of mechanics the fundamental basis of the electromagnetic theory, quantum mechanics, and in fact of all of theoretical physics.

Two general principles have determined the order of presenting the material: mathematical difficulty and order of historical development. Particle dynamics and problems of oscillations, involving ordinary differential equations and simple vector analysis, come first. Then follow vibrations and wave motion, introducing partial differential equations which can be solved by separation of variables, and Fourier series. Elasticity and hydrodynamics bring in more general partial differential equations, potential theory, and differential vector and tensor operations. In this way the mathematical foundation is built up on which most of the rest of mathematical physics is based. In the Appendixes we give the mathematical background of these various topics in sufficient detail to be used by the student familiar with the calculus and differential equations. It is natural that the historical order is in general the same as the order of increasing mathematical difficulty, for each branch of physics as it develops builds on the foundation of everything that has gone before.

1 2 43

We quote from the preface of *Introduction to Theoretical Physics:*
"In a book of such wide scope, it is inevitable that many important subjects are treated in a cursory manner. An effort has been made to present enough of the groundwork of each subject so that not only is further work facilitated, but also the position of these subjects in a more general scheme of physical thought is clearly shown. In spite of this, however, the student will of course make much use of other references, and we give a list of references, by no means exhaustive, but suggesting a few titles in each field which a student who has mastered the material of this book should be able to appreciate.

"At the end of each chapter is a set of problems. The ability to work problems, in our opinion, is essential to a proper understanding of physics, and it is hoped that these problems will provide useful practice. At the same time, in many cases, the problems have been used to extend and amplify the discussion of the subject matter, where limitations of space made such discussion impossible in the text. The attempt has been made, though we are conscious of having fallen far short of succeeding in it, to carry each branch of the subject far enough so that definite calculations can be made with it. Thus a far surer mastery is attained than in a merely descriptive discussion.

"Finally, we wish to remind the reader that the book is very definitely one on theoretical physics. Though at times descriptive material, and descriptions of experimental results, are included, it is in general assumed that the reader has a fair knowledge of experimental physics, of the grade generally covered in intermediate college courses. No doubt it is unfortunate, in view of the unity which we have stressed, to separate the theoretical side of the subject from the experimental in this way. This is particularly true when one remembers that the greatest difficulty which the student has in mastering theoretical physics comes in learning how to apply mathematics to a physical situation, how to formulate a problem mathematically, rather than in solving the problem when it is once formulated. We have tried wherever possible, in problems and text, to bridge the gap between pure mathematics and experimental physics. But the only satisfactory answer to this difficulty is a broad training in which theoretical physics goes side by side with experimental physics and practical laboratory work. The same ability to overcome obstacles, the same ingenuity in devising one method of procedure when another fails, the same physical intuition leading one to perceive the answer to a problem through a mass of intervening detail, the same critical judgment leading one to distinguish right from wrong procedures, and to appraise results carefully on the ground of physical plausibility, are required in theoretical and in experimental physics. Leaks in vacuum systems or in electric circuits have their counterparts in the many disastrous things that can happen to equations. And it is often as hard to devise a mathematical system to deal with a difficult problem, without unjustifiable approximations and impossible complications, as it is to design apparatus for measuring a difficult quantity or detecting a new effect. These things cannot be taught. They come only from that combination of inherent insight and faithful practice which is necessary to the successful physicist. But half the battle is over if the student approaches theoretical physics, not as a set of mysterious formulas, or as a dull routine to be learned, but as a collection of methods, of tools, of apparatus, subject to the same sort of rules as other physical apparatus, and yielding physical results of great importance. . . . The aim has constantly been, not to teach a great collection of facts, but to teach mastery of the tools by which the facts have been discovered and by which future discoveries will be made."

JOHN C. SLATER
NATHANIEL H. FRANK

CAMBRIDGE, MASS.,
  June, 1947.

CONTENTS

Chapter VIII
THE VIBRATING STRING

Chapter IX
WAVE PROPAGATION IN THE STRING

Chapter X
THE STRING WITH VARIABLE TENSION AND DENSITY

Chapter XI
THE VIBRATING MEMBRANE

CHAPTER I

THE LINEAR MOTION OF A PARTICLE

Newton's *Principia,* or *Mathematical Principles of Natural Philosophy,* published in 1687, formed the beginning of modern science, and remains its most famous and important single work. In the century before Newton, physics was gradually emerging from medieval superstition, in which the authority of Aristotle was the final arbiter of any scientific question, and was beginning to take on the modern attitude that the only way to see how nature behaves is to make an observation or an experiment. Galileo, Newton's most famous predecessor, knew that a force produced an acceleration, or change of velocity, of a body, and that no force was needed to keep it in uniform motion with constant velocity. Huygens showed that motion in a curved path, even with constant speed, involved an acceleration and required a force to maintain it. Copernicus established that the planets move around the sun, and Kepler used accurate astronomical observations to deduce detailed and correct laws about their motions. But it remained for Newton to make the synthesis of all these facts, to show that planets in the sky and bodies in the laboratory follow the same simple laws.

The existence of fundamental laws underlying the behavior of nature has furnished the guiding principle of natural science ever since. It has also formed the basis of most modern thought in philosophy, political science, economics, and the social sciences. Newton's laws, and the mechanical and astronomical phenomena which he explained by them, were fundamentally simple, and this simplicity led nonscientific interpreters of his principles to the erroneous view that the social and political sciences must be equally simple, an error that was widespread in the eighteenth century, and has persisted in some ways even to the present. Newton himself never fell into this error. As an experimental as well as a theoretical physicist, he well knew that there were many properties of nature other than those which he had explained: cohesion and interatomic and intermolecular forces, light with its phenomena of dispersion and interference and diffraction, and many others. But he believed firmly that his laws of motion, as well as his general approach to the problems of physics, would prove

1

to underlie these more complex aspects of nature as well as the simpler things that he was able to explain completely. In this belief he was correct; and it is for that reason that our study of theoretical physics, of the principles underlying the behavior of nature, must begin with Newton.

The basis of Newton's mechanics is his second law of motion, which states, in modern language, that the force acting on a body equals the time rate of change of its momentum. Thus any mechanical problem is really divided into two parts: first, given the forces, to find the motion; secondly, knowing the motion, or the positions of the particles, to find the forces acting on them. In a simple problem like planetary motion, these two aspects can be combined. The gravitational forces between planets and the sun can be written in terms of the locations of these bodies; the accelerations can be written in terms of the forces, and thus we secure differential equations expressing the second derivatives of the positions with respect to time (that is, the accelerations) in terms of the positions themselves. It is such differential equations that we must solve in the simpler types of mechanical problems. Problems involving elastic forces are similar; the forces can be written in terms of the strains, or deformations, of an elastic body, and Newton's law leads to a differential equation expressing the second time rate of change of strains (or again the accelerations) in terms of the strains themselves. It is such problems that are handled in the conventional subject of mechanics, and that we shall take up in this volume.

As soon as we come to somewhat more complicated problems, however, we see that this type of treatment is no longer possible. The simplest example of this is found in electromagnetic theory. There the forces between electrically charged particles cannot be expressed in terms of their positions, or even in terms of their positions and velocities. Instead, they depend on the past history of the particles in a complicated way. We can understand this from a simple example. An atom on the sun radiates light, an electromagnetic disturbance. In the process of radiating, it is acted on by a certain force, since the radiated light, at least in some cases, carries momentum with it. This light takes some eight minutes to reach the earth. When it reaches the earth, it can be absorbed by an atom on the earth, again an electromagnetic phenomenon, in which the absorbing atom is acted on by forces and absorbs energy. It is now clear that the electromagnetic forces exerted on the atom on the earth do not depend on the instantaneous position or velocity of the atom on the sun which is acting on it, but rather on the action of that atom some eight minutes previously, when it emitted its light.   To handle such problems, we have to introduce the idea of an electromagnetic field, an entity existing in empty space, really synonymous with light, carrying momentum and energy, which is acted on by matter, transports energy and momentum with the velocity of light to other matter at a distance, and in turn acts on that other matter.   In the sense that we retain the ideas of action and reaction between matter and the electromagnetic field, and of momentum and energy carried by the field as well as by matter, electromagnetic theory is based on Newtonian dynamics; but it is an involved relationship, and explains why electromagnetic theory and light are generally handled as a subject by themselves, to be treated by their own appropriate methods, rather than being considered a branch of mechanics.

An even more involved departure from the simple ideas of Newtonian mechanics is found when we study the behavior of atoms and molecules, and their constituents the electrons, protons, neutrons, and other elementary particles.   There it is found that even the fundamental postulates of Newtonian mechanics do not apply.   We cannot describe the motion of particles by specifying their coordinates, and stating that the time rate of change of momentum of a particle equals the force acting on it.   In fact, we cannot give any precise law whatever for determining the motion of an individual particle. We must, instead, introduce a wave field, reminding us strongly of the electromagnetic field, and we must assume that the correlation between this field and the motion of particles is purely statistical: the wave field determines the probability of finding the particle in a particular location, but no precise physical law, as far as we know now, can tell us just where it will be found.   This seems like a complete departure from Newtonian mechanics; nevertheless, in two rather different ways, Newtonian methods underlie even wave mechanics.   In the first place, wave mechanics reduces to Newtonian mechanics for large, heavy particles, in the sense that it predicts more and more precisely the law of motion of a particle, as the particle gets larger; and the limiting accurate law that is found in the limit of large objects is Newton's law.   In the second place, even for small objects, the concepts of energy, momentum, and other quantities found in Newtonian mechanics find their place, though with different interpretation, in wave mechanics, in such a way that a knowledge of Newtonian mechanics forms a necessary preliminary to the study of wave mechanics.

The facts we have outlined show how Newtonian mechanics under-

lies all of physics. Naturally some of its most important applications
are direct ones: all around us we study the motions of material objects,
and they are governed by mechanics. Its importance is thus practical,
as well as theoretical. We shall now proceed with its simplest example, the motion of a particle in a straight line, under the action of an
arbitrary force acting along the line of motion.

1. The Dynamics of Rectilinear Motion.—Let us consider a particle
moving along a straight line, under the action of an arbitrary force.
Examples of such motion are common: a ball thrown straight up
into the air and acted on by gravity and air resistance, or dropped
straight down in water and acted on by viscous friction; an object
sliding along a table subject to friction. The importance of the
problem lies not merely in the obvious examples, however, but in
the fact that many more complicated problems can be reduced to
it. Thus a rigid body pivoted on an axis, like a lever or a seesaw
or a pendulum, is described by one coordinate, the angle specifying
its orientation in space, and there is such a close analogy between
the rotational motion of this rigid body and the motion of a particle
in a straight line that the same mathematical methods can be used
for both. Even entirely nonmechanical problems can be treated
by similar mathematical methods. An electric circuit containing
resistance, inductance, and capacity, is mathematically equivalent
to a particle moving in a straight line, acted on by a force proportional
to its displacement, and a resisting force proportional to its velocity.
The same methods can be applied to both, as we shall show in the next
chapter. It is a result of this simple fact that electrical engineers,
who are familiar with electric circuits, have found themselves particularly fitted to discuss problems of mechanical and acoustical vibrations.
Our present topic, then, is far from an academic one; and a thorough
knowledge of the principles underlying it is fundamental to a great
variety of applications.

Let the coordinate measuring the position of the particle along
the line in which it moves be x. Then by elementary principles of
calculus the velocity of the particle is $v = dx/dt$, and its acceleration is

$$a = \frac{dv}{dt} = \frac{d^2x}{dt^2}. \tag{1.1}$$

Let the mass be m. Then we define the momentum as mv. Let the
force acting on it be F. Then Newton's second law of motion, which in
modern notation states that the force equals the time rate of change
of momentum, can be written in mathematical language as

$$\frac{d}{dt}\,(mv) = F. \tag{1.2}$$

This simple equation is the mathematical basis of the whole of mechanics. For an ordinary body, the mass m is a constant, independent of velocity or position. Thus we may carry out the differentiation in (1.2), using (1.1), and finding the alternative formulation

$$m\,\frac{d^2x}{dt^2} = ma = F. \tag{1.3}$$

In some cases the mass changes with time. One example is a rocket, which is continually shooting off part of its mass in the form of a jet. Another is the motion of a particle according to the theory of relativity, in which the mass of a body is a function of its velocity, varying according to the equation

$$m = \frac{m_0}{\sqrt{1 - v^2/c^2}}. \tag{1.4}$$

Here m_0 is its so-called "rest mass," or mass at sufficiently small velocities, so that the term v^2/c^2 in the denominator can be neglected, where c is the velocity of light, 3×10^{10} cm/sec, and m becomes infinite as the velocity approaches the velocity of light. In any such case, the two equations (1.2) and (1.3) are not equivalent to each other, since in carrying out the differentiation in (1.2) we should also find a term $v\,dm/dt$, and since in the case of a rocket we have to take account of the momentum of the jet as well as of that of the rocket. In all such cases (1.2), corresponding to Newton's original statement of his law, is correct, rather than (1.3).

In Eq. (1.2) or (1.3), provided that we know F, we have the information for computing the motion of the particle, or for finding x as a function of t, which is the goal in any mechanical problem. It is common in mechanics to treat problems where the force F depends on x, the position of the particle; on v, its velocity; and on the time t; but not on any other quantities. This does not mean that all forces fall into these categories. We saw in our introductory remarks that in electromagnetic theory, for example, much more complicated forces were possible. It means merely that, if we meet more complicated types of forces, they deserve a special treatment, and we shall handle them in some other branch of physics, not in mechanics.

The simplest examples of forces depending on x, as we saw in our introductory section, are gravitational forces and elastic forces. The simplest force depending on v is a frictional force, or force of viscous resistance. Forces depending on time fall in a slightly different category. Often we have two bodies acting on each other, one being so much larger than the other that the large one influences the motion of the small one profoundly, but the small one hardly affects the motion of the large one at all. In such a case we may first find how the large body moves without reference to the small one, so that we know its position as an explicit function of time. Then we consider the forces exerted by this body on the small one, and obviously these forces will depend explicitly on time, as well as on the position of the small body. We then solve for the motion of the small body, assuming that it does not react appreciably on the large one. In all such cases we are making approximations, neglecting the reaction of the small body on the large one. In a later chapter on the vibrations of coupled systems, we shall see in a special case how important these approximations are.

Another type of problem where we have a force depending on time is the electromagnetic problem. In the introductory section we considered the interactions between an atom emitting radiation on the sun, and another atom absorbing the radiation on the earth. Clearly the atom on the earth cannot react back in any ordinary sense on the atom on the sun. Thus the motion of the atom absorbing radiation on the earth can be handled by assuming that the electromagnetic force acting on it is a function of the time. Many important problems are of this type; in all such cases we should do well to ask ourselves whether the particle we are considering is not part of a larger system, and whether we are not neglecting the reaction of this particle on the larger system, a reaction that may or may not be negligible depending on circumstances.

Assuming that F depends on x, v, and t, and that the mass is a constant, Eq. (1.3) then becomes

$$m \frac{d^2x}{dt^2} = F\left(x, \frac{dx}{dt}, t\right).$$ (1.5)

This is a second-order differential equation for x as a function of t. There is no general method of finding analytic solutions for all such differential equations, and we are therefore driven to ask two sorts of questions: first, what general results can we deduce without getting an explicit solution, and second, how many types of problems can we solve explicitly, and how can we get approximate solutions if no exact solution is available?

We can deduce one very simple and very important general result from (1.5). Since it is a second order differential equation, its general solution must contain two arbitrary constants. These constants must be determined from additional information that we possess, aside from our information about the force. The common type of additional information is the statement of the value of x, the position, and v, the velocity, at a certain initial time. From the fact that there are just two arbitrary constants, we see that we can always set up a solution of (1.5) corresponding to the case where the particle starts from an arbitrary point x_0, with arbitrary velocity v_0, at the initial time t_0. The most familiar example is the elementary one of constant force, $F = $ constant, giving

$$x = x_0 + v_0(t - t_0) + \frac{1}{2}\frac{F}{m}(t - t_0)^2. \tag{1.6}$$

We see, however, that the possibility of writing the motion as a function of x_0, v_0, and t and t_0 is quite general, not limited to this case.

When we come to explicit ways of solving (1.5), several cases, familiar from the theory of differential equations, occur to us immediately. First and simplest, beyond the constant force taken up in (1.6), is that of a force depending only on the time: $F = F(t)$. Then obviously

$$x = x_0 + v_0(t - t_0) + \int_{t_0}^{t}\left[\int_{t_0}^{\tau_2}\frac{F}{m}(\tau_1)\,d\tau_1\right]d\tau_2. \tag{1.7}$$

Thus such a problem can always be solved explicitly, provided that the integration can be carried out. A second case that is easily solvable is that in which F is a sum of one constant times x, another constant times dx/dt, and an arbitrary function of time,

$$m\frac{d^2x}{dt^2} + a\frac{dx}{dt} + kx = F_1(t). \tag{1.8}$$

This is the case of a body acted on by a force proportional to the displacement, a resistance proportional to the velocity, and an arbitrary force depending on the time. We have already mentioned that it is mathematically equivalent to an electric circuit containing resistance, inductance, and capacity, with an arbitrary impressed emf. Mathematically, it is a linear differential equation with constant coefficients (linear because it contains only the first powers of d^2x/dt^2, dx/dt, and x), and can always be solved explicitly. We shall handle the general case in the next chapter. A third case that can always be solved is that in which the force depends only on the position, and is independent of velocity and time. In this case an integral, called the "energy integral," exists, and the resulting solution leads to the theorem of the conservation of energy. We shall take up this very important case later in this chapter.

Even if none of these methods of exact solution can be applied, it is still not an insuperable problem to obtain solutions of (1.5), in any case in which one is willing to take the trouble of using numerical methods. In the first place, the general case of (1.5) can be handled by the differential analyzer, a machine that solves ordinary differential equations by mechanical integration. In the second place, the numerical solution of such a differential equation is by no means a formidable task. The simplest method of numerical integration is described in Appendix I. It is based on dividing up the axis of time into finite intervals δt, and on computing the value of x at t_0, $t_0 + \delta t$, $t_0 + 2\ \delta t$, and so on. The derivative dx/dt at time $t_1 = t_0 + n\ \delta t$ is then approximated by

$$\frac{dx}{dt} \sim \frac{x(t_1) - x(t_1 - \delta t)}{\delta t} \tag{1.9}$$

and of d^2x/dt^2 by

$$\frac{d^2x}{dt^2} \sim \frac{(dx/dt)(t_1 + \delta t) - (dx/dt)(t_1)}{\delta t}$$
$$\sim \frac{x(t_1 + \delta t) - 2x(t_1) + x(t_1 - \delta t)}{(\delta t)^2}. \tag{1.10}$$

If a table of values of x has been computed for all values of t up to t_1, we can then compute $F(x, dx/dt, t)$, of (1.5), using the approximation (1.9), at time t_1. Then, using (1.10), and substituting into Eq. (1.5), we shall have an equation for computing $x(t_1 + \delta t)$. The process can then be repeated, finding next $x(t_1 + 2\delta t)$, and so on, so that the calculation can be extended as far as we please. The smaller the intervals δt, the better the approximations (1.9) and (1.10) become, and therefore the more accurate the results of the method. Examples are given in Appendix I, and problems including this method are given at the end of this chapter.

Still another approximate method that is useful in some cases is the expansion of x as a function of t in power series, and use of Eq. (1.5) to determine the coefficients of this power series. This method is described in Appendix II, and illustrations are given. Though this method is of great value in some differential equations that we shall meet in this book, there are few examples of (1.5) that we can conveniently solve by power series, in which simpler solutions are not available. All these numerical and approximate methods suffer in comparison with analytical solutions by the fact that they give us no general insight into the nature of the solutions, but only numerical information applicable to particular cases.

2. The Energy Integral.—Let us suppose that the force F, in Newton's equation of motion (1.5), is a function of the position x only. Then we have

$$m \frac{d^2x}{dt^2} = F(x). \qquad (2.1)$$

This equation can be solved, as follows: First we multiply each side by dx/dt, and integrate with respect to t, from time t_0 up to t:

$$m \int_{t_0}^{t} \frac{dx}{dt} \frac{d^2x}{dt^2} \, dt = \int_{t_0}^{t} F(x) \frac{dx}{dt} \, dt. \qquad (2.2)$$

Both these integrals can be transformed. First, we note that

$$\frac{d}{dt}\left(\frac{dx}{dt}\right)^2 = 2 \frac{dx}{dt} \frac{d^2x}{dt^2}.$$

Thus the left side of (2.2) is

$$\frac{m}{2} \int_{t_0}^{t} \frac{d}{dt}\left(\frac{dx}{dt}\right)^2 dt = \frac{m}{2}\left(\frac{dx}{dt}\right)^2 \Big|_{t_0}^{t},$$

or letting dx/dt be denoted by v, and its value at $t = t_0$ by v_0, this side is $mv^2/2 - mv_0^2/2$. On the right $\int F(dx/dt) \, dt = \int F \, dx$, where now the integral is from x_0 to x, if x_0 is the value of x at $t = t_0$, x at t. Then the equation is

$$\tfrac{1}{2}mv^2 - \tfrac{1}{2}mv_0^2 = \int_{x_0}^{x} F(x) \, dx. \qquad (2.3)$$

The quantity $mv^2/2$ is called the "kinetic energy," $\int F(x) \, dx$ is the work done by the force F on the particle while it is moving from x_0 to x, and our equation says that the work done by the force on the particle between two instants of time equals the increase in kinetic energy during the time.

We next define a potential energy $V(x)$, as follows: We consider a force $-F(x)$, equal and opposite to F, and balancing it, and find the work done by $-F(x)$ in moving from x_0 to x. This we define as the difference in potential energy between points x and x_0:

$$V(x) - V(x_0) = - \int_{x_0}^{x} F(x) \, dx. \qquad (2.4)$$

Differentiating with respect to x, we obtain the equivalent expression

$$F(x) = - \frac{dV(x)}{dx}. \qquad (2.5)$$

In terms of the potential energy, we may rewrite (2.3) in the form

$$\tfrac{1}{2}mv^2 + V(x) = \tfrac{1}{2}mv_0^2 + V(x_0) = E. \tag{2.6}$$

The quantity E, expressing the sum of kinetic and potential energies, which according to (2.6) stays constant during the motion, is defined as the energy, and (2.6) is the expression of the law of conservation of energy, for this particular case. We shall discuss it in detail in a later section; we shall now use it practically to complete the integration of (2.1).

Rewriting (2.6), with dx/dt in place of v, we have

$$v = \frac{dx}{dt} = \sqrt{\frac{2}{m}[E - V(x)]}. \tag{2.7}$$

Equation (2.7) allows us to find the velocity at every point of the motion. Dividing by the square root, multiplying by dt, and integrating, we have

$$t - t_0 = \int_{x_0}^{x} \frac{dx}{\sqrt{2(E - V)/m}}. \tag{2.8}$$

In (2.8) we have an explicit solution of our problem, giving t as a function of x, and involving only an algebraic process to give x as a function of t. The solution has two arbitrary constants, as it should: x_0 and E. Here x_0 is the value of x when $t = t_0$, as in Eqs. (1.6) and (1.7), and E is determined by (2.6) in terms of v_0, the velocity when $t = t_0$, and of x_0. As a simple example, consider a particle moving in a vertical direction under gravity. If x measures the height, the gravitational force is $F = -mg$, and

$$V(x) = V(x_0) + mg(x - x_0).$$

We then have, using (2.6) and (2.8),

$$t - t_0 = \int_{x_0}^{x} \frac{dx}{\sqrt{v_0^2 - 2g(x - x_0)}}.$$

Letting $z = v_0^2 - 2g(x - x_0)$, so that $dz = -2g\,dx$, this is

$$t - t_0 = -\frac{1}{2g} \int_{v_0^2}^{v_0^2 - 2g(x - x_0)} \frac{dz}{\sqrt{z}}$$

$$= -\frac{\sqrt{z}}{g} \Big|_{v_0^2}^{v_0^2 - 2g(x - x_0)}$$

$$= \frac{1}{g} \left[v_0 - \sqrt{v_0^2 - 2g(x - x_0)} \right].$$

Solving for x, this yields the result

$$x = x_0 + v_0(t - t_0) - \tfrac{1}{2}g(t - t_0)^2,$$

in agreement with (1.6). Obviously, in as simple a case as this, the method of the energy integral (2.8) is more complicated than a direct integration of the equation of motion (1.5). The value of the present method comes in more complicated problems that cannot be handled by elementary means. For instance, the pendulum with large amplitude can be solved by this method, leading to an elliptic integral. On the other hand, of course, in many cases the integration is too difficult to carry out.

3. Qualitative Use of the Energy Integral.—Even if the integral (2.8) cannot be evaluated explicitly, we can still use the method of the energy to get general information about the problem. Let us imagine V plotted as a function of x (see Fig. 1). Then we draw on the same graph a horizontal line at height E. The square root of the difference between the two curves is then proportional to the velocity of the particle at that point, by Eq. (2.7). Thus the velocity is real only where this difference is positive, and is imaginary elsewhere. If the velocity is real only in certain regions of x, this means that the motion can occur only within those regions. As the particle approaches the edge of such a region, the speed gets smaller and smaller, and finally at the edge the particle instantaneously comes to rest, then reverses, and travels away again. The possibility of going either toward or away from the boundary is shown by the two signs of the square root: the velocity at a given point of space is always the same in magnitude, but can be in either direction. If now the region where the kinetic energy is positive is bounded at both ends, then after reversing its motion at one edge, the particle will travel to the other, reverse, come back, and repeat the process indefinitely. Since at a given point the particle always travels with the same speed, it will always require the same time to traverse its path, and the motion will be periodic. Thus, if the total energy is E_1 (Fig. 1), the motion is periodic, confined between c and e. If it is E_2, either of two periodic motions is possible, between b and f, or between h and j. It is clearly a general result that any motion in one dimension in which the force depends only on the position, and in which the motion does not extend to infinity, is periodic.

If, on the other hand, the kinetic energy remains positive in one direction all the way to infinity, but becomes negative at a finite point in the other direction, the particle will come in from infinity, will reverse, and will return to infinity. This is the case for energy E_3, the particle coming in from the right, speeding up in the region about i, slowing down about g, speeding up about d, finally coming to rest at a, and reversing, traveling back to the right. An example of the first, periodic case is a particle vibrating in simple harmonic motion, and of the second nonperiodic case is a ball coming from infinity, hitting a wall, and being bounced back again, or a ball thrown up in the air and coming down again. Finally there is the possibility of a potential such that the kinetic energy is positive at all values of x. Then the particle persists in one direction forever, like a free particle, but generally travels with

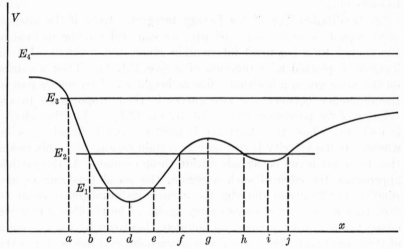

Fig. 1.—Potential energy as function of coordinate x.

a variable velocity. Such a case is found for energy E_4, where the particle starts from infinite distance in one direction, travels toward the center, speeds up and slows down corresponding to the minima and maxima of V, and finally goes to infinity in the other direction. It is to be noted that motions in the same potential field, but with different total energy, can have quite different characteristics under this classification. Thus oscillatory motions are always possible around minima in the potential energy, for small enough total energy. But it may be that for too high total energy the particle will be able to get entirely away from the neighborhood of the minimum, and will go to infinity. In Fig. 1, there are three points, d, g, and i, at which the force is zero, and the particle would stay at rest forever, if it were placed at one of these points. Of these, g is a position of unstable equilibrium, and a small impact would start the particle oscillating, about either d or i. On the other hand, d and i are both points of stable equilibrium, so that a particle at rest at either of these points would suffer only small oscillations about that point if struck a small impact.

A simple model that shows the properties of one-dimensional motion can be set up as follows: We imagine a track, like a roller coaster, set up, shaped just like the potential curve. Then we start a ball rolling on this track, starting from rest at a given height. Its motion will then approximate that of a particle in the corresponding potential field. The reason is that, since gravitational potential energy is proportional to height, the ball actually has the correct potential energy at any point, and consequently the correct speed. The only approximation made, other than friction, consists in neglecting the fact that part of the kinetic energy actually goes into up and down motion, and part into rotation, instead of all into horizontal motion. If the vertical scale is made such that the track actually rises only slightly from a horizontal plane, the errors are small. From such a model, we can see how motion may be oscillatory, if the track rises on the far side of a dip up to the height where the ball started, or how it can go to infinity if the track continues permanently at a lower level.

4. The Conservation of Energy.—The law of conservation of energy, which we expressed in Eq. (2.6), holds only in the case of a force depending only on position x, and not on velocity or time. Such a force is called a "conservative force"; other forces are called "nonconservative." To see what happens in the nonconservative case, let us assume that

$$F = -\frac{dV(x)}{dx} + F_1\left(x, \frac{dx}{dt}, t\right),$$

where part of the force is derivable from a potential function V, but the remaining part F_1 is nonconservative. Then, using steps similar to those used in deriving (2.6), we can prove the relation

$$\frac{d}{dt}\left(\frac{1}{2}mv^2 + V(x)\right) = F_1 v. \qquad (4.1)$$

That is, if there is a nonconservative part of the force, F_1, we find that the quantity $\frac{1}{2}mv^2 + V(x)$, which we may, if we choose, call the energy even in this case, is not conserved, or does not stay constant. Instead, its time rate of change is given by the product of the nonconservative part of the force, and the velocity. This product of force and velocity is the rate of working of the force, or the power.

Equation (4.1) is the closest approach to the conservation of energy that we have with nonconservative forces. If the nonconservative force is of the nature of a frictional or resistive force, it opposes the motion, or has the opposite sign to v. Thus it results in a decrease in energy with time. In a graphical discussion of the motion, as in Fig. 1, this means that the motion will have the general character of the motion without friction, but with a continually decreasing energy. Thus with an oscillatory motion the amplitude will constantly decrease until it stops, while with a motion that originally was not oscillatory it may become trapped in a minimum of potential, settle down to oscillate, and eventually come to rest. In any case, if the resistive force continues, the motion will finally stop.

Since friction is actually present in almost all mechanical motions, except the motions of the heavenly bodies, the law of conservation of energy would seem at first sight to have only very limited significance. The law was known, in its essential features, from the time of Newton on, but for over a hundred years after him it was regarded merely as a useful way of solving certain mechanical problems. It was not until the nineteenth century that the law acquired the importance that is now ascribed to it. Its importance became clear only when the mechanical nature of heat was discovered. In Newton's time, and for long after him, it was generally believed that heat was a form of fluid, generally called "caloric," which actually flowed from a hot body to a cold one; the calorie was regarded as a measure of the quantity of this fluid. Early in the nineteenth century, difficulties began to appear with this conception, associated with the tacit assumption that the caloric was conserved, as it certainly is in calorimetric experiments. These difficulties appeared, for instance, in Rumford's experiments in the boring of cannon. Rumford observed the great amount of heat liberated in this process. It had previously been assumed that in such a case caloric was somehow squeezed out of the material on which friction was exerted, but Rumford found more heat being produced than could have been reasonably supposed to be present in the metal before his experiments. He thus concluded that heat was actually being produced by the frictional process.

Since energy simultaneously disappears in such a process, as we have just seen, several scientists in the first half of the nineteenth century took the natural step of assuming that the heat was really a form of energy, interchangeable with mechanical energy, and that in frictional processes the decrease of mechanical energy is just balanced by increase of heat, whereas in a heat engine the reverse occurs, heat being lost and energy produced.   This point of view was made certain by Joule's measurement of the mechanical equivalent of heat, between 1840 and 1850, showing that the disappearance of 1 joule of mechanical energy always results in the appearance of 1/4.185 calories, no matter what sort of method is used to convert the energy into heat.   As a result of this discovery, the law of conservation of energy was elevated to the position that it holds at present, perhaps the most important of the laws of physics.

The rise of the electromagnetic theory in the latter half of the nineteenth century, with the work of Maxwell, Poynting, and others, still further emphasized the importance of the conservation of energy. We have pointed out the example of the radiation of light by an atom on the sun, some of the radiation later being absorbed by an atom on the earth.   With the development of the theory of the electromagnetic field, it became clear that that field carried energy.   An atom, or a radio antenna, that radiates an electromagnetic wave, has its own mechanical or electrical energy reduced, just as if it were being acted on by a frictional force; one speaks of the "radiation resistance" of an antenna.   But this decrease of energy is just balanced by the increase of energy in the electromagnetic field.   In turn, when some of the energy of the field is absorbed by another atom or antenna, the field loses energy, but the atom or antenna gains it, and it is observed as excitation of the atom, or as a received signal on the radio connected to the antenna.   Thus conservation of energy is observed in the electromagnetic theory, and in fact in all the various types of theory that have had to be introduced in the last few years to explain atomic and nuclear processes.

The conservation of energy of which we have just been speaking is really a conservation of the total energy of the universe; when energy of one form disappears, energy of another form appears. This does not mean, however, that the energy of any one portion of the universe stays constant.   Since we generally do not want to consider the whole universe as part of any mechanical problem, we constantly meet cases in which the energy of the particular system we are discussing changes with time.   Thus, in treating frictional forces in mechanics, we generally do not consider heat energy as a form of energy, but simply assume mathematically that energy is lost by action of the frictional forces, as we did in Eq. (4.1).   If we want to be more particular, and consider the thermal energy, we use the methods of thermodynamics or of statistical mechanics, in which these problems find their proper expression.   Or again, if we have two bodies, one large and one small, exerting forces on each other, and treat the force exerted by the large body on the small one as a force depending on time, we shall find that the energy of the small body changes with the time.   This does not mean that we are not having conservation, however.   The small body is simultaneously exerting forces on the large body, which make an exactly compensating change in the energy of the large body; but the total energy of the large body is so great in comparison with this change that the small change of energy can be neglected in considering the motion of the large body.   We shall meet many cases throughout our work in which the energy of that particular system which we consider is not conserved; this is entirely correct, but we should keep always in mind the fact that in every such case there is a compensating change of energy in the bodies that exert forces on the particular system we are considering.

5. Units.—When we come to solve practical problems in mechanics, we must understand the various systems of units.   Three systems are commonly used: the cgs (centimeter gram second), mks (meter kilogram second), and English system.   In the cgs system, masses are measured in grams, distances in centimeters, and time in seconds.   The unit of force is the dyne; by Eq. (1.3) it is the force that will give a mass of 1 gram an acceleration of 1 centimeter per second per second.   The unit of work, or of energy, is the erg, which by Eq. (2.3) is the work done by a force of 1 dyne moving through a distance of 1 centimeter.   The unit of rate of working, or power, by Eq. (4.1), is the dyne-centimeter per second, or erg per second.

In the mks system, masses are measured in kilograms, distances in meters, and time in seconds.   The unit of force is the newton; it is the force that will give a mass of 1 kilogram an acceleration of 1 meter per second per second.   By Eq. (1.3), 1 newton equals 10^5 dynes. The unit of work or of energy is the joule, the work done by a force of 1 newton moving through a distance of 1 meter.   By Eq. (2.3), 1 joule equals 10^7 ergs.   The unit of rate of working, or power, is the watt, the power produced by a force of 1 newton moving at the rate of 1 meter per second, or a rate of working of 1 joule per second.   By Eq. (4.1), 1 watt equals 10^7 ergs per second.   One kilowatt equals 1,000 watts.

In the English gravitational system, lengths are measured in feet, where 1 foot equals 30.48 centimeters, and 1 inch, a twelfth of a foot, equals 2.54 centimeters; 39.37 inches equals 1 meter.   Times in the English system are measured in seconds.   There is a certain standard weight, whose mass is 453.6 grams.   The force of gravity acting on this weight, at a standard latitude (this must be specified, for gravitational force depends slightly on latitude), is defined as the pound, the unit of force.   The gravitational acceleration g at standard latitude is 980.665 centimeters per second per second, or 32.174 feet per second per second.   Thus the gravitational force acting on 1 gram, at this latitude, by Eq. (1.3), is 980.665 dynes, so that the pound of force equals 453.6 × 980.665 dynes, or 444,820 dynes, or 4.448 newtons, and the newton equals 0.2248 pound of force.   The unit of mass in the English gravitational system is the slug, the mass that, when acted on by a force of 1 pound, is given an acceleration of 1 foot per second per second.   Since the standard pound, when acted on by gravity, is given an acceleration of 32.174 feet per second per second, the slug must be 32.174 times as great.   That is, the weight (gravitational attraction) of the slug is 32.174 pounds.   Its mass is then

$$32.174 \times 453.6 \text{ grams} = 14,594 \text{ grams} = 14.594 \text{ kilograms.}$$

The unit of work in the English system is the foot-pound, the work done by a force of 1 pound working through a distance of 1 foot.   It equals 1.356×10^7 ergs, or 1.356 joules.   The unit of rate of working, or power, is the foot-pound per second, which equals 1.356×10^7 ergs per second, or 1.356 watts.   Another unit of power is the horsepower, 550 foot-pounds per second, or 745.7 watts, or 0.7457 kilowatt.

The equations of this chapter will hold so long as any one of these three systems of units is used consistently.   Thus the transformations from one system to another that we have just given are not necessary in the solution of a problem using a single system of units.

Problems

1. A particle moves in a vertical line under the action of gravity and a viscous force $(-av)$, where v is its velocity.   Show that the velocity at any time is given by

$$v = \left(v_0 + \frac{mg}{a}\right) e^{-(a/m)t} - \frac{mg}{a}.$$

Show that this solution reduces properly to uniformly accelerated motion in the limiting case where the viscous resistance vanishes.   Illustrate this graphically, showing curves for several different values of a, and finally for $a = 0$, all for the same initial velocity v_0.

2. A raindrop weighs 0.1 g, and after falling from rest reaches a limiting speed of 1,000 cm/sec by the time it reaches the earth.   How long did it take to reach half its final speed?   Nine-tenths of its final speed?   How far did it travel before reaching half its final speed?   For how long could its velocity be described by the simple law $v = -gt$ to an error of 1 per cent?

3. At high velocities, the viscous resistance is proportional to the third power of the velocity.   Assuming this law, set up the differential equation for a particle falling under gravity and acted on by a viscous drag. Solve by power series, obtaining at least four terms in the expansion for v as a function of t. Draw graphs of velocity as a function of time, and discuss the solutions physically.

4. Set up the differential equation of the preceding problem in a form to solve by numerical integration. Carry through the integration of a particular case, and compare the numerical values of the resulting function with the values computed from the series of Prob. 3.

5. Using the same law of viscosity as in Prob. 3, but assuming no gravitational force, solve by direct integration of the differential equation for the case of a particle starting with given initial velocity and being damped down to rest. Show by power-series expansion of this function that it agrees with the special case of the power series of Prob. 3 obtained by letting the gravitational force be zero.

6. Suppose we have a rocket, shot off with initial velocity v_0, and thereafter losing mass according to the law $m = m_0(1 - ct)$, where m is the mass at any time, m_0 the initial mass at $t = 0$, c is a constant, and where the mass lost does not have appreciable velocity after it leaves the rocket. Show that, because of the loss of mass, the rocket is accelerated, just as if a force were acting on a body of constant mass. The rocket is acted on by a viscous resisting force in addition. Taking account of these forces, find the differential equation for its velocity as a function of time, and integrate the equation directly. Now find also the solution for v as a power series in the time. Show that the resulting series agrees with that obtained by expanding the exact solution. Calculate the limiting ratio of successive terms in the power series, as we go out in the series, and from this result obtain the region of convergence of the series. Is this result reasonable physically? What happens in the exact solution outside the range of convergence?

7. For the case of linear motion with varying mass, where the mass gained or lost by the body m under consideration has a velocity v_1 before entering or leaving m, show that the appropriate form of Newton's second law is

$$F = m\frac{dv}{dt} + (v - v_1)\frac{dm}{dt}.$$

8. A particle of mass m is projected vertically upward with an initial velocity v_0. If the viscous force due to air resistance is of magnitude kv^2, show that the particle returns to its initial position with a speed v_1 given by

$$\frac{1}{v_1^2} = \frac{1}{v_0^2} + \frac{k}{mg}.$$

9. Find a series solution for the differential equation $m\,dv/dt + kv = c/t$, where c is a constant, representing a damped motion under the action of an external force that decreases inversely proportionally to the time, the series having the form $v = a_1/t + a_2/t^2 + \cdots\cdot$ Show that this series is divergent for all values of t. Show that the differential equation is formally satisfied by the expression $v = e^{-t}\int_{-\infty}^{t}\frac{e^t}{t}\,dt$. This solution is convergent for t negative. The integral $\int_{-\infty}^{t}\frac{e^t}{t}\,dt$ is known as the "exponential integral function," and is important in physics and mathematics. It is frequently calculated by using the above divergent series. Explain how this procedure might be valid.

10. Suppose a particle is acted on by a damping force proportional to the velocity, and to a force that varies sinusoidally with the time. Solve the resulting differential equation for velocity as function of time, by the series method, by expanding the force in power series in the time. Can you recognize the analytical form of the resulting power series?

11. A beam of high-energy electrons is projected into a region of uniform electric field in a direction parallel to the lines of force, so that the motion is rectilinear under a constant force. Using the relativistic mass $m = m_0/\sqrt{1 - v^2/c^2}$, where m_0 is the rest mass (a constant), v is the velocity, and c the velocity of light, and the corresponding relativistic momentum mv, discuss the motion. Integrate the equations of motion directly, and show that your results reduce to the non-relativistic formulas as v/c gets small compared with unity. Show that the rate of working by the field on the electrons is equal to the rate of change of $m_0c^2/\sqrt{1 - v^2/c^2}$, and write the law of conservation of energy for the motion.

12. A beam of uniformly spaced electrons moving with velocity v_0 along the x axis enters a region of width d in which there is an electric field $E_x = E \sin \omega t$. Integrate the equations of motion to obtain the equation for the transit time $(t - t_0)$ across the region d for an electron entering the field at time t_0. Consider the case for which the transit angle $\omega(t - t_0)$ is small compared with unity. Investigate the velocity distribution of the electrons leaving the field. Discuss how this distribution changes with the frequency of the electric field.

13. Solve the problem of the undamped oscillator, for which the force is $-kx$, by the method of the energy integral.

14. Discuss the problem of the physical pendulum with arbitrary amplitude by the graphical method. Show that for low energies the motion is oscillatory, but for high energies it is a continuous rotation. Sketch the qualitative form of curves for angular displacement as a function of time, for several energies, in both the oscillatory and rotatory ranges.

15. Set up the problem of the physical pendulum by the method of the energy integral, and show that t as a function of the angle is given by an elliptic integral. (*Hint:* Use the information about elliptic integrals given in B. O. Peirce, *A Short Table of Integrals*, (Ginn and Company), or similar reference; note that $1 - \cos \theta = 2 \sin^2 \tfrac{1}{2}\theta$.)

16. Let a particle move in a field whose potential is $-1/x + 1/x^2$. Show by graphical methods that for small total energy the motion is oscillatory, but that for larger energy it is nonperiodic and extends to infinity. Find the energy that forms the dividing line between these two cases. Compute the limiting frequency of the oscillatory motion as the amplitude gets smaller and smaller, by expanding the potential energy about its minimum in power series, retaining only its quadratic term, and comparing with the linear oscillator whose potential energy would be given by that term. Describe qualitatively how the frequency changes when the amplitude increases.

17. Solve directly the problem of the motion of a particle moving in a field of potential $-1/x + 1/x^2$, using the energy integral. Show that the mathematical solution has the physical properties found in Prob. 16.

18. Using the solution of Prob. 17, find the period of oscillation of the oscillatory solutions in the potential $-1/x + 1/x^2$, as functions of the energy. To do this, note that the two ends of the path are the values of x for which $\sqrt{2(E - V)/m} = 0$. Thus the integral $\int_{x_0}^{x_1} \dfrac{dx}{\sqrt{2(E - V)/m}}$ from one of these points to the other will give just the half period.   Show that the period approaches the value found in Prob. 16 for small oscillations.

19. A particle of mass m moves in rectilinear motion with a potential energy given by $V(x) = 2cx^2 - cx^4$, where c is a constant.   Determine the range of energies for periodic motion, nonperiodic motion with reversal of direction, and nonperiodic, nonreversing motion.   What is the period of small oscillations?

20. A particle of mass m is subject to a linear restoring force whose force constant is proportional to the time.   Solve for the motion, using a power-series expansion.

21. A linear oscillator is acted on by a frictional force varying with the square of the speed, and starts from rest at a distance a from the center of attraction Find the position of the first turning point of the motion.

CHAPTER II

THE LINEAR OSCILLATOR

A linear oscillator is a particle acted on by a force proportional to its displacement, another force proportional to its velocity, and a third force that is a function of time, so that its motion is governed by the differential equation (1.8) of Chap. I. Because of the wide variety of systems that lead to the same differential equation, and hence are identical in their mathematical treatment, it is one of the most important problems of mechanics, as well as one of the simplest. It is met first of all in elastic vibrations. If an elastic body, such as a spring, is displaced from its position of equilibrium, the force restoring it to this position is, to a good approximation, proportional to the displacement. This is Hooke's law, and it holds provided that the displacement is small enough so as to lie within the elastic limit. A body governed by this law, and displaced, executes simple harmonic motion, its displacement varying sinusoidally with the time. In all real cases, there is a frictional force preventing the oscillation from continuing forever. If this friction arises from immersion in a viscous fluid, air being an example, the frictional force is proportional to the velocity. As a result of the friction, the amplitude gradually decreases with the time, instead of remaining constant. Such a motion is called a "damped oscillation." If the body is acted on by an external force varying with the time, we describe the resulting motion as a "forced motion." On account of the linear nature of the differential equation, this forced motion can always be written as the sum of two parts: a motion determined only by the external force, and called the "steady-state oscillation"; and a motion identical with what we should have without external force, and therefore damped out with the time. This latter motion is called the "transient," and its amplitude and phase are adjusted in each case to meet the initial conditions, the values of x_0 and v_0 at $t = t_0$.

We can solve the problem of the linear oscillator for any type of external force depending only on the time. Two methods of carrying this out are commonly used. One is that of analyzing the force as a sum of sinusoidal functions of the time. This analysis is called a "Fourier analysis," and we shall find later that it can be carried out for any arbitrary function. On account of the linear character of the differential equation, we can then solve the equation for each of the sinusoidal functions separately, and then add the results. For a sinusoidal impressed force, the displacement is also sinusoidal, apart from the transient. The amplitude of the forced oscillation is small if the frequency of the external force is widely different from the frequency with which the particle would oscillate in its free oscillation, generally called the "natural" or "resonant frequency" of the oscillator. On the other hand, if the external force has a frequency that is nearly the same as the natural frequency, the amplitude of the forced oscillation is very large. This phenomenon is called "resonance." In this case, the phase relation between external force and velocity is such that the external force does a large amount of work on the particle, which in turn is dissipated in the frictional resistance (and, in turn, as we emphasized in Chap. I, reappears as heat). The other method of handling external forces consists in considering the force as a succession of impulses, each acting for a very short time only. Such an impulse suddenly changes the velocity of the particle, and then leaves it oscillating freely. The resulting motion is the transient, or damped oscillation, which we mentioned earlier. By superposing such treatments from all the successive impulses, we get the complete forced motion.

The phenomena we have described are common to all problems that mathematically reduce to the equation of the linear oscillator, and we shall discuss them all in this chapter. Let us consider some of the other problems that lead to the same mathematical formulation. First are more complicated cases of elastic vibrations. A vibrating string, or membrane, or bar or plate, or air column, can oscillate in a great number of modes, or overtones. Each one of these, however, has properties almost exactly like a linear oscillator. In Chap. VII, we shall find this to be expressed mathematically by saying that, in any complicated oscillating system, we can introduce normal coordinates, one corresponding to each overtone or mode, and we shall find that the differential equation governing each of these normal coordinates is Eq. (1.8) of Chap. I. Thus our present treatment underlies the whole theory of mechanical vibrations of any degree of complexity, and hence the theory of acoustics. Furthermore, electrical oscillations of an oscillating circuit containing inductance, resistance, capacity, and an impressed emf, satisfy just the same equations. There is a further variety of electromagnetic oscillations behaving in the same way. These are oscillations of electromagnetic resonant cavities: it is possible to have electromagnetic oscillations within closed cavities with conducting walls, analogous to acoustical oscillations in the air inside an organ pipe, and these oscillations have normal modes that act like linear oscillators. Such oscillations play the same part in the very high, or microwave, frequencies of electromagnetic theory that oscillating circuits do at lower frequencies.

A further class of oscillations mathematically equivalent to the linear oscillator is found in wave mechanics, in the study of dispersion, the interaction of atoms and molecules with light. Light is an electromagnetic oscillation of very high frequency. It exerts forces on the atoms and molecules of matter. It is an interesting feature of wave mechanics that, as far as this interaction is concerned, any atomic or molecular system acts strictly like a collection of linear oscillators, one having the resonant frequency of each spectrum line. Some of these oscillators correspond to electronic oscillations, others to the slower oscillations of whole atoms and groups of atoms. The theory governing them, in every case, is the simple theory that we shall take up in this chapter. Resonance is particularly in evidence in this case, and shows itself in the phenomenon of anomalous dispersion. If light having nearly the frequency of one of the atomic or molecular resonant frequencies falls on matter, the atoms or molecules will oscillate with large amplitude, and since they contain electric charges, they will produce a correspondingly large electromagnetic field of the same frequency. This field will reinforce the incident field, changing its properties, and the net result is a change in the velocity of propagation, or of the index of refraction. Since a change of index of refraction with wave length is called "dispersion," we have as a result a large dispersion near each atomic resonance, and this is called "anomalous dispersion." Furthermore, the light will be absorbed by the atom or molecule near this resonance frequency, causing an absorption band in the spectrum of the material. The absorbed light is sometimes dissipated in heat, sometimes reappears as radiation of another wave length. These subjects must be discussed by the methods of quantum theory, or wave mechanics; but they lead back to the theory of the linear oscillator.

As a result of the analogy between the mechanical linear oscillator and the oscillating electric circuit, the same notation can be used for both mechanical and electrical problems. It has become customary in recent years to use the electrical notation in discussing the mechanical oscillator, and we shall follow this custom. Thus we shall speak of such things as impedance, resistance, reactance, Q, etc., in our mechanical discussion.   This carrying over of the notation of one field into another can be of more than symbolic importance; for it may well be that a problem has been discussed completely in the theory of electric circuits, and has not happened to be treated for the corresponding case of mechanical oscillations.   In such a case, if we use the same notation for both, we can carry the result over bodily from one field to the other.   Such carrying over has been of great practical importance in the recent development of the theory of vibrations.

1. Free Oscillations.—Our first problem will be that in which there is no external force varying with time, the problem of free oscillations.   The differential equation, from (1.8), Chap. I, is then

$$m \frac{d^2u}{dt^2} + a \frac{du}{dt} + ku = 0, \tag{1.1}$$

in which we have used u for the displacement of the particle, and where the restoring force, the force resulting from Hooke's law, and pushing the body back to its position of equilibrium $u = 0$, is $-ku$, and the resisting force, arising from viscous resistance, is

$$-av = -a \frac{du}{dt}.$$

We know from the theory of differential equations that such a linear homogeneous differential equation with constant coefficients (linear because it contains no powers of u or its derivatives higher than the first, homogeneous because it contains no term independent of u or its derivatives), can always be solved by assuming $u = Ae^{pt}$, where A and p are constants.   Making this assumption, and substituting in (1.1), the exponential cancels, and we have the solution

$$u = Ae^{pt}, \tag{1.2}$$

where A is arbitrary, and where

$$mp^2 + ap + k = 0, \qquad p = -\frac{a}{2m} \pm \sqrt{\left(\frac{a}{2m}\right)^2 - \frac{k}{m}}. \tag{1.3}$$

We notice immediately that, if the resistive term a is large, so that $(a/2m)^2 > k/m$, the square root in (1.3) is real, but, if

$$\left(\frac{a}{2m}\right)^2 < \frac{k}{m},$$

it is imaginary. The limiting case between the two, where

$$\left(\frac{a}{2m}\right)^2 = \frac{k}{m},$$

is called "critical damping." We notice also that, because of the two signs before the square root, two values of p are possible. Thus we really have two solutions like (1.2), one with each of the two values of p, and in general with different constants A. One of the fundamental properties of the linear differential equation, as (1.1), is that the sum of any two solutions is itself a solution. Thus the sum of the two functions like (1.2) is a solution of the problem. From this point on we can better handle the two cases separately, first that of greater than critical damping, second that of less than critical damping.

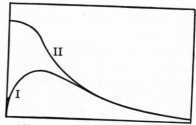

Fig. 2.—Displacement as function of time, greater than critical damping. Curve I: initial displacement = 0. Curve II: initial velocity = 0.

If the damping is greater than critical, both values of p, which we may call p_+ and p_-, depending on which sign we use in (1.3), are real and negative. We may write the general solution as

$$u = A_+ e^{p_+ t} + A_- e^{p_- t}. \tag{1.4}$$

This is the sum of two exponentials each decreasing with the time. The constants A_+ and A_- are chosen to satisfy the initial conditions that $u = u_0$ and $v = v_0$ when $t = t_0$. Thus they satisfy the equations

$$u_0 = A_+ e^{p_+ t_0} + A_- e^{p_- t_0}, \qquad v_0 = p_+ A_+ e^{p_+ t_0} + p_- A_- e^{p_- t_0}.$$

Typical curves of u as a function of time, for this case of large damping, are shown in Fig. 2. The case of critical damping must be handled separately. Then, since $p_+ = p_-$, the solution (1.4) would really contain only one arbitrary constant, and could not be the general solution. In this special case, however, the function te^{pt}, where $p = -a/2m$, is a solution of the equation of motion, as we can see by direct substitution in (1.1). Thus for critical damping the solution is

$$u = (A + Bt)e^{pt}, \qquad p = -\frac{a}{2m}.$$

It is clear that, in this case, since we have two arbitrary constants A and B, we can satisfy our initial conditions at $t = 0$.

For damping less than the critical value, the two values of p in (1.3) are conjugate complex numbers. (We assume that the reader is familiar with simple properties of complex numbers. If he is not, he will find the necessary properties discussed in Appendix III.) Then the two exponentials e^{p_+t} and e^{p_-t} are conjugate complex numbers. In order that u may be real, which it must be in any ordinary problem, we must then have A_+ and A_- also conjugate complex numbers; for then the two quantities $A_+e^{p_+t}$ and $A_-e^{p_-t}$ which we must add to get u, by (1.4), will also be conjugate complex numbers, and, the sum of any complex number and its conjugate is real. We note, however, that the sum of a complex number and its conjugate is twice the real part of the complex number. Thus the solution (1.4) for u becomes in this case twice the real part of $A_+e^{p_+t}$. Since A_+ is quite arbitrary, we may define a new A twice as great, so that then u will be simply the real part of Ae^{p_+t}. If we denote the real part of a complex number by Re, and if we define

$$\sqrt{\left(\frac{a}{2m}\right)^2 - \frac{k}{m}} = j\omega_1, \qquad \text{where } j = \sqrt{-1} \qquad (1.5)$$

we then find in this case of less than critical damping

$$u = Re A e^{-(a/2m)t} e^{j\omega_1 t}. \qquad (1.6)$$

The complex number A can be written in either of the two convenient forms

$$A = A_1 - jA_2 = A_0\, e^{j\varphi}, \qquad (1.7)$$

where A_1, A_2, A_0, φ are real. The constants have the following relations to each other:

$$\begin{aligned} A_1 &= A_0 \cos \varphi, & A_2 &= -A_0 \sin \varphi, \\ A_0 &= \sqrt{A_1^2 + A_2^2}, & \varphi &= -\tan^{-1} \frac{A_2}{A_1}. \end{aligned} \qquad (1.8)$$

In terms of the two expressions (1.7), we find

$$\begin{aligned} u &= e^{-(a/2m)t}(A_1 \cos \omega_1 t + A_2 \sin \omega_1 t) \\ &= A_0\, e^{-(a/2m)t} \cos (\omega_1 t + \varphi). \end{aligned} \qquad (1.9)$$

The constants A_1 and A_2, or A_0 and φ, are to be found by writing u and $v = du/dt$, at time $t = t_0$, and setting them equal to u_0 and v_0. The most convenient form to use for this is a modification of (1.9),

$$u = Ae^{-(a/2m)(t-t_0)} \cos [\omega_1(t - t_0) + \varphi], \qquad (1.10)$$

in which the constants are determined by the equations

$$u_0 = A \cos \varphi$$

$$v_0 = A \left[-\left(\frac{a}{2m}\right) \cos \varphi - \omega_1 \sin \varphi \right].$$

The motion (1.9), or (1.10), is called "damped simple harmonic motion." If $a = 0$, so that u varies sinusoidally with the time, it is simple harmonic motion. Clearly the greater a is, the more rapid the damping. A typical example of damped simple harmonic motion is shown in Fig. 3. The quantity A of (1.10) is called the "amplitude," φ is the initial phase, ω_1 the angular frequency. The period T, or the time after which the sinusoidal function repeats itself, and the

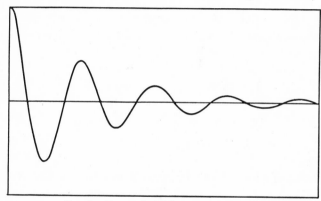

Fig. 3.—Damped simple harmonic motion.

frequency f, the number of oscillations per second, or the reciprocal of T, are related to ω_1 by the equations

$$f = \frac{1}{T} = \frac{\omega_1}{2\pi}. \tag{1.11}$$

The quantity $(a/2m)T$ is sometimes called the "logarithmic decrement." As we see from Eq. (1.9), it is the natural logarithm of the ratio of the values of u at two times differing by a period; for example, at two successive maxima of oscillation, as in Fig. 3.

2. The Rate of Damping, and Q.—In the study of resonant circuits, it has proved to be useful to introduce a constant Q, related to the sharpness of tuning of a circuit, or to its rate of damping, and closely related to the logarithmic decrement $(a/2m)T$ which we have just discussed. Since resonance is such a widespread phenomenon in mechanical oscillations, it seems useful to introduce the definition

MECHANICS

of Q here too. Let us start by pointing out the resemblance between Eq. (1.1) and the corresponding equation for a series resonant circuit. If we have a circuit containing resistance R, inductance L, and capacity C in series, and if we use q, the charge on one plate of the condenser, as the variable describing the circuit, then from the theory of oscillating circuits we know that the differential equation describing the circuit is

$$L \frac{d^2q}{dt^2} + R \frac{dq}{dt} + \frac{q}{C} = 0.$$

Thus, comparing with (1.1), there is an analogy between L and m, R and a, and $1/C$ and k. Following Eqs. (1.5) and (1.6), the free oscillations of the circuit, in the case of less than critical damping, are given by

$$q = ReAe^{-(R/2L)t}e^{j\omega_1 t}, \qquad \omega_1 = \sqrt{\left(\frac{1}{LC}\right) - \left(\frac{R}{2L}\right)^2}. \qquad (2.1)$$

For many purposes it is desirable to introduce an angular frequency ω_0, defined by the equation

$$\omega_0 = \sqrt{\frac{1}{LC}}. \qquad (2.2)$$

which by (2.1) equals the angular frequency with which the circuit would oscillate if the damping term were zero. Then we shall define the Q of this circuit by the equation

$$Q = \frac{\omega_0 L}{R}. \qquad (2.3)$$

In terms of this definition, we have from (2.1)

$$\omega_1 = \omega_0 \sqrt{1 - \left(\frac{1}{2Q}\right)^2}. \qquad (2.4)$$

When Q is large compared with unity, it has a very simple meaning. In that case, by (2.4), ω_1 and ω_0 differ only by small quantities of the second order, which we shall neglect. Then (2.1) becomes

$$q = ReAe^{-(1/2Q)\omega_0 t}e^{j\omega_0 t}. \qquad (2.5)$$

The square of the magnitude of q then varies with time according to the exponential $e^{-(1/Q)\omega_0 t}$. We shall see shortly that the energy of the oscillator is proportional to the square of the magnitude of q, so that it decreases, in the damped oscillation, according to this exponential. If we find the relative change in energy in a period, by differentiating this expression with respect to time, multiplying by the period, and dividing by the exponential itself, we have

$$\frac{\text{Change of energy in one period}}{\text{Total energy}} = -\frac{1}{Q}\,\omega_0 T,$$

so that, remembering that $\omega_0 T = 2\pi$ (to the approximation to which $\omega_0 = \omega_1$),

$$Q = 2\pi \times \frac{\text{total energy}}{\text{decrease of energy in one period}}. \tag{2.6}$$

The formula (2.6) is sometimes used as the definition of Q. As we have seen, it agrees with our definition (2.3) in case ω_1 is approximately equal to ω_0, which means, by (2.4), in case $(1/2Q)^2$ can be neglected compared with unity. When Q is of the order of magnitude of unity, it is no longer legitimate to find the change of energy in a period by differentiating the exponential with respect to time, and multiplying by the period; we must rather speak of a logarithmic decrement, as in the preceding section. We notice that the definition of logarithmic decrement previously given can be expressed in the form

$$\text{Logarithmic decrement} = \frac{\pi}{Q}\frac{\omega_0}{\omega_1} = \frac{\pi}{Q} \quad \text{if } \omega_1 = \omega_0.$$

Returning now to Eq. (1.1) for the mechanical oscillator, it is useful to introduce definitions of Q and of ω_0 analogous to those of Eqs. (2.2) and (2.3). In terms of the constants of (1.1), these definitions are

$$\omega_0 = \sqrt{\frac{k}{m}}, \qquad Q = \omega_0\,\frac{m}{a}, \qquad a = \frac{m\omega_0}{Q}, \qquad k = m\omega_0^2. \tag{2.7}$$

In terms of Q and ω_0, we may rewrite (1.1) in the form

$$m\left(\frac{d^2u}{dt^2} + \frac{\omega_0}{Q}\frac{du}{dt} + \omega_0^2 u\right) = 0. \tag{2.8}$$

We shall henceforth consider (2.8) as a standard form for writing the differential equation of an oscillator, and shall use the constants in this form, rather than in terms of a and k as in (1.1).

3. Forced Oscillations and Resonance.—In the present section we shall assume that our oscillator is acted on by an external force varying sinusoidally with the time. That is, we assume that the force is given by

$$F = Re(F_0\,e^{i\omega t}), \tag{3.1}$$

where F_0 is a complex constant representing the amplitude of the force. Relations similar to (1.7) and (1.8) hold by which we can express F_0 in terms of its real and imaginary parts, or in terms of its magnitude and phase angle. To get our differential equation of motion, we insert the force (3.1) in the right side of Eq. (2.8). We may handle the problem in complex form by inserting, not (3.1), but the complex quantity $F_0 e^{j\omega t}$ of which the force is the real part. Then we shall find a complex solution for u, whose real part will give the solution of our actual problem, by an argument closely analogous to that used in deriving Eq. (1.6).

The equation of motion is then

$$m\left(\frac{d^2u}{dt^2} + \frac{\omega_0}{Q}\frac{du}{dt} + \omega_0^2 u\right) = F_0\, e^{j\omega t}. \tag{3.2}$$

We solve it by assuming that u varies as $e^{j\omega t}$, so that differentiating u with respect to t is equivalent to multiplication by $j\omega$. Substituting, we have

$$m\left(-\omega^2 + j\frac{\omega\omega_0}{Q} + \omega_0^2\right)u = F_0\, e^{j\omega t},$$

or

$$u = \frac{(F_0/m)e^{j\omega t}}{-\omega^2 + \omega_0^2 + j\,(\omega\omega_0/Q)}. \tag{3.3}$$

Instead of finding the displacement u, it is often convenient to solve for the velocity $v = du/dt = j\omega u$, in the forms

$$v = \frac{F_0\, e^{j\omega t}}{Z}, \quad \text{where } Z = R + jX,\ R = \frac{m\omega_0}{Q},\ X = m\omega - m\frac{\omega_0^2}{\omega} \tag{3.4}$$

or

$$v = \frac{(F_0/m\omega_0)}{z}\, e^{j\omega t}, \quad z = r + jx, \quad r = \frac{1}{Q}, \quad x = \frac{\omega}{\omega_0} - \frac{\omega_0}{\omega}. \tag{3.5}$$

In any of these forms, we must remember that the actual solution of the problem is given by the real part u or of v.

We have written our solution in various forms, (3.3) to (3.5), that are convenient under different circumstances. Equation (3.3) is the form that is perhaps most familiar for mechanical applications. Equation (3.4) is written by analogy with the corresponding electric circuit. We have seen that u corresponds to the charge q in a series resonant circuit; then v, or du/dt, corresponds to the current i in such a circuit, and $F_0 e^{j\omega t}$ corresponds to the impressed emf. Furthermore, since m corresponds to L, $m\omega_0/Q$ to R, and $m\omega_0^2$ to $1/C$, the quantities

R, X, and Z of Eq. (3.4) correspond to resistance, reactance, and complex impedance of such a circuit. We see from (3.4) that the mechanical impedance Z is given by the ratio of impressed force to velocity, as the electrical impedance of a circuit is given by the ratio of impressed emf to current. Equation (3.5) is a version of (3.4) in which the resistance, reactance, and complex impedance have been reduced to dimensionless form.

The solutions (3.3), (3.4), or (3.5) represent the phenomenon of resonance: as the external frequency ω approaches the resonant frequency ω_0, the denominator becomes small, so that the amplitude of the displacement or velocity becomes large. Furthermore, when $\omega = \omega_0$, the denominator of (3.3) becomes pure imaginary, the denomi-

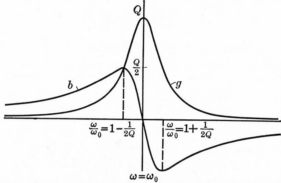

FIG. 4.—Conductance and susceptance as function of frequency.

nators of (3.4) and (3.5) real, so that the displacement is 90° out of phase with the force, and the velocity is in phase with the force, resulting in a maximum dissipation of energy. These phenomena are shown graphically in Fig. 4. In that figure we plot real and imaginary parts of $1/z$ as a function of ω/ω_0. We may define

$$y = \frac{1}{z} = g + jb = \frac{r - jx}{r^2 + x^2}, \tag{3.6}$$

where y, g, and b are dimensionless quantities proportional to the complex admittance, the conductance, and the susceptance, in the electrical analogy. Then Fig. 4 shows the conductance and susceptance as functions of the frequency. The behavior shown in Fig. 4 is characteristic of all resonances, the conductance rising to a maximum at resonance, and falling off rapidly on both sides of it, while the susceptance is zero at resonance, but rises to peaks of large magnitude and opposite sign on each side of the resonant frequency, falling off as the frequency departs considerably from resonance.

For a resonance whose Q is large compared with unity, we can derive important relations between the width of the resonance peak and Q. We shall find that in such a case the peak is narrow, so that we can discuss it on the assumption that the frequency is close to ω_0. In this case we may approximately write

$$x = \frac{\omega^2 - \omega_0^2}{\omega \omega_0} = \frac{(\omega - \omega_0)(\omega + \omega_0)}{\omega \omega_0} \sim \frac{2(\omega - \omega_0)}{\omega_0}. \tag{3.7}$$

We notice from (3.5) and (3.6) that the quantity g, proportional to the conductance, equals Q at resonance; we can then estimate the width of the resonance peak by asking where g equals $Q/2$, or half its maximum value. This comes when $x^2 = r^2$, or when

$$\frac{\omega - \omega_0}{\omega_0} = \pm \frac{1}{2Q}. \tag{3.8}$$

If we let $\Delta\omega$ be the difference between the two values of ω of (3.8), we have

$$\frac{\Delta\omega}{\omega_0} = \frac{1}{Q}.$$

The quantity $\Delta\omega$ is often called the "half width" of the resonance peak. If we wish to express the relation in terms of frequency f instead of angular frequency ω, we remember by (1.11) that they are proportional to each other, so that the half width Δf expressed in frequency is given by

$$\frac{\Delta f}{f_0} = \frac{1}{Q}. \tag{3.9}$$

We can also easily get the behavior of the susceptance curve in the neighborhood of the resonance, by finding the maximum and minimum of b, which is defined as a function of x by (3.6). We find that the maximum and minimum of b come at the same points, given by (3.8), at which the conductance equals $Q/2$, or half its maximum height; and furthermore we find that at that point the susceptance b is also equal to $\pm Q/2$, or is numerically equal to the conductance at those points. These relations are clear from Fig. 4.

Another graphical way of exhibiting the resonance is shown in Fig. 5, where we plot b as a function of g, regarding the frequency as a parameter. We may regard the plane of Fig. 5 as a complex plane, so that we are plotting values of the complex admittance for all values of frequency.   The resulting curve is a circle, tangent to the imaginary axis at the origin, and extending out along the real axis to the value Q. To prove this, we solve for g and b from (3.6), use r from (3.5), and show that g and b satisfy the equation

$$\left(g - \frac{Q}{2}\right)^2 + b^2 = \left(\frac{Q}{2}\right)^2, \tag{3.10}$$

which is clearly the equation of the circle just described.   To show the way in which g and b vary with frequency, we plot in Fig. 5 the points corresponding to certain values of x, which by (3.7) measures the frequency.   Remembering that the complex vector out to an arbitrary point of the circle of Fig. 5 represents the complex admittance corresponding to the appropriate frequency, we see that far from resonance this admittance is zero, but as resonance is approached, the magnitude of the admittance rapidly increases, to the value Q at resonance, decreasing again to zero on the other side of resonance, and simultaneously the phase shifts through 180°, from

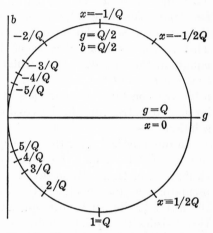

FIG. 5.—Susceptance as function of conductance near resonance.

an angle of 90° between force and velocity at low frequencies, through 0° at resonance, to −90° at high frequencies, with a phase angle of ±45° at the two points $x = \pm 1/Q$, the points given in (3.8).

4. Superposition of Transient and Forced Oscillation.—In Sec. 3 we found the displacement or velocity of the oscillator when acted on by a sinusoidal impressed force; the solution was given in (3.3), (3.4), or (3.5).   This cannot be the complete solution, however, for it has no arbitrary constants, so that we cannot satisfy arbitrary initial conditions by means of it.   We shall next inquire how to get a complete solution.   The answer is well known from the theory of differential equations.   Our Eq. (3.2) is a linear second order differential equation with constant coefficients.   It is an inhomogeneous equation; that is, the term that appears on the right side does not involve the dependent variable u or any of its derivatives, while each term of the left side is linear in the variable or one of its derivatives. The related homogeneous equation is that in which the external force is zero, so that the right side of the equation is zero; that is, it is Eq. (2.8). When we have an inhomogeneous equation like (3.2), the related homogeneous equation is often called the "auxiliary equation," and the general solution of the auxiliary equation, which in this case is given by (1.10), containing the proper number of arbitrary constants, is called the "complementary function." A particular solution of the inhomogeneous equation, such as (3.3), (3.4), or (3.5) in our case, is called a "particular integral." Then in the theory of differential equations we learn the following result: the complete solution of the inhomogeneous equation equals the sum of a particular integral, and of the complementary function. The proof is obvious. Because of the linear nature of the differential equation, the sum of the particular integral and the complementary function satisfies the differential equation, and since it contains two arbitrary constants (in our case of a second order equation) it can be used to satisfy any initial conditions, and is therefore a complete solution.

In our physical case, the particular integral is the steady-state or forced oscillation, and the complementary function is the damped oscillation, or transient, so that we say that the general motion of an oscillator is a superposition of the forced oscillation, and of a transient, the latter having such an amplitude and phase that the sum of the two satisfies the initial conditions. Rewriting the forced oscillation from (3.3), and the transient from (1.10), using (2.4) and (2.7), our complete solution is

$$u = Re\left[\frac{(F_0/m)e^{j\omega t}}{-\omega^2 + \omega_0^2 + j(\omega\omega_0/Q)} + A e^{[-\omega_0(t-t_0)/2Q]} e^{j\omega_0\sqrt{1-[1/(2Q)]^2}(t-t_0)}\right]. \tag{4.1}$$

Here the complex amplitude A is to be so chosen that both u and du/dt of (4.1) have their prescribed values at $t = t_0$. We shall not write down the explicit equations for doing this, but the way of setting them up is obvious.

In Fig. 6 we show several cases of superposition of forced oscillations and transients, calculated by Eq. (4.1). They are all calculated on the assumption that both displacement and velocity are zero at $t = 0$, the commonest case in practice, and that the external force then commences to act. Case (a) is one in which the external frequency is rather different from the natural frequency. In case (b) the external frequency is close to the natural frequency. In this case the steady-state motion and transient have almost the same frequency, so that we have the phenomenon of beats, in which the amplitude pulsates between a large and a small value. This occurs whenever two approximately equal frequencies are superposed, as we can see from the simple trigonometrical identity

$$\cos \omega_1 t + \cos \omega_2 t = 2 \cos\left(\frac{\omega_1 - \omega_2}{2}\right) t \cos\left(\frac{\omega_1 + \omega_2}{2}\right) t, \quad (4.2)$$

showing that the result is a sinusoidal vibration whose frequency is the average of the two frequencies, but whose amplitude is modulated

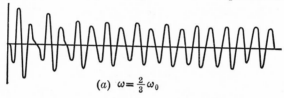

$$(a) \quad \omega = \tfrac{2}{3}\omega_0$$

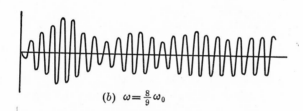

$$(b) \quad \omega = \tfrac{8}{9}\omega_0$$

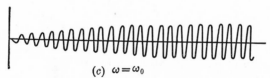

$$(c) \quad \omega = \omega_0$$

FIG. 6.—Superposition of forced oscillation and transient.

with the slow difference frequency between the two vibrations. Since the transient gradually dies down, however, the amplitude of the beats grows less and less, until gradually only the forced motion remains. In case (c) the external frequency is exactly equal to the natural frequency. Here there are no beats, the amplitude merely building up exponentially to its final value. In all these cases, as we see from (4.1), the amplitude of the transient falls to $1/e$ of its initial value in Q/π periods, and after a sufficient lapse of time, the transient has damped down practically to zero, and the steady-state motion alone remains.

5. Forced Motion under General External Forces.—If we are given an arbitrary external force, say $F(t)$, we show in Appendix VI that it is possible to write it as a sum of sinusoidal terms,

$$F(t) = Re \left(\sum_n F_n \, e^{j\omega_n t} \right). \tag{5.1}$$

Thus any sound may be considered as made up of a superposition of pure tones, and any light as a superposition of pure colors. Now suppose we find the forced motion resulting from each of these sinusoidal vibrations separately, and then add them. The result will be the solution of the whole problem. That is to say, if the inhomogeneous part of an inhomogeneous linear differential equation is a sum of terms, and if we have particular integrals of the equations formed by taking each one of these separately, a particular integral of the whole problem is a sum of the particular integrals of the separate problems. The property by which we can add solutions to get the complete solution is called the "principle of superposition." It is a property of linear differential equations such as our present one, and is a principle of widespread application in physics, where it leads to the possibility of coexistence of different sound waves, light waves, and other such disturbances, in the same region of space, without disturbing each other. To prove the principle of superposition in this particular case, we start with our equation of motion

$$m \left(\frac{d^2u}{dt^2} + \frac{\omega_0}{Q} \frac{du}{dt} + \omega_0^2 u \right) = \sum_n F_n \, e^{j\omega_n t} \tag{5.2}$$

We assume that $u_n(t)$ is a solution of the equation in which we have only the nth term of the summation on the right-hand side, obtained as in (3.3), so that

$$m \left(\frac{d^2u_n}{dt^2} + \frac{\omega_0}{Q} \frac{du_n}{dt} + \omega_0^2 u_n \right) = F_n \, e^{j\omega_n t} \tag{5.3}$$

Adding the equations (5.3), it is at once obvious that the summation $\sum_n u_n$ satisfies (5.2). In considering our solution physically, it is clear, for instance from (3.3), that those terms of (5.1) whose frequencies happen to lie near the natural frequency of the oscillator will produce much greater response than the other terms of the summation.

There is another quite different solution for arbitrary external forces, which is more convenient than the one just described in discussing transients when an external force is suddenly applied, and for similar problems. Suppose we divide up the time axis into short intervals δt, and consider a force that equals $F(t)$ during a certain interval δt, but is zero at all other times. Such a force acting through an infinitesimal time, multiplied by the time through which it acts, is called an "impulse." Let us consider the force that is equal to $F(t)$ from t_0 to $t_0 + \delta t$, zero at other times, and let us consider the motion of the oscillator after this impulse acts at $t = t_0$, assuming that u is zero at all times up to t_0. Since the oscillator is at rest with $u = 0$ to a high approximation during δt, the only force acting on it is $F(t)$. By Newton's second law we then have approximately

$$mv(t_0 + \delta t_0) = F \, \delta t_0. \tag{5.4}$$

That is, the momentum after the action of the impulse equals the magnitude of the impulse (remembering that the initial momentum is zero). After the infinitesimal time interval in which the impulse acts, the motion will be a transient, with initial displacement zero, initial velocity given by (5.4). We readily find, using (1.10), that this transient may be written

$$u = \frac{F(t_0)}{m\omega_0} \frac{e^{-(\omega_0/2Q)(t-t_0-\delta t_0)}}{\sqrt{1 - (1/2Q)^2}} \sin\left[\omega_0 \sqrt{1 - \left(\frac{1}{2Q}\right)^2} (t - t_0 - \delta t_0) \right] \delta t_0 \tag{5.5}$$

for all times subsequent to the short interval δt_0. In Eq. (5.5) we have a particular solution of the problem of the motion of a particle subject to our impulse.

We may now consider the problem in which the force $F(t)$ has been acting since $t = -\infty$. Each interval of time δt_0 will have contributed a solution like (5.5), at all subsequent times. On account of the linearity of the problem, we can superpose solutions corresponding to all the various impulses that have preceded the time t at which we wish to find the motion. That is, we may sum (5.5) over t_0, from $-\infty$ to the time t when we want the solution, since all past impulses contribute to the displacement, but not future impulses. As δt_0 becomes small, we can change the summation to an integration, obtaining

$$u(t) = \int_{-\infty}^{t} \frac{F(t_0)}{m\omega_0} \frac{e^{-(\omega_0/2Q)(t-t_0)}}{\sqrt{1 - (1/2Q)^2}} \sin\left[\omega_0 \sqrt{1 - \left(\frac{1}{2Q}\right)^2} (t - t_0) \right] dt_0. \tag{5.6}$$

In (5.6) we have a general solution of the problem of the motion of the linear oscillator, subject to an external force $F(t)$ which is an arbitrary function of time. No additional transient term involving arbitrary constants is needed; for this would represent a transient existing at $t = -\infty$, which would have damped to zero at any finite time. This method of solution is sometimes called "Green's method." That method is a general one for handling inhomogeneous linear differential equations, by dividing up the range of the independent variable as we have done, finding the solution for the case where the inhomogeneity is confined to a small interval [as (5.5)], and adding the resulting solutions. One precaution should be mentioned regarding (5.6): as we have set it up, we have used a real solution for u, and have assumed that the force F is real, not the real part of a complex number. This should be borne in mind in applying it.

6. The Energy and the Linear Oscillator.—In the equation of motion for the oscillator,

$$m\left(\frac{d^2u}{dt^2} + \frac{\omega_0}{Q}\frac{du}{dt} + \omega_0^2 u\right) = F(t),$$

the damping force $-(m\omega_0/Q)(du/dt)$ and the external force $F(t)$ are nonconservative, while the restoring force $-m\omega_0^2 u$ is derivable from a potential. This potential energy is clearly

$$V(u) = \frac{m}{2}\,\omega_0^2 u^2.$$

Following Eq. (4.1) of Chap. I, we then may write the energy equation in the form

$$\frac{d}{dt}\left(\frac{1}{2}\,mv^2 + \frac{1}{2}\,m\omega_0^2 u^2\right) = -m\,\frac{\omega_0}{Q}\,v^2 + Fv. \tag{6.1}$$

If there is no damping, and no external force, the energy of course stays constant. In that case we have

$$u = A\cos\omega_0 t, \qquad v = -\omega_0 A\sin\omega_0 t,$$
$$\tfrac{1}{2}mv^2 = \tfrac{1}{2}m\omega_0^2 A^2\sin^2\omega_0 t, \qquad \tfrac{1}{2}m\omega_0^2 u^2 = \tfrac{1}{2}m\omega_0^2 A^2\cos^2\omega_0 t,$$
$$E = \tfrac{1}{2}mv^2 + \tfrac{1}{2}m\omega_0^2 u^2 = \tfrac{1}{2}m\omega_0^2 A^2.$$

This expresses the way in which the energy is proportional to the square of the amplitude.

If the damping and external forces in (6.1) are small, the energy will change by only a small fraction of itself in the course of a period. In that case we may treat the motion as simple harmonic, but with an amplitude that varies slowly with time. We may average the right side of (6.1) over a period. In that case, the damping term may be written in terms of the amplitude A, and we have

$$\frac{d}{dt}\left(\frac{1}{2}\, m\omega_0^2 A^2\right) = \frac{dE}{dt} = -\frac{\omega_0}{Q}\, E + \overline{Fv}, \qquad (6.2)$$

where $\overline{Fv}$ represents the average of Fv over a period. If the external force F is absent, (6.2) leads to an exponential decrease of energy with time, at a rate as given in Eq. (2.6). If, however, there is an external force, the term $\overline{Fv}$ can have either sign, depending on the phase relations between force and velocity, so that the energy can either increase or decrease with time. In the steady-state motion, after the decay of the transient, the amplitude is independent of time, so that the energy stays constant. In that case, (6.2) shows that the external force must be working on the oscillator at just the right rate to balance the dissipation of energy into the frictional resistance. By (6.2), this rate of working is proportional to the energy, or the square of the amplitude, of the oscillator. Thus in a case of resonance, when the amplitude is large, the dissipation of energy will be correspondingly large. Equation (6.2) can sometimes be profitably used to get a simple approximate solution for the time rate of change of energy, without going through the complete details of the solution for u as a function of time.

The linear oscillator forms a simple and instructive example of the discussion of energy in Chap. I. The potential energy curve, analogous to Fig. 1, is a parabola, so that the motion is always periodic, no matter what the energy. It is not merely periodic, it is sinusoidal, in the absence of nonconservative forces, and the period is independent of the amplitude, a very important characteristic of the linear oscillator. This of course has been proved by the methods of this chapter; we can also use the energy integral to solve it, as in Eq. (2.8) of Chap. I, and Prob. 13, Chap. I. If we have damping and external forces, we have just seen in detail how the energy changes with time, with corresponding changes in amplitude.

The energy method suggests an important respect in which our discussion of the linear oscillator can throw light on a more difficult problem. In the neighborhood of any minimum of potential energy, the potential energy function can be expanded in Taylor's series, the first term being proportional to $(u - u_0)^2$, where u_0 is the position of the minimum, so that the corresponding force is proportional to $-(u - u_0)$. That is, for small enough energies, motion in the neighborhood of any potential minimum is simple harmonic. A potential minimum is a point of stable equilibrium, so that we have the general result that simple harmonic motion is possible around any position of stable equilibrium. Examples have been encountered in Probs. 16 and 19, Chap. I. Furthermore, if there is damping, or an external force, in such a case, we may use the methods of the present chapter to discuss it. The difference between a general potential minimum and the case of the linear oscillator is that, in the general case, called the "nonlinear oscillator," the frequency of oscillation depends on the amplitude, and the motion, though periodic, is not sinusoidal. As a result of the dependence of frequency on amplitude, the resonance phenomenon with a nonlinear oscillator is quite different from the linear case. If an external force whose frequency equals that of the free oscillations of infinitesimal amplitude is impressed on a nonlinear oscillator, the oscillation will start to build up as in the linear case; but with increasing amplitude the natural frequency will change, the external force will no longer be in resonance with the velocity, the mean rate of working of the external force on the oscillator will fall off, and the amplitude will not build up as it would do with the linear oscillator. The problem of the nonlinear oscillator is an important one, but we shall not go into it in detail. Clearly in the conservative case it can be handled by the methods of Chap. I. If in addition there are nonconservative forces acting, which are small enough so that they do not change the energy greatly during a period, we can apply an analysis similar to Eq. (6.2), to find the rate of change of total energy, and thus obtain considerable qualitative information about the system, even without quantitative solutions.

Problems

1. Show directly that the solution $A_1 \cos \omega t + A_2 \sin \omega t$ for the particle moving with simple harmonic motion can also be written $A_0 \cos (\omega t + \varphi)$. Find A_0 and φ as functions of A_1 and A_2, and vice versa.

2. A pendulum 1 m long is held at an angle of 1° to the vertical, and released with an initial velocity of 5 cm/sec toward the position of equilibrium. Find the amplitude and phase of the resulting motion.

3. A circuit contains resistance, inductance, and capacity, but there is no impressed emf. Solve the differential equation in series, and show by comparison of the first few terms that the series represents the function

$$e^{-(R/2L)t}(A_1 \cos \omega t + A_2 \sin \omega t),$$

where $\omega^2 = 1/LC - R^2/4L^2$.

4. In an oscillatory circuit, show that the phases of the charge and the current differ by 90°.

5. A coil has a resistance of 0.7 ohm, inductance of 5 henrys. Until $t = 0$, no current is flowing in the coil. At that moment, a battery of 5 volts emf is connected to it. After 5 sec, the battery is short-circuited and the current in the coil allowed to die down. Compute the current as a function of the time, drawing a curve to represent it.

6. A coil having $L = 10$ henrys, $R = 1$ ohm, has no current flowing in it until $t = 0$. Then it has an applied voltage increasing linearly with the time, from zero at $t = 0$ to 1 volt at $t = 1$ sec. After $t = 1$, the emf remains equal to 1 volt. By series methods find the current at any time, and plot the curve.

7. A coil of resistance 2 ohms, inductance 10 millihenrys, is connected to a condenser of capacity 10 mf. At $t = 0$, the condenser is charged to a potential of 100 volts, and no current is flowing. Find the charge on the condenser at any later time, and also the current flowing. What are the period and logarithmic decrement of the circuit? What would the resistance have to be, leaving inductance and capacity the same, such that the system would be critically damped?

8. Prove that the displacement of a particle in damped oscillation is given by

$$u = e^{-\frac{\omega_0 t}{2Q}} \left(u_0 \cos \omega_0 \sqrt{1 - \left(\frac{1}{2Q}\right)^2} \, t + \frac{(v_0/\omega_0) + (u_0/2Q)}{\sqrt{1 - (1/2Q)^2}} \sin \omega_0 \sqrt{1 - \left(\frac{1}{2Q}\right)^2} \, t \right)$$

where u_0, v_0 are initial values of displacement and velocity. Pass to the case of critical damping, by letting $1 - (1/2Q)^2$ approach zero. Show that the resulting motion has one term of the form $te^{(-\omega_0 t/2Q)}$, and prove directly that this satisfies the differential equation.

9. Letting $Q = \frac{1}{4}$, draw curves for u as a function of t, representing the damped motion for the case where the initial velocity is zero but the initial displacement is not, and also for the case where the initial displacement is zero but the velocity is not.

10. A pendulum is damped so that its amplitude falls to half its value in 1 min. Its actual period is 2 sec. Find the change in the period which there would be if the damping were not present. (*Hint:* Use power series expansion for frequency, treating $1/Q$ as a small quantity.)

11. A radio receiving station has a circuit tuned to a wave length of 500 m. It is desired to have the tuning sharp enough so that a frequency differing from this by 10,000 cycles/sec gives only 1 per cent as much response as the natural frequency, for the same amplitude of signal. Work out reasonable values of resistance, inductance, and capacity to accomplish this.

12. A tuning fork of pitch C (256 vibrations per second) is so slightly damped that its amplitude after 10 sec is 10 per cent of the original amplitude. It is set into oscillation, first by another fork of the same pitch, then by one a semitone higher, both vibrating with the same amplitude. Find the ratio of amplitudes of forced motion in the two cases. What will be the pitch of the forced vibration in the second case?

13. The support of a simple pendulum moves horizontally back and forth with simple harmonic motion. Show that this sets the pendulum into forced motion, as if there were a force applied directly to the bob. Show that the motion has the following behavior: The pendulum pivots about a point not its point of support, but such that, if it were really pivoted there, its natural period would be the actual period of the forced motion. Discuss the cases where the pivotal point is below the point of support; above the point of support. Neglect transients.

14. A particle subject to a linear restoring force and a viscous damping is acted on by a periodic force whose frequency differs from the natural frequency by a small quantity. The particle starts from rest at $t = 0$, and builds up the motion. Discuss the whole problem, including initial conditions. Consider what happens in the limiting case when the frequency gets nearer and nearer the natural frequency, and the damping gets smaller and smaller. Compare with the results of Fig. 6.

15. Show that for a particle subject to a linear restoring force and viscous damping the maximum amplitude occurs when the applied frequency is less than the natural frequency. Find this frequency. Show that maximum energy is attained when the applied frequency equals the natural frequency. What are the maximum amplitude and maximum energy?

16. The motion of an anharmonic undamped oscillator is described by

$$ m \left(\frac{d^2u}{dt^2} + \omega_0^2 u + au^2 \right) = 0, $$

where a is a small quantity. Solve this equation by successive approximations, expanding u in a power series in powers of a.

17. If the oscillator in Prob. 16 is acted on by a force $A \cos pt + B \cos qt$, show that the steady-state solution contains terms of frequencies $2p$, $2q$, $q + p$, $q - p$, $2q + p$, $2q - p$, etc. Note that superposition does not hold for the equation above. These new frequencies are called "combination tones."

18. Show that in general a linear homogeneous differential equation of the nth order with constant coefficients has n independent exponential solutions of the sort we have considered.

19. Show that if we have n independent solutions of an $n$thorder differential equation, then an arbitrary linear combination of these solutions, containing n coefficients, is a general solution of the equation.

20. A particle can move along a straight line and is attracted toward two points on the line with forces proportional to the distances of the particle from the centers of attraction. Find the motion, showing that it is simple harmonic, and obtain a formula for the period.

21. Two masses m_1 and m_2 are connected by a spring. When m_1 is held fixed, m_2 oscillates with a frequency f. Find the frequency of linear oscillations when m_2 is held fixed and when both particles are free to move.

22. A linear oscillator of mass m, natural frequency ω_0, and of finite Q, initially at rest, is acted on by an external force $F(t)$ which is zero until $t = 0$, has a constant value F_0 from $t = 0$ to $t = T$, and is zero after $t = T$. Find the motion of the oscillator for all values of t.

23. Solve Prob. 22 if the external force is given by $F(t) = F_0 \sin (\omega_1 t - \delta)$ for all values of t greater than zero, and zero before $t = 0$. Discuss the dependence of the solution on the initial phase lag δ.

24. Solve Prob. 22 for the case where the external force is given by $F(t) = F_0 \sin \omega t$, $0 \leq t \leq T$, and zero otherwise.

CHAPTER III

MOTION IN TWO AND THREE DIMENSIONS

In the preceding two chapters we have been considering the motion of a particle along a line; mathematically, we have had one differential equation, determining the one dependent variable, the coordinate, as a function of the time. We have found that the energy is conserved if the force depends only on position, not on velocity or time, and that in that case we can always solve the problem of the motion explicitly. Even if there are nonconservative forces, depending on velocity and time, we can solve the problem in which the forces are linear functions of displacement and velocity. That problem was that of the linear oscillator, the case of elastic vibrations, or of Hooke's law, and forms one of the two perhaps most celebrated problems of mechanics. The other, which led Newton to his original formulation of the laws of motion, is the problem of planetary motion, the motion of a particle (in this case a planet) around a center of attraction exerting a force inversely proportional to the square of the distance of the particle from the center (gravitational force). It is an example of motion in several dimensions, and it introduces some fundamentally new features. In the first place, when the motion occurs in two or more dimensions, it is not necessarily true that a force that depends only on position is conservative; our first problem will be to find what additional conditions are imposed on a force, in order that it be conservative. Secondly, the energy integral by itself is not enough to permit a complete solution of a conservative problem. There is, in fact, no general way of getting a solution of a dynamical problem of motion in several dimensions. In some cases, there are additional integrals of the equations of motion; that is, additional quantities which, like the energy, remain constant during the motion. We shall find that the case of planetary motion has such an integral: the angular momentum. When we have as many such integrals as there are dimensions, we can solve the problem, but in general such integrals do not exist.

We shall now proceed to consider the general problem of the dynamics of a particle in two or three dimensions, and the conditions for a conservative force. Then we shall consider motion in a central

43

field, as a special example of such motion. We shall handle that problem by elementary methods; but in the next chapter we shall go over the same problem by more powerful methods, the methods of generalized coordinates and Lagrange's equations, mathematical tools that often greatly simplify the solution of problems in several dimensions.

1. The Dynamics of Motion in Two or Three Dimensions.—A particle in three dimensions requires three quantities to measure its position; the simplest way to set up these three quantities is to use rectangular coordinates, x, y, and z. We may, if we choose, regard these three coordinates as being the components of a vector $\mathbf{r}$, pointing out from the origin to the position of the particle. Similarly the velocity is a vector, whose components along the x, y, and z axes are

$$v_x = \frac{dx}{dt}, \qquad v_y = \frac{dy}{dt}, \qquad v_z = \frac{dz}{dt}$$

and the acceleration is a vector with components

$$a_x = \frac{dv_x}{dt} = \frac{d^2x}{dt^2}, \qquad a_y = \frac{dv_y}{dt} = \frac{d^2y}{dt^2}, \qquad a_z = \frac{dv_z}{dt} = \frac{d^2z}{dt^2}.$$

The momentum is a vector, defined by the equation momentum $= m\mathbf{v}$, and the force $\mathbf{F}$ is a vector with components F_x, F_y, F_z. Then Newton's second law becomes a vector equation, whose components are

$$\frac{d}{dt}(mv_x) = F_x, \qquad \frac{d}{dt}(mv_y) = F_y, \qquad \frac{d}{dt}(mv_z) = F_z, \qquad (1.1)$$

or, if the mass m is constant,

$$ma_x = m\frac{d^2x}{dt^2} = F_x, \qquad ma_y = m\frac{d^2y}{dt^2} = F_y, \qquad ma_z = m\frac{d^2z}{dt^2} = F_z.$$
$$(1.2)$$

If the force components are functions of the position, velocity, and time, as in Chap. I, we have in (1.2) three simultaneous differential equations for x, y, and z, as functions of time. In general, each of the equations will contain all three variables (for each component of force will ordinarily depend on x, y, and z, as well as three components of velocity), so that the mathematical problem of solving (1.2) is in general formidable. Much of the rest of this book will be devoted to ways of handling these simultaneous equations.

We can obtain one general result in this case, as in the one-dimensional case. This is the theorem, first proved in Eq. (2.3), Chap. I, that the work done on a particle in a certain displacement equals the increase of kinetic energy in that displacement. We proceed as in the one-dimensional case. We take the first of the three Eqs. (1.2), multiply by dx/dt, and integrate with respect to t, from time t_0 to t, proceeding as in the derivation of (2.3), Chap. I. Then we find

$$\frac{1}{2} mv_x^2 - \frac{1}{2} mv_{x0}^2 = \int_{t_0}^{t} F_x \frac{dx}{dt} dt. \tag{1.3}$$

We must look more critically at this equation, however, before accepting it. The force component F_x, we remember, depends in general on x, y, z, dx/dt, dy/dt, dz/dt, and t. We cannot evaluate the integral on the right side of (1.3) unless we know x, y, z, dx/dt, dy/dt, dz/dt as functions of time; that is, unless we know the complete details of the motion. We assume that we know these details, in setting up Eq. (1.3). Proceeding similarly with the y and z components, and adding, we have

$$\tfrac{1}{2}m(v_x^2 + v_y^2 + v_z^2) - \tfrac{1}{2}m(v_{x0}^2 + v_{y0}^2 + v_{z0}^2)$$
$$= \int_{t_0}^{t} (F_x v_x + F_y v_y + F_z v_z) \, dt.$$

We may express this equation in shorter form by using vector notation (the reader who is not familiar with vector methods will find a brief account of the necessary relations in Appendix IV). We have

$$\tfrac{1}{2}mv^2 - \tfrac{1}{2}mv_0^2 = \int_{t_0}^{t} \mathbf{F} \cdot \mathbf{v} \, dt. \tag{1.4}$$

Then, as in one dimension, we define $\tfrac{1}{2}mv^2$ as the kinetic energy, $\mathbf{F} \cdot \mathbf{v}$ as the rate of working of the force, so that (1.4) states that the total work done by the force on the particle, from time t_0 to t, equals the increase of kinetic energy during that time interval. As with the one-dimensional case, the work done can be rewritten in the form

$$\text{Work done} = \int(F_x \, dx + F_y \, dy + F_z \, dz) = \int \mathbf{F} \cdot \mathbf{ds,} \tag{1.5}$$

where $\mathbf{ds}$ is the vector displacement, whose components are dx, dy, dz. In (1.5), remembering that the force depends on position, velocity, and time, in the general case, we cannot carry out the integration unless we know the complete details of the motion, so that at each instant of time along the path we know how to find the force.

Since the work-energy relation of (1.4) demands that the complete details of the motion be known, it is clear that it cannot be useful in the general case in solving for the motion. It is useful only if it leads to the conservation of energy, and we surely cannot expect conservation, by analogy with the one-dimensional case, if the force depends on the velocity or on the time explicitly. Therefore we shall now consider the special case in which the force depends only on the position, and shall inquire in what cases that results in conservation of energy.

2. The Conservation of Energy in Two and Three Dimensions.— If F_x, F_y, F_z depend on x, y, and z, but not on the velocity or time, the integral (1.5), representing the work done, becomes a line integral. That is, we can compute it if we know the line, or path, along which the motion occurs, without knowing the time at which the particle reached each point of the path in its motion. To compute it, using the vector form of (1.5), we proceed as follows: We divide the path into small intervals **ds**; we compute the force acting on the particle in each of those intervals, which we can do since the force depends only on the position; we take the component of force in the direction of **ds,** and multiply by the magnitude of **ds** (in other words, we find **F · ds**); finally, we sum over all elements **ds** of the path. Thus the work done, (1.5), depends in this case on the path, as well as on the initial point x_0, y_0, z_0, and the final point x, y, z, between which the motion occurs. We shall now ask under what conditions we can get conservation of energy.

In Chap. I, Eqs. (2.4) to (2.6), the essential step in deriving the conservation of energy, beyond what we have already established in Eq. (1.4) or (1.5), was Eq. (2.4):

$$V(x) - V(x_0) = - \int_{x_0}^{x} F \, dx.$$

This allowed us to write the work done as the difference between the potential energies at the initial and final points, and when inserted in the work-energy equation, which in our present case is (1.4), it allowed us to define a total energy that stayed constant. The same situation holds in the present case: if we can write the work done, $\int$**F · ds** of (1.5), as the difference between the potential energies at the two end points of our path, or can write

$$V(x,y,z) - V(x_0,y_0,z_0) = - \int_{x_0y_0z_0}^{xyz} \mathbf{F} \cdot \mathbf{ds}, \qquad (2.1)$$

then we can insert this relation in (1.4), with the result

$$\tfrac{1}{2}mv^2 + V(x,y,z) = \tfrac{1}{2}mv_0^2 + V(x_0,y_0,z_0) = E, \qquad (2.2)$$

where, as in Chap. I, E is the total energy, and stays constant during the motion. The difference between the present case and the previous one is that, before, we could always write the work done as the difference of potential energies, provided that the force was a function of position only. Here, on the contrary, it is only in an exceptional case that the relation (2.1) is correct. For we see what it means: the line integral of $\mathbf{F} \cdot \mathbf{ds}$, from the starting point $x_0 y_0 z_0$ to the final point xyz, must depend only on these end points of the path, and be independent of the particular path along which we travel from the initial to the final point.

Let us first show, by simple examples, that in some cases the line integral of the force times the displacement is independent of path, and in other equally simple cases it is not. We consider the two cases of two-dimensional motion,

$$(a) \qquad\qquad F_x = x, \qquad F_y = 0,$$
$$(b) \qquad\qquad F_x = y, \qquad F_y = 0. \qquad\qquad (2.3)$$

In case (a), the work done is $\int_{x_0 y_0}^{xy} x\,dx = \frac{1}{2}(x^2 - x_0^2)$, a quantity depending only on the end points of the path, so that a potential energy function can be immediately set up. In case (b), however, the work done is $\int_{x_0 y_0}^{xy} y\,dx$. This is the formula for the area under the curve connecting the point $x_0 y_0$ and the point xy in the xy plane. Obviously this area can be anything we please, depending on the particular curve chosen to connect these two points. Hence in case (b) no potential energy function can be set up. In these two cases it is easy to see whether there is conservation of energy or not, and to set up the potential energy when there is, but in the general case it is not so simple. We shall therefore consider next the general problem of setting up a test to show in any particular case whether the force is conservative or not.

We shall first find a necessary condition for a force to be conservative, by assuming that a potential energy function V exists, and showing that this leads to a necessary relation among the force components F_x, F_y, and F_z. Let us find the work done in the small displacement of components dx, dy, dz. By (2.1), we have

$$V(x + dx, y + dy, z + dz) - V(x,y,z) = -(F_x\,dx + F_y\,dy + F_z\,dz).$$

On the other hand, by the fundamental theorem of partial differentiation, this can be rewritten

$$V(x + dx, y + dy, z + dz) - V(x,y,z) = \frac{\partial V}{\partial x}\,dx + \frac{\partial V}{\partial y}\,dy + \frac{\partial V}{\partial z}\,dz.$$

Equating, we have

$$F_x = -\frac{\partial V}{\partial x}, \qquad F_y = -\frac{\partial V}{\partial y}, \qquad F_z = -\frac{\partial V}{\partial z}. \qquad (2.4)$$

In vector language, the vector of components $\partial V/\partial x$, $\partial V/\partial y$, $\partial V/\partial z$, is called the "gradient" of V, abbreviated grad V, so that we have

$$\mathbf{F} = -\text{ grad } V. \qquad (2.5)$$

Now we may differentiate the first of Eqs. (2.4) with respect to y, the second with respect to x; noting that a second partial derivative with respect to two variables is independent of the order of differentiation, we have

$$\frac{\partial F_x}{\partial y} = -\frac{\partial^2 V}{\partial y \, \partial x} = -\frac{\partial^2 V}{\partial x \, \partial y} = \frac{\partial F_y}{\partial x}. \qquad (2.6)$$

Proceeding similarly with the other pairs of variables, we obtain the three conditions

$$\frac{\partial F_z}{\partial y} - \frac{\partial F_y}{\partial z} = 0, \qquad \frac{\partial F_x}{\partial z} - \frac{\partial F_z}{\partial x} = 0, \qquad \frac{\partial F_y}{\partial x} - \frac{\partial F_x}{\partial y} = 0. \qquad (2.7)$$

These equations may also be expressed in vector language, for the three quantities of (2.7) are the three components of the vector defined as the curl of $\mathbf{F}$. Thus we have

$$\text{curl } \mathbf{F} = 0 \qquad (2.8)$$

as a necessary condition for the existence of a potential function. This results from the vector relation that the curl of any gradient is zero, a relation that we have proved in (2.6) and (2.7), since we made no assumption in (2.5) beyond that of letting $\mathbf{F}$ be the gradient of a scalar quantity.

Equation (2.7) or (2.8) forms a simple test for the existence of a potential function, if we are given the components of force. Applying to the two examples of (2.3), we find at once that case (*a*) has a force whose curl is zero, and case (*b*) does not, so that our previous conclusion is verified regarding these two cases. The test is simple to apply in any case, and is a very valuable and important one. Before we leave it, we should point out that it is not only a necessary condition for the existence of a potential energy, but also a sufficient condition. We prove this from Stokes's theorem, discussed in Appendix IV. Stokes's theorem can be stated in words in the following way: Suppose we have a closed path, and a vector function such as $\mathbf{F}$, and that we find the line integral $\int \mathbf{F} \cdot \mathbf{ds}$ around the complete path, from

a starting point back to the same starting point.   Assume also that
we have some surface in space, arbitrary except that its bounding
edge is formed by the closed path just mentioned.   We divide up this
surface into small elements of area, at each element find the component
of curl **F** normal to the element, multiply this normal component of
curl **F** by the element of area, and integrate over the surface, forming
the surface integral of the normal component of curl **F**.   Then Stokes's
theorem states that the line integral of the tangential component of
F around the path, $\int$**F** $\cdot$ **ds**, taken in a path in the counterclockwise
sense about the surface, equals the surface integral of the normal
component of curl **F**, over the arbitrary surface spanning the path.

We can apply this theorem in the following way in our present case:
We wish to prove that, if curl **F** = 0, the line integral $\int_{x_0 y_0 z_0}^{xyz}$ **F** $\cdot$ **ds**
from $x_0 y_0 z_0$ to xyz is independent of the path.   Let us consider two
paths a and b leading from $x_0 y_0 z_0$ to xyz.   The difference between
the line integrals along the paths a and b connecting $x_0 y_0 z_0$ and xyz
is evidently the integral around the complete path, from $x_0 y_0 z_0$ to
xyz along a, and back again along b; for reversing the direction of a
line integral merely changes the sign of the integral.   Thus we wish
to prove that the line integral of **F** $\cdot$ **ds** around the complete path is
zero.   But, since by hypothesis curl **F** = 0, Stokes's theorem tells us
that this line integral is zero, and our result is proved.

Since the vanishing of curl **F** is a sufficient as well as a necessary
condition for the existence of a potential energy function, we can
now proceed in the following way to find the potential energy in any
particular case: First, if we are given **F** as a function of x, y, and z,
we compute curl **F**, and see if it is zero.   If it is, then we know that
the line integral $\int_{x_0 y_0 z_0}^{xyz}$ **F** $\cdot$ **ds** is independent of the path used in
traveling from $x_0 y_0 z_0$ to xyz.   Then we may use (2.1) to find
$V(x,y,z) - V(x_0,y_0,z_0)$, by integrating **F** $\cdot$ **ds** along any arbitrary path
from $x_0 y_0 z_0$ to xyz.   Naturally we use the path along which the
mathematical problem of computing the integral is the simplest.   We
may be sure that we should have found the same answer by using any
other path.   This then gives a complete solution to the problem of
setting up the potential energy, once the force is known.   It of
course defines only the difference of potential energy between two
points; this is always the case in the determination of potential
energy.   We may always choose the value of potential energy at a
particular point $x_0 y_0 z_0$ at will, making whatever choice seems convenient.   A similar arbitrary constant will enter into the total energy.

E, in (2.2), but it will always cancel out when we make practical use of the energy method, for we always take the difference between the potential energy at two points, or else use the difference $E - V$.

Before leaving the problem of potential energy functions and conservative fields, we shall describe graphical methods of plotting them which are very useful in visualizing the situation. If a potential energy function exists, we may draw surfaces (in three dimensions) or curves (in two dimensions) on which the potential energy is con-

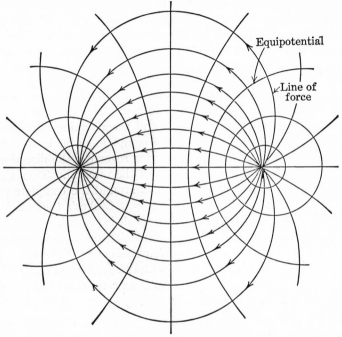

Fig. 7.—Equipotentials and lines of force for an attracting and a repelling center.

stant. These are called "equipotentials." For instance, in case (*a*), Eq. (2.3), the equipotentials are the lines $x =$ constant; in the case of a central field, in which the potential depends on the distance from an attracting center, they are concentric spherical surfaces with centers at the centers of attraction. We may also draw lines that at every point are in the direction of the force vector through that point; these are called "lines of force." Such lines of force and equipotentials are familiar, for instance, from the case of electrostatic forces.

In Fig. 7, we show equipotentials and lines of force for a simple two-dimensional problem of one attracting and one repelling center of force, which is similar to the magnetic problem of lines of force around a bar magnet.   We note that the equipotentials and lines of force intersect at right angles.   This is a general relationship, which can be proved very easily.   By definition, no work can be done in a displacement from one point to another of the same equipotential.   Thus the force can have no component along the direction of any displacement lying on the equipotential; hence it must be at right angles to the equipotential.   This provides a simple graphical way of sketching in the lines of force when the equipotentials are known, or vice versa. More than this, the method of the potential allows us to compute forces in many cases more conveniently than by direct calculation.   In a number of types of problems, such as gravitational, electrostatic, and magnetostatic problems, the potential energy of a particle at a given point can be written as the sum of the potential energies of interaction between the particle and a number of point masses, or charges, or poles, each of which contributes a term to the potential energy depending only on the distance.   This potential energy can then be easily calculated.   After finding the total potential energy, we take its gradient to find the force.   This is simpler than the method of directly computing the force; for in that method, we find the force of attraction or repulsion exerted by each of the attracting or repelling centers of force, and must then find the vector sum of these forces.   It is generally more trouble mathematically to find this vector sum, than to add the potential energies, which are scalars, and then to take the gradient of the resulting function.

In problems of motion in two and three dimensions, the potential can often be used to discuss the nature of the motion qualitatively, much as we have done for one-dimensional motion in Chap. I, Sec. 3. Thus for two-dimensional motion, we may plot the potential energy V as a function of the coordinates x and y.   We imagine a ball to roll on the resulting surface; its motion gives an approximate picture of the actual motion of the particle.   Thus, if the potential energy surface has a minimum, a bowl-shaped depression, the ball can oscillate in its neighborhood, showing that there are stable orbits near potential minima.   On the other hand, if the ball has too much energy, it can climb over the potential maximum between one depression and another, as one can climb over a mountain pass from one valley to another.   Using such pictures, and drawing on our intuitive knowledge of the rolling of balls, we can get much insight into the orbits of two-dimensional problems; but likewise we can easily convince ourselves that the problem is vastly more complicated than for one dimension. The reason fundamentally is that, instead of having the velocity at a given point uniquely determined by the energy, except for the question of whether it moves in the positive or negative direction, as it is in one dimension, we find in the two-dimensional problem that the direction of the velocity at a given point is not determined by the energy at all, but only its magnitude. Thus we can have an infinite variety of orbits, and except in the very simplest case the discussion of these orbits is exceedingly difficult.

3. Motion of a Particle in a Central Field.—In the preceding section, we have seen that not all force fields in which the force is a function of position only are conservative. We found a simple test to tell whether any given force field is conservative, however, and set up a method for finding the potential energy from the force, if it is conservative. For a conservative force, we have shown that the law of conservation of energy holds, as in the one-dimensional problem. But we have mentioned that we cannot take the further step that was possible in the one-dimensional case, and derive a general method of solution of the equations of motion, based on the energy integral. We shall now consider the special case of central motion, in which we can get an explicit solution; by studying it, we shall see why the method we use there cannot be applied in the general case, and shall get an insight into the difficulties of the general problem. We shall handle this problem in the present chapter by very elementary methods, postponing until the next chapter a more general discussion.

By a central field we mean a force field in which the force always points directly toward or away from a central point, which we may choose to be the origin, and furthermore in which the magnitude of the force depends only on the distance from the central point. In this case we can easily prove by elementary methods that the force is conservative. Let the magnitude of the force be $F(r)$, where r is the distance from the center to the point in question. Consider the quantity $\mathbf{F} \cdot \mathbf{ds}$, which we must sum to find the work done along an arbitrary path. We may find this by multiplying the magnitude of the force by the component of $\mathbf{ds}$ along the force. Since the force is along r, this component of $\mathbf{ds}$ is simply dr, the change in r. Thus (2.1) becomes

$$V(x,y,z) - V(v_0,y_0,z_0) = - \int_{r_0}^{r} F(r) \, dr. \tag{3.1}$$

where the integral obviously depends only on the values of r at the initial and final points. As a result, the potential energy can be written as a function of r: $V = V(r)$. We clearly have from (3.1)

$$F(r) = -\frac{dV}{dr}.$$

If we remember that $r = \sqrt{x^2 + y^2 + z^2}$, so that

$$\frac{\partial r}{\partial x} = \frac{x}{r}, \qquad \frac{\partial r}{\partial y} = \frac{y}{r}, \qquad \frac{\partial r}{\partial z} = \frac{z}{r}, \qquad (3.2)$$

we may find the components of F, using (2.4), in the form

$$F_x = \frac{x}{r} F(r), \qquad F_y = \frac{y}{r} F(r), \qquad F_z = \frac{z}{r} F(r). \qquad (3.3)$$

Equation (3.3) expresses a general central force in terms of its components. It is a simple exercise to verify the fact that this force has a curl equal to zero, by substituting in (2.7), and using (3.2).

There are a number of very familiar and important examples of central forces in physics. Most famous is the gravitational attraction between two spherical masses, which can be shown to act as if each mass were concentrated at its center, and to result in an attractive force proportional to the product of the masses, and inversely proportional to the square of the distance between. That is, if M and m are the two masses, r the distance between, we have

$$F(r) = -\gamma \frac{Mm}{r^2}, \qquad (3.4)$$

where γ is called the "gravitational constant." Its value in the cgs system is 6.658×10^{-8}; that is, if M and m are in grams, r in centimeters, $F(r)$ will come out in dynes. In the mks system, the constant is 6.658×10^{-11}; we shall not have occasion to use it in the English system. With the force given by (3.4), the potential energy may be written

$$V(r) = -\gamma \frac{Mm}{r}.$$

As we have mentioned before, we could add any arbitrary constant to this value; our choice is dictated by convenience, and amounts to choosing the potential energy to be zero at infinity.

A second famous example of central forces is the attraction or repulsion between point charges in electrostatics. Coulomb's law states that two point charges, of magnitude q and q', repel each other with a force

$$F(r) = \frac{qq'}{r^2} \qquad (3.5)$$

if q and q' are expressed in electrostatic units, r in centimeters, and F in dynes, or with a force

$$F(r) = \frac{qq'}{4\pi\epsilon_0 r^2} \tag{3.6}$$

where

$$\epsilon_0 = 8.85 \times 10^{-12} \text{ farads per meter,}$$

where q and q' are expressed in coulombs, r in meters, and F in newtons. We note that, if q and q' are of opposite sign, the force will be negative, representing an attraction instead of a repulsion. The potential energy for the Coulomb law is

$$V(r) = \frac{qq'}{r} \tag{3.7}$$

for cgs units as in (3.5), and

$$V(r) = \frac{qq'}{4\pi\epsilon_0 r} \tag{3.8}$$

for mks units as in (3.6).

Another simple and familiar central force is an attraction to the origin, proportional to the distance from it:

$$F(r) = -ar, \qquad V(r) = \tfrac{1}{2}ar^2.$$

The components of force in this case are

$$F_x = -ax, \qquad F_y = -ay, \qquad F_z = -az,$$

so that the equations of motion (1.2) break up into three separate equations, one involving x, the next y, the last z only, which can be solved independently, each leading to simple harmonic motion as in the preceding chapter. This is the case of the three-dimensional linear oscillator.

More generally, we notice that all the examples we have mentioned are special cases of the general formula

$$F(r) = \text{constant } r^n, \tag{3.9}$$

where n is an integer, with a potential energy

$$V(r) = -\text{constant } \frac{r^{n+1}}{n+1},$$

which holds except when $n = -1$. The gravitational and Coulomb cases correspond to $n = -2$, the three-dimensional linear oscillator to $n = 1$. The cases for other values of n are of less physical interest, but they are sometimes encountered. Fortunately the method of solution that we shall now describe holds quite generally, not merely for any value of n in (3.9), but for any arbitrary central force.

The first point to notice about motion under a central force is that the motion takes place in a plane. Suppose the motion starts with a certain initial velocity $\mathbf{v}_0$ (a vector) at time t_0. A plane is determined by the radius vector $\mathbf{r}_0$, of components x_0, y_0, z_0, and by the velocity $\mathbf{v}_0$, and the motion never leaves this plane. To see this, we notice that at t_0 there is no force perpendicular to the plane. Thus there is no component of acceleration perpendicular to it, so that the velocity remains in the plane. Carrying on from instant to instant, the same plane will be determined at any later instant by radius vector and velocity vector, and this plane will remain permanently the plane of the orbit. Thus we may take x and y axes in this plane, and the problem becomes a two-dimensional one.

Considering central motion in a plane, we know from elementary mechanics that the problem is greatly simplified if we introduce polar coordinates, with the origin at the center of attraction. Kinematically we describe the particle by the polar coordinates r, θ, defined in terms of x and y by the relations

$$x = r \cos \theta, \qquad y = r \sin \theta. \tag{3.10}$$

The components of velocity and acceleration, denoting time derivatives by a single dot and second time derivatives by a double dot, are

$$\dot{x} = \dot{r} \cos \theta - r\dot{\theta} \sin \theta, \qquad \dot{y} = \dot{r} \sin \theta + r\dot{\theta} \cos \theta$$
$$\ddot{x} = \ddot{r} \cos \theta - 2\dot{r}\dot{\theta} \sin \theta - r\dot{\theta}^2 \cos \theta - r\ddot{\theta} \sin \theta$$
$$\ddot{y} = \ddot{r} \sin \theta + 2\dot{r}\dot{\theta} \cos \theta - r\dot{\theta}^2 \sin \theta + r\ddot{\theta} \cos \theta \tag{3.11}$$

We next find components of velocity and acceleration, not in the xy coordinates, but along the directions of increasing r and of increasing θ. Calling these v_r, v_θ, a_r, a_θ, we have

$$v_r = \dot{x} \cos \theta + \dot{y} \sin \theta = \dot{r}$$
$$v_\theta = -\dot{x} \sin \theta + \dot{y} \cos \theta = r\dot{\theta}$$
$$a_r = \ddot{x} \cos \theta + \ddot{y} \sin \theta = \ddot{r} - r\dot{\theta}^2$$
$$a_\theta = -\ddot{x} \sin \theta + \ddot{y} \cos \theta = 2\dot{r}\dot{\theta} + r\ddot{\theta}. \tag{3.12}$$

To make connections with elementary work, we remember that the angular velocity is defined by

$$\omega = \dot{\theta}$$

and the angular acceleration by

$$\alpha = \ddot{\theta}.$$

Then the component of velocity in the direction of increasing θ is $r\omega$. The component of acceleration along r includes not only $\ddot{r}$, generally called the "radial acceleration," but also the term

$$-r\omega^2 = -\frac{v_\theta^2}{r},$$

the centripetal acceleration, or the acceleration toward the origin that results from uniform motion in a circle of radius r. The acceleration along the direction of increasing θ includes not only the term $r\alpha$, but also the term $2\dot{r}\dot{\theta}$, which is usually not computed in elementary treatments, but which may be called the "Coriolis acceleration," since the force associated with it is called the "Coriolis force."

For a general force, with components F_r, F_θ along the directions of increasing r and θ, the equations of motion become

$$m\frac{d^2r}{dt^2} - mr\left(\frac{d\theta}{dt}\right)^2 = F_r, \qquad mr\frac{d^2\theta}{dt^2} + 2m\frac{dr}{dt}\frac{d\theta}{dt} = F_\theta. \quad (3.13)$$

The second of these equations may be rewritten in the form

$$\frac{d}{dt}\left(mr^2\frac{d\theta}{dt}\right) = rF_\theta. \quad (3.14)$$

The quantity $mr^2(d\theta/dt)$ is called the "angular momentum," mr^2 the "moment of inertia," rF_θ the "moment" of the force F, or the "torque." Thus, if the angular momentum is called p, the moment of inertia I, and the torque M, we have

$$p = I\omega, \qquad \frac{dp}{dt} = M. \quad (3.15)$$

In the general case, r and θ are mixed up inextricably in the equations of motion (3.13) and (3.14), and we are no nearer a solution in polar coordinates than we were in rectangular coordinates. For a central force, however, the torque M is zero, so that (3.15) states that the angular momentum is constant. That is, this forms an integral of the motion, just as the energy does. This allows us to carry out a complete solution of the problem.

To make use of the constancy of angular momentum in the central field problem, we write θ in terms of r and p. We have

$$mr^2\frac{d\theta}{dt} = p, \qquad \frac{d\theta}{dt} = \frac{p}{mr^2}. \quad (3.16)$$

We can then use this in the first equation of (3.13), which becomes

$$m\frac{d^2r}{dt^2} = F(r) + \frac{p^2}{mr^3}. \quad (3.17)$$

That is, we have reduced the problem to a one-dimensional one of motion along r; the apparent force, however, is not merely $F(r)$, but there is an additional force tending to increase r, inversely proportional to r^3, resulting from the rotation. This is the centrifugal force, a fictitious force that must be added in the radial problem to make it formally like a one-dimensional problem.

Having reduced our problem to a one-dimensional one, we can use the method of conservation of energy to get a complete solution. We can set up an effective potential energy, $V'(r)$, given by

$$V'(r) = V(r) + \frac{p^2}{2mr^2} \qquad (3.18)$$

whose negative derivative with respect to r gives the apparent force on the right side of (3.17). We can then proceed just as in Chap. I, Eq. (2.8), and find the solution for time as a function of r:

$$t - t_0 = \int_{r_0}^{r} \frac{dr}{\sqrt{2(E - V')/m}}. \qquad (3.19)$$

From Eq. (3.19), we can find r as a function of time, in terms of three arbitrary constants: the energy E, the angular momentum p, and the value of radius r_0 when time is t_0. Having found r as a function of time, we can use (3.16) to get θ as a function of time, by a single integration, introducing one additional arbitrary constant, the value θ_0 when $t = t_0$. These four constants are the proper number for our problem, which contains two second order differential equations, each of which requires two arbitrary constants. If we are given our initial conditions by the statement that the positions and velocities have specified values at $t = t_0$, we can determine the energy and angular momentum from these initial conditions. The angular momentum can be found directly from (3.16), and the energy from the equation

$$
\begin{aligned}
E &= \frac{1}{2} m(v_r^2 + v_\theta^2) + V(r) \\
&= \frac{1}{2} m \left(\frac{dr}{dt}\right)^2 + \frac{1}{2} mr^2 \left(\frac{d\theta}{dt}\right)^2 + V(r) \\
&= \frac{1}{2} m \left(\frac{dr}{dt}\right)^2 + V'(r).
\end{aligned}
\qquad (3.20)
$$

It is interesting and significant to note from these formulas that the extra term $p^2/2mr^2$ which must be added to $V(r)$ to get the effective potential energy $V'(r)$ is just the kinetic energy $\frac{1}{2}I\omega^2$ associated with the rotational motion. The fact that this contributes the centrifugal force term to the equation of radial motion is a result of the fact that, when the angular momentum remains constant, this term in the kinetic energy depends on r, so that it acts in a sense like a potential energy.

4. The Inverse Square Law.—If two particles attract each other according to the inverse square law, the center of mass of the system remains fixed, and either one may be considered as attracted to this center of mass with a force varying inversely as the square of the distance from the particle to the center of mass. Familiar examples are a planet attracted by the sun, and an electron (according to classical mechanics) attracted by a positive nucleus. A particle moving according to such a force obeys Kepler's laws: first, the particle travels in an ellipse or hyperbola, or their special cases a circle or parabola, with the attracting center at one of the foci; secondly, the radius vector from the center to the particle sweeps out equal areas in equal times; thirdly, for the elliptical orbits, which result in periodic motions, the squares of the periods of rotation are proportional to the cubes of the major axes of the orbits. In the present section we shall prove these results, and show how they fit in with our general treatment of the central field problem.

We begin by considering a few simple properties of the conic sections, the ellipse and hyperbola (and their limiting cases the circle and parabola). In Fig. 8 we show an ellipse and a hyperbola. The fundamental geometrical definition of the ellipse states that the sum of the distances from the two foci to any point on the ellipse is a constant, which we shall call $2a$. A little reflection will show that the major axis, or longest diameter, of the ellipse, must equal $2a$, so that a is the semimajor axis. The distance between foci is called $2a\epsilon$, where ϵ, which must clearly be less than unity, is called the "eccentricity." If the eccentricity is zero, the ellipse degenerates to a circle; if it is unity, and simultaneously the major axis becomes infinite, the ellipse becomes a parabola. Let us find the equation of the ellipse in polar coordinates, the right-hand focus being the origin. If r is the distance from the origin to a point of the ellipse, r' the distance from the other focus to the same point, then by the law of cosines we have

$$r' = \sqrt{r^2 + (2a\epsilon)^2 + 2r(2a\epsilon)\cos\theta}.$$

Writing the equation of the ellipse in the form $r + r' = 2a$, squaring and canceling terms, we have

$$r = \frac{a(1 - \epsilon^2)}{1 + \epsilon \cos \theta}.$$ (4.1)

Similarly we consider the hyperbola.   Here the difference between the distances of any point of the curve to the two foci is constant. As before, we call the constant 2a, and see that it equals the shortest

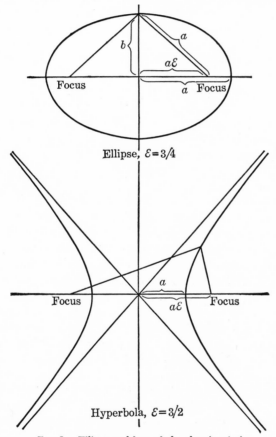

Fig. 8.—Ellipse and hyperbola, showing foci.

distance between the two branches of the hyperbola.   Again we call the distance between foci 2aε, where now the eccentricity ε is greater than unity.   The equation of the hyperbola is $r' - r = 2a$ (for the right-hand branch), and, proceeding as before, this becomes

$$r = \frac{a(\epsilon^2 - 1)}{1 - \epsilon \cos \theta}.$$ (4.2)

We note that, since ϵ is greater than unity for the hyperbola, the denominator can become zero, and r infinite, for two values of θ, the asymptotes. On the other hand, in the equation (4.1) for the ellipse, the denominator never becomes zero, and r always stays finite.

We shall now prove Kepler's first law, that the orbit of a particle moving according to the inverse square law is a conic section. For definiteness, we assume that the particle is a mass m, moving under the gravitational attraction of a mass M which is so large that it can be assumed to remain fixed at the origin (as, for instance, the sun). Then Eq. (3.17) becomes

$$m \frac{d^2r}{dt^2} = -\gamma \frac{mM}{r^2} + \frac{p^2}{mr^3}. \tag{4.3}$$

Also from (3.16) we have

$$\frac{d\theta}{dt} = \frac{p}{mr^2}. \tag{4.4}$$

We now wish to derive the equation of the orbit, the relation between r and θ, eliminating the time, to show that this equation takes the form (4.1) or (4.2). This is most easily done by making the substitution $u = 1/r$. Making this substitution, we have

$$\frac{dr}{dt} = -\frac{1}{u^2} \frac{du}{d\theta} \frac{d\theta}{dt} = -\frac{p}{m} \frac{du}{d\theta}$$

$$\frac{d^2r}{dt^2} = -\frac{p}{m} \frac{d^2u}{d\theta^2} \frac{d\theta}{dt} = -\left(\frac{p}{m}\right)^2 \frac{d^2u}{d\theta^2} u^2.$$

Substituting into (4.3), we have

$$\frac{d^2u}{d\theta^2} + u = \gamma \frac{m^2M}{p^2}. \tag{4.5}$$

Equation (4.5) is of a familiar type; if θ were the time instead of the angle, it would be the equation for simple harmonic motion, with a constant impressed force. Its general solution may be written in the form

$$u = \frac{1}{r} = \gamma \frac{m^2M}{p^2} + A \cos(\theta - \theta_0). \tag{4.6}$$

We may now compare the solution (4.6) with Eqs. (4.1) and (4.2) for the ellipse and hyperbola. Clearly they are of the same form. If we choose the orientation of the orbit so that $\theta_0 = 0$, then by comparison we see that A is related to the eccentricity by the relation

$$A = \pm \epsilon \gamma \, \frac{m^2 M}{p^2}. \tag{4.7}$$

Then we have

$$a = \frac{p^2}{\gamma m^2 M |\epsilon^2 - 1|}. \tag{4.8}$$

With this assumption, (4.6) then becomes equivalent to (4.1) or (4.2), depending on whether ϵ is less than or greater than unity, so that we have proved Kepler's first law.

Next we consider Kepler's second law, that the area swept out by the radius vector is proportional to the time. This is a direct consequence of (4.4), and holds for any central motion in which the angular momentum is conserved, not merely for motion under the inverse square law. In time dt, the radius vector will sweep out a small triangle of altitude r, base $r \, d\theta$, in consequence of the increase of θ. This triangle has an area $\frac{1}{2} r^2 \, d\theta$. Thus the rate of sweeping out of area is

$$\frac{d \, (\text{area})}{dt} = \frac{1}{2} r^2 \frac{d\theta}{dt} = \frac{p}{2m} \tag{4.9}$$

and is constant, on account of the constancy of angular momentum p.

We may now use Kepler's second law to give a derivation of his third law, relating the period of rotation to the major axis of the ellipse, in the elliptical case. Integrating (4.9) about a complete period, we have

$$\text{Period } T = \frac{2m}{p} \, (\text{area}). \tag{4.10}$$

We may find the area of the elliptical orbit from the semimajor axis a and the semiminor axis b. We have found the former in (4.8). To find b, we note from Fig. 8 that the quantities $a\epsilon$, b, and a form the two legs and the hypotenuse of a right triangle, so that

$$b = a \sqrt{1 - \epsilon^2}.$$

The area of an ellipse is $\pi a b$. Thus, substituting in (4.10), we have

$$\left(\frac{T}{2\pi}\right)^2 = \frac{m^2(1 - \epsilon^2)a^4}{p^2} = \frac{a^3}{\gamma M}. \tag{4.11}$$

Thus we verify Kepler's third law that the square of the period of rotation is proportional to the cube of the major axis of the orbit, independent of the minor axis, and also independent of the mass of the particle. We note that, as the major axis becomes infinite, the period also becomes infinite; naturally the hyperbolic orbits all require infinite time for the particle to traverse them, so that there is nothing equivalent to Kepler's third law for them.

5. The Energy Method for the Inverse Square Law.—We have so far based our solution of the problem of motion under the inverse square law on the equation of motion, (4.3). We may also proceed

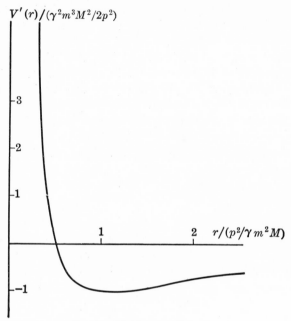

FIG. 9.—V' (r) as function of r.

by use of the energy method, as in Eqs. (3.18) to (3.20). The energy, from (3.18) and (3.20), is

$$E = \frac{1}{2} m \left(\frac{dr}{dt}\right)^2 + \frac{p^2}{2mr^2} - \gamma \frac{mM}{r}. \tag{5.1}$$

Before using this to discuss the motion, let us compute the energy in terms of the properties of the orbit, using the methods of Sec. 4. Since the energy remains constant during the motion, we may compute E at any instant, and the convenient time at which to make the calculation is the time at which $dr/dt = 0$, or at the maximum or minimum value of r. From (4.6) and (4.7) we have

$$\frac{1}{r_{\min,\max}} = \gamma \frac{m^2M}{p^2} (1 \pm \epsilon), \tag{5.2}$$

where the + sign gives the minimum r, the − sign the maximum.

Substituting these values in (5.1), we find

$$E = \frac{\gamma^2 m^3 M^2}{2p^2} (\epsilon^2 - 1). \tag{5.3}$$

That is, the energy is positive for the hyperbolic orbits, negative for the elliptical orbits. Using (4.8), we can rewrite this

$$E = \pm \gamma \frac{mM}{2a}, \tag{5.4}$$

where the $+$ sign is used for hyperbolic, the $-$ for elliptical, orbits. From (4.11) and (5.4) we see the interesting facts that all elliptic orbits of the same major axis have the same energy, and also the same period. We may combine the formulas into the expression

$$\frac{T}{2\pi} = \gamma M \left(\frac{m}{-2E}\right)^{3/2}. \tag{5.5}$$

To discuss the motion qualitatively, using the energy integral, we may plot the effective potential energy

$$V'(r) = \frac{p^2}{2mr^2} - \gamma \frac{mM}{r} \tag{5.6}$$

as in Fig. 9. We see that this effective potential energy has a minimum, at a value of r given by

$$-\frac{p^2}{mr^3} + \gamma \frac{mM}{r^2} = 0, \qquad r = \frac{p^2}{\gamma m^2 M},$$

which comes about when the attractive force is balanced by the centrifugal force. The corresponding value of $V'(r)$ is easily seen to be $-\gamma mM/2r$. If the energy has this value, the motion is in a circular orbit. We note that in this orbit the potential energy is $-\gamma mM/r$, and the term $p^2/2mr^2$, which in this case is the complete kinetic energy, since the term in $(dr/dt)^2$ is zero, is $\gamma mM/2r$. Thus in the case of the circular orbit, the kinetic energy is minus half the potential energy, so that the total energy is half the potential energy. It can be proved, by methods more advanced than we are employing at the moment, that this result is true for the elliptical orbits as well, if we state it in terms of time averages: the average kinetic energy is half the negative of the average potential energy, or the negative of the total energy. This is a general result for inverse square forces; an analogous result holds for other central forces.

For energies between the energy of the circular orbit, and zero, it is clear from Fig. 9 that a line of constant energy intersects the curve of $V'(r)$ twice, so that the motion takes place between two values of r, given by (5.2), where ϵ in (5.2) can be found by solving (5.3) for ϵ as a function of E. These orbits are the elliptical orbits. On the other hand, for positive energies, it is obvious from Fig. 9 that the orbit is not periodic, but rather that the particle comes in from infinity to a minimum distance, reverses, and recedes to infinity again. This is the description, in terms of r, of the hyperbolic orbits.

We may use the method of energy in the familiar way to find r, and also θ, as functions of time. For r, we have

$$dt = \frac{dr}{\sqrt{(2/m)[E + (\gamma mM/r) - (p^2/2mr^2)]}}.$$

This can be integrated, though we shall not carry it through; it is essentially the same problem taken up in Probs. 16, 17, and 18 of Chap. I. If we integrate from r_{min} to r_{max} of (5.2), we shall have half the period, and we find easily that the period is given by (5.5), which we have already found by another method. Also we can find θ. From (3.16) we may write

$$dt = \frac{mr^2}{p} d\theta.$$

We write r in terms of θ, from (4.1). This expression can be integrated to give t as a function of θ, and here as before we can find the period, by carrying out the integral from $\theta = 0$ to 2π, again with the same result as before.

We have now given a fairly complete discussion of the motion of a particle under the action of the inverse square law. One obvious example of this theory is the motion of the planets, comets, and other bodies around the sun, for which the theory was originally devised. The planets move in elliptical orbits of slight eccentricity, almost circular. Some of the comets move in much more eccentric elliptical orbits, and occasional objects enter the solar system from outside, in hyperbolic orbits.

A second example is found in atomic structure, where the hydrogen atom consists of a light body, an electron, moving under the electrostatic inverse square attraction about a heavy nucleus. Atoms are really governed by wave mechanics, not by Newtonian mechanics. Nevertheless there are such widespread analogies between the two theories that a thorough knowledge of planetary motion has been of the greatest value in working out the explanation of atomic structure. There can be hyperbolic as well as elliptical orbits in such problems.   Our analysis is only slightly changed if the inverse square law is repulsive, rather than attractive, as would be the case with the repulsion between two like electric charges.   In this case, the energy term in $1/r$, in (5.6), will be positive, so that the effective potential energy will have no minimum, but will always be greater than the value zero which it has at infinity.   Thus there are no periodic orbits in this case, only hyperbolic orbits.   This problem is met when the nuclei of atoms are bombarded with heavy positively charged particles, as alpha particles.   Rutherford's experiments, which verified the existence of atomic nuclei, consisted of a study of the scattering of alpha particles by atoms, and the distribution in angle of the scattered particles.   The calculation was made by the methods of the present chapter, and the excellent agreement between experiment and theory allowed him to draw the definite conclusion that the atoms contained nuclei repelling according to the inverse square law, and allowed him further to estimate the nuclear charges rather accurately.   These calculations of course were made using Newtonian mechanics; it is an interesting fact that for this particular problem wave mechanics gives just the same formula as classical mechanics, so that the agreement with experiment is not destroyed.

In addition to the inverse square law, we can of course use the energy method for discussing other cases of central motion.   Only two other cases of central motion are easy to discuss analytically. First there is the case of a restoring force proportional to the displacement, which we have already mentioned.   Then there is the rather remarkable case of a force inversely proportional to the cube of the distance, in which, as for instance we see from (3.17), the restoring force term has the same dependence on r as the centrifugal force term. If there is no external force at all, (3.17) of course tells us that during the motion r decreases from infinity, goes to a minimum distance, and then increases to infinity again; for the motion is uniform motion in a straight line, and r is the distance from a point on this line to the origin.   In the case of the inverse cube force, we have just the same variation of r with time, only the effective force on the right side of (3.17) is not related in the normal way to the angular momentum, so that the angle must be calculated somewhat differently in (3.16).

Aside from these two cases of the force proportional to r, and inversely as r^3, we must resort to the energy method to get a discussion of the motion.   By that method we can get immediate answers to questions as to whether the motion is periodic or not, and over what

ranges of energy.   One case in which the energy method has been
particularly important is the problem of atoms with many electrons,
in wave mechanics.   The electrons group themselves about the nucleus
so as to give essentially a central field, when we average over time.
In discussing the motion of an electron in such a field, in wave mechanics, we find that the first step is to carry through a similar discussion
of motion by the energy method using classical mechanics; the wave
mechanical solution is based on this classical solution.   It thus comes
about that, in the development of atomic theory, at the hands of Bohr,
Sommerfeld, Hartree, and others, the study of central motion has
been a constant and valuable guide.

Problems

1. Let $F_x = y$, $F_y = -x$, $F_z = 0$.   Prove that this vector field represents a
force tangent to circles about the origin in the xy plane.   Compute $\int \mathbf{F} \cdot \mathbf{ds}$ around
such a circle.   Find the curl of the force, and discuss the question as to whether it
is a conservative field or not.

2. In the gravitational field of a mass m, the potential is given by $-\gamma m/r$,
where r is the distance from the mass, given by $r^2 = x^2 + y^2 + z^2$, if the mass is
at the origin.   Obtain the components of the force vector by direct differentiation.
Find the curl of the force, and show that it is zero.

3. Find which ones of the following forces are derivable from potentials, and
describe the physical nature of the force fields.   Set up the potential in cases
where that can be done:

(a) $\qquad\qquad F_x = \dfrac{y}{x^2 + y^2}, \qquad F_y = \dfrac{-x}{x^2 + y^2}, \qquad F_z = 0.$

(b) $\qquad\qquad F_x = \dfrac{y}{\sqrt{x^2 + y^2}}, \qquad F_y = \dfrac{-x}{\sqrt{x^2 + y^2}}, \qquad F_z = 0.$

(c) $\qquad\qquad F_x = xf(r), \qquad F_y = yf(r), \qquad F_z = zf(r),$

where $f(r)$ is an arbitrary function of the distance from the origin.

(d) $\qquad\qquad\qquad F_x = f_1(x), \qquad F_y = f_2(y), \qquad F_z = f_3(z).$

4. Taking the potential field from Prob. 2, find the line integral $\int \mathbf{F} \cdot \mathbf{ds}$
around a square of arbitrary size in the xy plane, with the origin at its center.
Show by direct calculation that the integral always vanishes.   Do the same for a
path made up as follows: the part of the square of side $2a$, made of lines at $x = -a$,
$y = \pm a$, which lies at negative values of x, and the part of the circle of radius
a, center at the origin, which joins onto and completes the figure for positive x's.

5. A particle of mass m is attracted to a center by a force $-\gamma mM/r^2$.   Find
the necessary relation between energy and angular momentum for perihelion and
aphelion distances to be equal, so that the orbit is circular.   Check this relation
by elementary discussion, balancing the centrifugal force in the circular motion
against the attraction.

6. A particle in an inverse square field executes an elliptical motion with the
center of attraction as a focus.   Find the period of this motion, by considering

the radial motion and using the energy integral, and show that the result agrees with that found in Eq. (5.5).

7. Suppose a particle of mass m, charge e, collides with a very heavy particle that has charge e', so that it repels with a potential energy $ee'/4\pi\epsilon_0 r$, using mks units. The first particle is moving with a velocity v_0 at a great distance, and is aimed so that, if it continued in a straight line, it would pass by the center of repulsion at a minimum distance R. Note that this determines the angular momentum. Using the energy method, find the perihelion distance as a function of R and the velocity of the particle.

8. Discuss in detail the motion of the particle in Prob. **7**, showing that it will be deflected so that after the collision the line of travel will make an angle φ with the initial direction, where $\tan\dfrac{\varphi}{2} = \dfrac{ee'}{4\pi\epsilon_0 m v_0^2 R}$. Such deflections are observed in collisions between alpha particles and atomic nuclei, in Rutherford's scattering experiments.

Suggestions: The particle executes a hyperbolic orbit, and the desired angle is the angle between the asymptotes. Now the equation of a hyperbola is given in (4.2), and the asymptotes come when the denominator is zero, giving the angle of the asymptotes in terms of ϵ. We need then only determine ϵ in terms of energy and angular momentum.

9. A two-dimensional linear oscillator is attracted to a center by a force proportional to the distance, or $F_x = -ax$, $F_y = -ay$. Solve in rectangular coordinates, separating variables, showing that x and y execute independent simple harmonic vibrations with the same frequency. Prove that the resulting orbit is an ellipse, with its center at the center of attraction.

10. Taking the solution of Prob. **9** in rectangular coordinates, find the angular momentum vector by ordinary vector formulas from the displacement and velocity, and prove by direct computation that it remains constant. Find the angular momentum as a function of the dimensions of the elliptical orbit, and show its connection with the area of the orbit.

11. Set up the problem of the two-dimensional linear oscillator, as in Prob. **9**, using polar coordinates. Separate variables, solve the radial problem by the energy method, compute the period in this way, and show that it is in agreement with the period as found in Prob. **9**.

12. Suppose in a two-dimensional oscillator that the force constants along the two axes are only slightly different from each other. Prove that the orbit resembles an ellipse, of slowly changing shape and size. [*Hint:* Show that $x = A \cos(\omega t - \alpha)$, $y = B \cos(\omega t - \beta)$, where A, B, α, and β, are constants, is the equation of the ellipse. Then show that the equation of the path of the oscillator can be written in this form, if α and β are slowly changing functions of time.]

13. A particle moving in two dimensions is attracted by two centers, of the same strength, attracting with a force proportional to the inverse square of the distance. Compute and plot a number of equipotentials, showing that for some energies the motion must be entirely confined to the region around one or the other center, while for larger energies it can surround both centers.

14. A particle moves in three dimensions under the action of a force of attraction to a center, depending only on the distance. Set up the problem in spherical coordinates. Show that the variables can be separated. Show that energy, total angular momentum, and the component of angular momentum along the axis of coordinates, all remain fixed. Using the obvious fact that the motion occurs in a plane and is just like the two-dimensional central motion in that plane, show that the periods of the motions in θ and φ are the same.

15. A particle moves in a plane under the action of a nonconservative force $F_x = 0$, $F_y = f(x)$. Show that the orbit is given by the solution of the equation $\dfrac{d^2y}{dx^2} + Af(x) = 0$, where A is a constant. Discuss the motion in detail when $f(x)$ is a linear function of x.

16. If a planet moving in a circular orbit were suddenly stopped, find how long it would take for it to fall into the sun in terms of its original period.

17. The eccentricity of the earth's orbit around the sun is $\frac{1}{60}$. For how many days of the year is the distance from sun to earth greater than the semimajor axis of the orbit? What are the times of describing the two halves of the orbit, bounded by the *latus rectum* passing through the sun (that is, the straight line perpendicular to the major axis passing through the sun)?

18. A particle performs circular motion in a central field. It is then slightly displaced from the circular orbit. Show that r oscillates about the value characteristic of the circular orbit, in a stable oscillation, only if $-(r/f)(df/dr) < 3$, where $f(r)$ is the force as a function of r, and where the quantity is to be computed at the radius of the circular orbit.

19. A particle moves in the xy plane. Find expressions for the x and y components of acceleration if the xy axes rotate with constant angular velocity ω about the z axis.

20. In a magnetic field **B**, a charge e experiences a force equal to $e(\mathbf{v} \times \mathbf{B})$, where **v** is the velocity vector. An electron moves in an electric field whose potential depends only on the distance from the z axis, and in a uniform magnetic field pointing along the z axis. Set up the equations of motion in a cylindrical coordinate system rotating with a constant angular velocity ω about the z axis. Find the angular velocity ω for which the Coriolis acceleration vanishes, and show that to the first order in the magnetic field the motion of the electron in this rotating system is determined by the electric field alone, but that there is a fictitious potential energy term proportional to the square of the magnetic field and to the square of r. The angular frequency that is found in this way is called the "Larmor frequency."

21. A particle of mass m slides on the inside of a vertical circular track of radius r, the coefficient of friction being μ. If it starts from rest at the end of a horizontal diameter, how high will it rise on the opposite side of the track?

22. Discuss the motion of a projectile in air, assuming a viscous resistance proportional to the speed of the projectile.

23. Show that for an elliptical orbit of small eccentricity ϵ, the radius vector from sun to planet sweeps out an angle θ in time t, given very nearly by

$$\theta = \frac{2\pi t}{T} + 2\epsilon \sin \frac{2\pi t}{T},$$

where T is the period of the motion.

CHAPTER IV

LAGRANGE'S AND HAMILTON'S EQUATIONS

In the preceding chapter we took up the problem of motion in a central field, and we found that it is natural to introduce polar coordinates on account of the symmetry of the problem. This is a simple example of a very common situation, in which the use of coordinates other than rectangular is highly desirable. In Sec. 3 of that chapter we carried out a transformation of the equations of motion from rectangular to polar coordinates and such a transformation can always be carried out, in an analogous way. There is an easier way to make the transformation, however, and that is by the method worked out by the eighteenth century mathematician Lagrange. Lagrange's equations allow us to set up Newton's equations of motion rather easily in terms of any generalized coordinates; that is, in terms of any set of variables capable of describing the positions of all the particles in the system. They contribute nothing new in a physical sense, for they are based on Newton's equations; but they are a valuable addition to the mathematical technique of dealing with mechanical problems. They are useful not only in setting up problems of motion of particles in various coordinate systems, but also for problems involving constraints. As an example, we may have a particle sliding down an inclined plane. If we look at the problem in a general sense, it takes two coordinates, the horizontal and vertical displacements, to describe the motion of the particle. However, there is a condition of constraint: the particle must move on the surface of the plane. Lagrange's method allows us at once to set up an equation of motion for the single remaining coordinate, which may, for instance, be taken as the distance measured along the surface of the plane. We shall find many illustrations of the usefulness of Lagrange's equations in later chapters.

1. Derivation of Lagrange's Equations.—As a first step in the derivation of Lagrange's equations, we must describe the generalized coordinates in terms of which we wish to express the equations of motion. We start with rectangular coordinates. For generality, we assume that our mechanical system may consist of several particles, each with its own x, y, and z coordinates. Thus to describe the system we need three times as many coordinates as there are particles. To simplify notation, let us call these coordinates $x_1, x_2, \ldots x_n$, where x_1, x_2, x_3 would be the x, y, and z of the first particle, x_4, x_5, and x_6 of the second, and so on, n equaling three times the number of particles. We now wish to express the equations of motion, not in terms of $x_1 \ldots x_n$, but in terms of n other quantities, $q_1 \ldots q_n$, which are functions of the x's. These q's are the generalized coordinates. For example, in our case of planetary motion, where we had one particle moving in a plane, so that we needed only x and y to describe it (x and y being then x_1 and x_2, in our present notation), the two quantities q_1 and q_2 would be r and θ, the polar coordinates.

In some problems, certain constraints exist, limiting the motion of the particles. For instance, a bead may be constrained to slide along a curved wire. In such cases, certain relations between the x_i's are imposed by the constraints, as in our example, where the x_i's must be related by the equations describing the shape of the wire. In such a case, fewer than n generalized coordinates are required to describe the system. For instance, in our example, we need only one coordinate, the distance measured along the wire from a fixed point to the bead. The number of generalized coordinates required to determine the system completely, in a problem involving constraints, is called the "number of degrees of freedom" of the system. A problem involving constraints may be brought into our general framework by choosing the generalized coordinates in such a way that the constraints are expressed by stating that certain ones of the generalized coordinates are constant. For instance, if a bead is constrained to move on a circular wire, we choose polar coordinates with center at the center of the circle, and can express the constraint by the equation $r = $ constant, so that we are left with just one degree of freedom, described by the generalized coordinate θ.

We shall now write the functional relationship between the x's and q's in the form

$$x_i = x_i(q_1 \cdots q_n), \qquad i = 1 \cdots n,$$

where by $x_i(q_1 \ldots q_n)$ we mean some definite function of the q's, and where for the present we take no explicit account of the constraints. The corresponding equations in Chap. III were Eqs. (3.10), $x = r \cos \theta$, $y = r \sin \theta$. As in Chap. III, we shall want expressions for the velocity components $\dot{x}_i$ in terms of the q's and $\dot{q}$'s. Remembering that the q's are functions of time, the general equations of which (3.11) of Chap. III are a special case are

$$\dot{x}_i = \sum_j \frac{\partial x_i}{\partial q_j}\, \dot{q}_j. \tag{1.1}$$

These express the $\dot{x}$'s as linear functions of the $\dot{q}$'s, the coefficients $\partial x_i/\partial q_j$ being functions of the coordinates. We shall shortly want to use the partial derivative of $\dot{x}_i$ with respect to $\dot{q}_j$, keeping the q's, and the other $\dot{q}$'s, constant. From (1.1) it is

$$\frac{\partial \dot{x}_i}{\partial \dot{q}_j} = \frac{\partial x_i}{\partial q_j}. \tag{1.2}$$

In terms of the x's, we may write Newton's equations of motion in the form

$$\frac{d}{dt}\,(m_i \dot{x}_i) = m_i \ddot{x}_i = F_i, \tag{1.3}$$

where m_i is the mass associated with the coordinate x_i (that is, for $i = 1, 2, 3$, m_i would be the mass of the first particle, for $i = 4, 5, 6$ the mass of the second particle, and so on), and F_i is the component of force associated with this same coordinate. We now wish to write these equations in terms of the q's and $\dot{q}$'s.

It turns out to be a simplification if we introduce at the outset the idea of kinetic energy, momentum, and work done. Let the kinetic energy be T. It is defined as usual by the equation

$$T = \sum_i \tfrac{1}{2} m_i \dot{x}_i^2. \tag{1.4}$$

Using (1.1), we may express T in terms of the $\dot{q}$'s; it becomes a quadratic expression in the $\dot{q}$'s, the coefficients depending on the q's. We note that $\partial T/\partial \dot{x}_i = m_i \dot{x}_i$, the component of momentum associated with the ith coordinate. There is a corresponding relation in terms of the generalized coordinates. In (1.4), assuming the $\dot{x}_i$'s expressed in terms of the q_i's and $\dot{q}_i$'s by use of Eq. (1.1), we define a generalized momentum p_i associated with the coordinate q_i by the equation

$$\frac{\partial T}{\partial \dot{q}_i} = p_i. \tag{1.5}$$

For instance, in polar coordinates, as in the last chapter, we can find the kinetic energy directly, without considering the rectangular coordinates. There are two components of velocity: along r, the velocity component is $\dot{r}$, and along θ it is $r\dot{\theta}$, or $r\omega$, where ω is the angular velocity. Thus the kinetic energy is $T = \tfrac{1}{2} m(\dot{r}^2 + r^2 \dot{\theta}^2)$.

The radial momentum is $\partial T/\partial \dot{r} = m\dot{r}$, as we should expect, and the momentum associated with θ is $mr^2\dot{\theta}$, which by Eq. (3.16) of Chap. III is the angular momentum.

The work done by the forces F_i, in a small displacement, is

$$dW = \sum_i F_i \, dx_i. \tag{1.6}$$

We can express this in terms of the q's as follows: it is

$$dW = \sum_{ij} F_i \frac{\partial x_i}{\partial q_j} \, dq_j = \sum_j Q_j \, dq_j, \qquad Q_j = \sum_i F_i \frac{\partial x_i}{\partial q_j}. \tag{1.7}$$

Since the work done is the product of a Q_j with a displacement dq_j, we call the Q_j's the generalized forces associated with the generalized coordinates q_j. In polar coordinates, if F_r is the component of force along r, and M is the moment of the force about the axis, the work done is $F_r \, dr + M \, d\theta$; hence F_r and M are the generalized forces associated with r and θ, respectively. As we see by our illustration of polar coordinates, we can generally find the expressions for kinetic energy, momentum, and generalized forces, in terms of generalized coordinates, without writing down explicitly the transformations from rectangular to generalized coordinates.

We are now ready to find the form that Newton's equations (1.3) take in generalized coordinates. Let us compute the time rate of change of the generalized momentum p_i, as defined in (1.5), and see what relation this has to the generalized force. We have

$$p_i = \frac{\partial T}{\partial \dot{q}_i} = \sum_j m_j \dot{x}_j \frac{\partial \dot{x}_j}{\partial \dot{q}_i} = \sum_j m_j \dot{x}_j \frac{\partial x_j}{\partial q_i}$$

where we have used (1.2). Taking the time derivative, this gives

$$\frac{dp_i}{dt} = \sum_j \left(m_j \ddot{x}_j \frac{\partial x_j}{\partial q_i} + m_j \dot{x}_j \frac{d}{dt} \frac{\partial x_j}{\partial q_i} \right). \tag{1.8}$$

Since $\partial x_j/\partial q_i$ is a function of the q's, which in turn are functions of time, we have

$$\frac{d}{dt} \frac{\partial x_j}{\partial q_i} = \sum_k \frac{\partial^2 x_j}{\partial q_i \, \partial q_k} \dot{q}_k.$$

Substituting in (1.8),

$$\frac{dp_i}{dt} = \sum_j m_j \ddot{x}_j \frac{\partial x_j}{\partial q_i} + \sum_{jk} m_j \dot{x}_j \frac{\partial^2 x_j}{\partial q_i \, \partial q_k} \dot{q}_k. \tag{1.9}$$

Using (1.3) and (1.7), the first term on the right of (1.9) is the generalized force Q_i. The second term remains, however, and can be put in a simple form. Let us compute $\partial T/\partial q_i$. This is

$$\frac{\partial T}{\partial q_i} = \sum_j m_j \dot{x}_j \frac{\partial \dot{x}_j}{\partial q_i} = \sum_j m_j \dot{x}_j \frac{\partial}{\partial q_i} \left(\sum_k \frac{\partial x_j}{\partial q_k} \dot{q}_k \right)$$

where we have used (1.1). But this is just the last term of (1.9), so that we have

$$\frac{dp_i}{dt} = Q_i + \frac{\partial T}{\partial q_i} \tag{1.10}$$

which holds in consequence of Newton's law, and hence is the generalization of the equation of motion that holds in generalized coordinates. The terms $\partial T/\partial q_i$ are fictitious forces that appear because of the curvature of the generalized coordinates. For instance, in polar coordinates, where $T = (m/2)(\dot{r}^2 + r^2\dot{\theta}^2)$, we have $\partial T/\partial r = mr\dot{\theta}^2$, the centrifugal force, so that Eq. (1.10) for r becomes equivalent to Eq. (3.13) of Chap. III; and $\partial T/\partial \theta = 0$, so that there is no fictitious force connected with the angle, and the torque equals the time rate of change of angular momentum, as shown in Eq. (3.14) of Chap. III.

In Eq. (1.10), taken with the definition (1.5) of the generalized momentum, we have a general formulation of the equations of motion in any coordinates. To use this, we must express the kinetic energy in terms of the generalized coordinates and velocity components. Then we may rewrite the equation in the form

$$\frac{d}{dt}\left(\frac{\partial T}{\partial \dot{q}_i}\right) - \frac{\partial T}{\partial q_i} = Q_i \tag{1.11}$$

where Q_i is the generalized force, so defined that the work done in a small displacement is $Q_i \, dq_i$. This equation takes a simple form if the forces Q_i are derivable from a potential function. In this case, the work done by the forces Q_i in a small displacement is by definition $-dV$, where V is the potential function. Thus in this case

$$Q_i = -\frac{\partial V}{\partial q_i} \tag{1.12}$$

so that (1.11) becomes

$$\frac{d}{dt}\left(\frac{\partial T}{\partial \dot{q}_i}\right) = \frac{\partial T}{\partial q_i} - \frac{\partial V}{\partial q_i}. \tag{1.13}$$

That is, in this case, the time rate of change of generalized momentum equals the negative derivative with respect to q_i of an effective potential energy, equal to $V - T$, where T is to be expressed in terms of coordinates and velocities. Thus, in the case of central motion, (1.13) for r becomes

$$m\ddot{r} = -\frac{\partial}{\partial r}\left[V(r) - \frac{m}{2}r^2\dot{\theta}^2 \right].$$

This leads to the equation of motion (3.13) of Chap. III.

Lagrange introduced a function L, generally called the "Lagrangian function," and defined by the equation

$$L = T - V \qquad (1.14)$$

where T is to be expressed in terms of the coordinates and velocities, V in terms of the coordinates. In terms of L, remembering that V is independent of the velocities, we may rewrite (1.13) in the form

$$\frac{d}{dt}\left(\frac{\partial L}{\partial \dot{q}_i}\right) - \frac{\partial L}{\partial q_i} = 0. \qquad (1.15)$$

The equations (1.15) are in the form called "Lagrange's equations." They hold, as we see from their derivation, for external forces derivable from a potential function. If the forces are not so derivable, we may use Eq. (1.11) instead. If part of the forces are derivable from a potential function V, and part (as, for example, frictional forces) are not, we may define the Lagrangian function by (1.14) from the potential function V, and may call the remaining forces, not derivable from a potential, Q_i'. Then the corresponding equations are

$$\frac{d}{dt}\left(\frac{\partial L}{\partial \dot{q}_i}\right) - \frac{\partial L}{\partial q_i} = Q_i'. \qquad (1.16)$$

In terms of the Lagrangian function (1.14), we may rewrite the definition (1.5) of the momenta in the form

$$\frac{\partial L}{\partial \dot{q}_i} = p_i. \qquad (1.17)$$

2. Hamilton's Equations.—Hamilton, who followed Lagrange by a number of years, expressed the equations of motion in a different form that makes more explicit use of the momenta, and is more convenient for some purposes. Hamilton introduced a so-called "Hamiltonian function" H, defined by the equation

$$H = \sum_i p_i\dot{q}_i - L. \qquad (2.1)$$

In this expression, the p_i's are to be computed from (1.17). They are functions of coordinates and velocities, so that H would be a function of coordinates and velocities, as it is written. However, the next step in setting up Hamilton's equations is to use (1.5), or (1.17), to express the velocity components in terms of the momenta, and hence to express H in terms of coordinates and momenta. Thus let us take our case of polar coordinates. We have already seen in this case that $p_r = m\dot{r}$, $p_\theta = mr^2\dot{\theta}$. Then $\dot{r} = p_r/m$, $\dot{\theta} = p_\theta/mr^2$, and

$$H = p_r\left(\frac{p_r}{m}\right) + p_\theta\left(\frac{p_\theta}{mr^2}\right) - \frac{m}{2}\left[\left(\frac{p_r}{m}\right)^2 + r^2\left(\frac{p_\theta}{mr^2}\right)^2\right] + V$$

$$= \frac{p_r^2}{2m} + \frac{p_\theta^2}{2mr^2} + V.$$

That is, since $p_r^2/2m + p_\theta^2/2mr^2$ is the kinetic energy, expressed in terms of the momenta, we have in this case $H = T + V$. We can easily show that this relation holds in a very general case. For using (1.4), (1.1), the kinetic energy is

$$T = \frac{1}{2}\sum_{ijk} m_i \frac{\partial x_i}{\partial q_j}\frac{\partial x_i}{\partial q_k}\,\dot{q}_j\dot{q}_k,$$

a quadratic function of the velocity components. If we differentiate with respect to one of the velocity components, to get the corresponding momentum, we note that we get terms both from differentiating the first factor $\dot{q}_j$, when j happens to equal the index in question, and also from differentiating the second $\dot{q}_k$, when k equals the index in question. Thus we have

$$\frac{\partial T}{\partial \dot{q}_s} = p_s = \sum_{ij} m_i \frac{\partial x_i}{\partial q_j}\frac{\partial x_i}{\partial q_s}\,\dot{q}_j.$$

Multiplying by $\dot{q}_s$, and summing over s, we have at once

$$\sum_s p_s\dot{q}_s = 2T \tag{2.2}$$

from which

$$H = 2T - L = T + V \tag{2.3}$$

or the Hamiltonian function equals the total energy, expressed as a function of coordinates and momenta.

Having set up the Hamiltonian function by (2.1), and having expressed it in terms of the coordinates and momenta, we next compute $\partial H/\partial q_i$. We have

$$H = \sum_j p_j \dot{q}_j(p_k, q_k) - L[\dot{q}_j(p_k, q_k), q_j].$$

Thus, remembering that the variables are the p's and q's,

$$\frac{\partial H}{\partial q_i} = \sum_j p_j \frac{\partial \dot{q}_j}{\partial q_i} - \sum_j \frac{\partial L}{\partial \dot{q}_j} \frac{\partial \dot{q}_j}{\partial q_i} - \frac{\partial L}{\partial q_i}.$$

By (1.17), the first two terms cancel, so that by (1.15) we have

$$\frac{dp_i}{dt} = -\frac{\partial H}{\partial q_i}. \tag{2.4}$$

That is, when expressed in the Hamiltonian form, in terms of the coordinates and momenta, the Hamiltonian function, or total energy, forms the effective potential energy function, so that, if there is a term like $p^2/2mr^2$ of Eq. (3.18), Chap. III, in the kinetic energy, which depends on the coordinates, this leads to an effective force like the centrifugal force, as we saw in Eq. (3.17), Chap. III. We may also compute $\partial H/\partial p_i$. We have

$$\frac{\partial H}{\partial p_i} = \dot{q}_i + \sum_j p_j \frac{\partial \dot{q}_j}{\partial p_i} - \sum_j \frac{\partial L}{\partial \dot{q}_j} \frac{\partial \dot{q}_j}{\partial p_i}.$$

The last two terms cancel as a result of (1.17), leaving

$$\frac{dq_i}{dt} = \frac{\partial H}{\partial p_i}. \tag{2.5}$$

Equations (2.4) and (2.5) are called "Hamilton's equations." We see that (2.4) is equivalent to Lagrange's equation (1.15), and (2.5) is equivalent to the definition (1.17) of momenta in terms of the Lagrangian function. In a case in which there is an external force Q_i' not derivable from a potential, as in (1.16), we see immediately that (2.4) is to be rewritten in the form

$$\frac{dp_i}{dt} = -\frac{\partial H}{\partial q_i} + Q_i'. \tag{2.6}$$

Since H represents the total energy, according to (2.3), we should be able to prove the law of conservation of energy very simply from it, and this is actually the case. Let us find dH/dt, remembering that H is explicitly a function of the q_i's and p_i's. We have

$$\frac{dH}{dt} = \sum_i \left(\frac{\partial H}{\partial q_i} \frac{dq_i}{dt} + \frac{\partial H}{\partial p_i} \frac{dp_i}{dt} \right).$$

Using Hamilton's equations (2.5) and (2.6), this becomes

$$\frac{dH}{dt} = \sum_i \left[\frac{\partial H}{\partial q_i} \frac{\partial H}{\partial p_i} + \frac{\partial H}{\partial p_i} \left(-\frac{\partial H}{\partial q_i} + Q_i' \right) \right]$$
$$= \sum_i Q_i' \frac{dq_i}{dt}$$

showing that, if the forces are derivable from a potential function, so that $Q_i' = 0$, the energy is conserved; and, if there are forces Q_i' not derivable from a potential, the time rate of change of energy is the rate of working of these forces Q_i'.

The Hamiltonian function in the case of a conservative force provides a very simple way of setting up the energy integral: it is simply $H(q_i, p_i) = E = $ constant. This is a convenient way to express the energy integral if some of the momenta remain constant, in which case it is more convenient to express the kinetic energy in terms of them than in terms of the velocities. An example was seen in Eqs. (3.18) and (3.19) of the preceding chapter, in the problem of central motion, where the angular momentum stays constant, and it was convenient to set up an effective potential energy in which one term was the kinetic energy of angular motion, expressed in terms of the angular momentum. We now see that this was simply part of the Hamiltonian function, so that we understand why this term in the kinetic energy acted like part of an effective potential energy.

For actual solution of mechanical problems, Hamilton's equations are generally not any more convenient than Lagrange's equations, though as we have just seen it is often convenient to introduce the momenta, and hence to use essentially the Hamiltonian form. The great importance of the Hamiltonian methods comes in the insight they give into branches of mechanics more advanced than those we shall take up in this volume.

Two very important developments of mechanics are based entirely on Hamilton's equations: statistical mechanics, and wave mechanics. Wave mechanics in its structure shows a remarkable similarity to some of Hamilton's ideas. Hamilton was led to his equations by analogies between the propagation of a wave of light and the motion of material particles. That was a hundred years ago; and it was only recently that Schrödinger found that this analogy was not merely a mathematical device, as Hamilton had thought, but that it expressed a deep and underlying physical similarity between the two phenomena, as a result of which there really is a wave motion associated with the motion of any particle. It is only natural for this reason that the Hamiltonian methods in mechanics, to which Hamilton was led by his deep physical insight, have proved the most valuable methods in the most recent developments of mechanics. Furthermore, it now appears that wave mechanics has certain essential statistical features: it is not able to predict with certainty the motion of a particle, but only to state which motions are more probable, which less probable. In this respect it shows an analogy that is fundamental, not merely superficial, with statistical mechanics, the branch of mechanics that treats the statistical motion of great groups of particles, as the atoms and molecules of matter, and that draws conclusions regarding their average behavior, and the thermodynamic properties that follow from them. It is natural to find in this connection that statistical mechanics is based almost of necessity on Hamiltonian methods, a fact that was recognized in the latter half of the nineteenth century by Boltzmann and Gibbs. Considering these applications of Hamiltonian methods, it seems that the proper place to develop them in detail, in the present state of mechanical theory, is in connection with a treatment of the related subjects of wave mechanics and statistical mechanics, and not in connection with classical mechanics. We shall therefore not find further use for them in this volume.

3. The Uses of Generalized Coordinates and Lagrange's Equations. The only reason for introducing generalized coordinates, and using Lagrange's equations, in any mechanical problem, is to make it easier to solve. One sort of case in which the method is useful was illustrated in the problem of central motion, in the preceding chapter. By using polar coordinates, we found that the equations for r and θ could be separated from each other, and solved completely, whereas if we had used rectangular coordinates the two coordinates x and y would have been inextricably mixed up in the two simultaneous equations of motion, and we should not have been able to find a solution. Such a use is often called "separation of variables." We shall meet another example in the next section, where we take up the problem of the spherical pendulum. In all such cases, Lagrange's equations form the easiest way of getting the equations of motion in the appropriate generalized coordinates.

We must not get the idea, however, that the only use of Lagrange's equations is in introducing curvilinear coordinates in problems of the dynamics of particles.   We have already mentioned the usefulness of these methods in problems involving constraints.   For example, one may have a particle sliding on an inclined surface, or a bead sliding along a frictionless wire, or a particle constrained to move on the surface of a sphere or other surface, as the bob of a spherical pendulum must move in a sphere.   Then we may often satisfy the conditions of constraint by suitable choice of the generalized coordinates.   Thus, with the spherical pendulum, we may take spherical polar coordinates, r, θ, φ.   We may then arbitrarily set r constant, equal to R, the radius of the sphere, and write Lagrange's equations for θ and φ.   To justify this, we note that the component of the external and centrifugal force normal to the sphere will be exactly balanced by the reaction of the constraint, a force normal to the sphere, just as the weight of a body resting on a table is exactly balanced by the upward push of the table.   That is, considering Lagrange's equation in the form (1.11), if q_i is a generalized coordinate normal to the surface in which the body is constrained to move, a normal force Q_i will automatically be set up so that the equation will be satisfied by the value $q_i = 0$.

As examples of problems involving constraints, we may go further than particles constrained to move along fixed paths, and may consider, for instance, an Atwood's machine, two weights hung by a string over a pulley.   This can be described very easily by a single generalized coordinate.   In the general problem of coupled systems, and in fact in all problems of interaction of different particles or systems, Lagrange's method is very useful, as we shall see.   One particularly important application will be found in Chap. VI, the motion of rigid bodies.   A rigid body consists of a great many particles (really the molecules) held together by constraints that allow the body to rotate as a whole, but not to change its shape or size.   Its position and orientation in space can then be described completely by six generalized coordinates, three fixing the position of its center of gravity, three the orientation about the center of gravity.   We shall find it easy to set up the equations of motion by Lagrangian methods.

4. The Spherical Pendulum.—The spherical pendulum, which we have just mentioned, is an interesting example of the use of Lagrange's equations, and also of the general methods of solving mechanical problems.   By a spherical pendulum we mean a mass m, so small in its dimensions that it can be considered a point mass, suspended from a fixed point by a weightless string, or better a weightless rod, of length R.   It is more general than the ordinary pendulum, in that it is not confined to move in a plane, but the weight can move to any point of a spherical surface of radius R. Thus it can, as a special case, execute plane motion, like an ordinary pendulum, passing through the bottom point of the sphere; but it can also rotate about that bottom point, execute approximately elliptical paths, and carry out quite a variety of motions, and our general solution will include all of these.

Let us describe the position of the mass by using spherical polar coordinates, as shown in Fig. 10. On account of the constraint imposed by the fixed length of the rod, the coordinate r will always be constant, equal to R, so that we need use only two coordinates in Lagrange's equations, θ and φ. We are now directed first to compute the kinetic energy T, in terms of θ and φ and their time derivatives. The component of velocity in the direction of increasing θ is $R\dot{\theta}$. In the direction of increasing φ, the radius vector for rotation is $R \sin \theta$, so that the component of velocity is $R \sin \theta \, \dot{\varphi}$. Thus we have

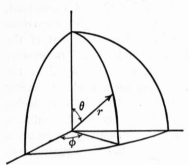

Fig. 10.—Spherical polar coordinates.

$$T = \tfrac{1}{2}m(R^2\dot{\theta}^2 + R^2 \sin^2\theta \, \dot{\varphi}^2).$$

Next we must find the potential energy. If g is the acceleration of gravity (980.6 cm/sec², or 9.806 m/sec², or 32.174 ft/sec², as we saw in Sec. 5, Chap. I), the potential energy may be written

$$V = mgR \cos \theta$$

or mgh, where h is the height above a fixed plane, the plane passing through the origin. Thus the Lagrangian function L is

$$L = \tfrac{1}{2}m(R^2\dot{\theta}^2 + R^2 \sin^2\theta \, \dot{\varphi}^2) - mgR \cos \theta.$$

We then have for the momenta

$$p_\theta = \frac{\partial L}{\partial \dot{\theta}} = mR^2\dot{\theta}, \qquad p_\varphi = \frac{\partial L}{\partial \dot{\varphi}} = mR^2 \sin^2\theta \, \dot{\varphi}. \qquad (4.1)$$

Lagrange's equation for θ is then

$$\frac{d}{dt}(mR^2\dot{\theta}) - \frac{\partial L}{\partial \theta} = 0, \qquad mR^2\ddot{\theta} - mR^2 \sin \theta \cos \theta \, \dot{\varphi}^2 - mgR \sin \theta = 0$$
$$(4.2)$$

and for φ

$$\frac{d}{dt}(mR^2 \sin^2\theta \,\dot{\varphi}) = 0, \qquad \frac{dp_\varphi}{dt} = 0. \qquad (4.3)$$

From (4.3) we see that p_φ, the component of angular momentum along the vertical axis, in Fig. 10, is independent of time. This is a result of the fact that the torque, considered as a vector, has no component along this axis, a fact that will be clearer after the discussion of the next chapter, in which we shall show that the torque, a vector, equals the time rate of change of angular momentum, also a vector.

We may now use the constancy of p_φ, as we used the constancy of angular momentum in the central field problem, to carry out a solution of our problem. Writing $\dot{\varphi}$ in terms of p_φ, (4.2) becomes

$$mR^2\ddot{\theta} = \frac{p_\varphi^2 \cos\theta}{mR^2 \sin^3\theta} + mgR \sin\theta. \qquad (4.4)$$

This is an equation for θ alone, so that the problem is reduced to a problem of one degree of freedom. It is not, however, an elementary differential equation whose solution we can work out, so that we are forced to the method of energy to get information about the solution. The Hamiltonian function is

$$H = \frac{p_\theta^2}{2mR^2} + \frac{p_\varphi^2}{2mR^2 \sin^2\theta} + mgR \cos\theta = E. \qquad (4.5)$$

Thus the effective potential energy for motion of θ consists of the last two terms of (4.5),

$$V' = \frac{p_\varphi^2}{2mR^2 \sin^2\theta} + mgR \cos\theta. \qquad (4.6)$$

In Fig. 11 we plot values of V'/mgR, for a series of values of the parameter $p_\varphi^2/2m^2gR^3$, where

$$\frac{V'}{mgR} = \frac{p_\varphi^2}{2m^2gR^3} \frac{1}{\sin^2\theta} + \cos\theta. \qquad (4.7)$$

We see that, when $p_\varphi = 0$, the effective potential (4.7) stays finite everywhere, having a maximum at $\theta = 0$ (the top of the sphere) and a minimum at $\theta = \pi$ (the bottom). This is the case for the ordinary pendulum. For a small energy there is oscillation, approximately simple harmonic for small amplitudes, about the bottom of the sphere. For larger energies the amplitude increases, and as the potential energy curve departs more and more widely from the parabola that approximates it for $\theta = \pi$, the motion departs more and more from simple harmonic.   Finally, for energies great enough to carry the particle over the maximum of potential energy at $\theta = 0$, the motion becomes a rotational one, with larger velocities at the bottom of the path, smaller at the top.   The solution for θ as a function of t in this case involves elliptic functions.

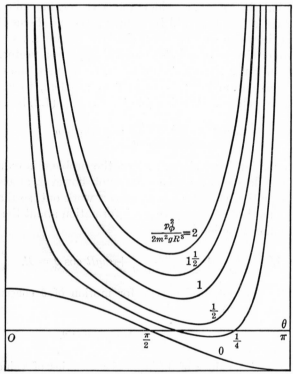

Fig. 11.—Effective potential V'/mgR of spherical pendulum, as function of angle θ, for various values of p_φ.

For p_φ different from zero, the character of the motion becomes quite different.   The effective potential energy in this case becomes infinite at both $\theta = 0$ and π, so that the motion never reaches those two points.   There is a single minimum of V', and the motion of θ takes the form of an oscillation about this minimum.   For a value of E as given by the minimum for a given p_φ, θ stays constant, and we have the case of the conical pendulum.   For slightly larger energy, there is an oscillation of small amplitude in θ, while of course at the same time φ is increasing almost uniformly with the time, as we see from (4.1), combined with the fact that θ stays almost constant in this case.   For considerably higher energy, the amplitude of oscillation gets larger and larger, so that the pendulum swings nearer to the top and bottom position of the sphere, but never reaches these points.

The general solution is too difficult to work out analytically, but we can discuss the small oscillations about the conical pendulum solution, and the method we use in doing this is one that can often be applied in similar problems.   To do this, we approximate a curve of V' as a function of θ, in Fig. 11, by a parabola that fits it at its minimum.   The parabola corresponds to a linear restoring force or simple harmonic motion, which we have if the amplitude of oscillation is sufficiently small.

Equally well we may consider the effective force, the right side of (4.4), which of course is the negative derivative of the effective potential (4.6).   This effective force is zero at the minimum of the effective potential, or at the

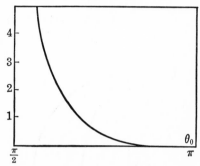

Fig. 12.—Function $-\dfrac{\sin^4\theta_0}{\cos\theta_0}$ as function of θ_0, giving value of $p_\varphi{}^2/m^2gR^3$ for which angle of conical pendulum is θ_0.

angle of rotation of the conical pendulum, and to get the simple harmonic approximation we expand the effective force in Taylor's series about this point, and use only the linear term.   Setting the effective force equal to zero, we have

$$-\frac{\sin^4\theta_0}{\cos\theta_0} = \frac{p_\varphi^2}{m^2gR^3}. \tag{4.8}$$

In Fig. 12 we show the function $-\sin^4\theta_0/\cos\theta_0$ as a function of θ_0. It is positive only between $\theta_0 = \pi/2$ and π, so that the angle of the conical pendulum must lie in the lower half of the sphere.   Figure 12 shows that, as p_φ increases, the pendulum rises more and more into the horizontal plane $\theta = \pi/2$.   Solving for $\dot\varphi$ from (4.1), (4.8) gives the angular velocity of rotation of the conical pendulum as

$$\dot\varphi = \sqrt{\frac{g}{R(-\cos\theta_0)}}. \tag{4.9}$$

This is what we should find from an elementary discussion.   Figure 13 shows the forces acting on the mass as it rotates.   These forces consist of a tension T acting upward toward the point of support, and the gravitational force mg acting down.   The resultant of these must be a force $m\dot{\varphi}^2$ times the radius of the circle in which the mass rotates, pointing inward toward the vertical axis, since this is the force necessary to produce the centripetal acceleration. Letting $\theta_0' = \pi - \theta_0$, and drawing the force triangles, we then have

$$mg \tan \theta_0' = m\dot{\varphi}^2 R \sin \theta_0', \qquad \dot{\varphi}^2 = \frac{g}{R \cos \theta_0'} = \frac{g}{R(-\cos \theta_0)}, \quad (4.10)$$

agreeing with (4.9).

Next we find the restoring force if the pendulum is displaced slightly from the angle in which it rotates as a conical pendulum. Differentiating the force on the right side of (4.4) with respect to θ, and setting $\theta = \theta_0$, we find the Taylor's expansion

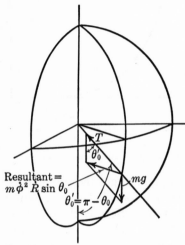

Effective force =

$$mgR\left(\frac{1 + 3 \cos^2 \theta_0}{\cos \theta_0}\right)(\theta - \theta_0) \cdots .$$

Thus the equation of motion (4.4) becomes

$$\ddot{\theta} =$$

$$\frac{g}{R}\left(\frac{1 + 3 \cos^2 \theta_0}{\cos \theta_0}\right)(\theta - \theta_0) \cdots .$$

Remembering that $\cos \theta_0$ is negative, this is the equation of a simple harmonic oscillation in θ,

Fig. 13.—Forces on spherical pendulum.

with an angular frequency

$$\omega_\theta = \sqrt{\frac{g}{R}\left(\frac{1 + 3 \cos^2 \theta_0}{-\cos \theta_0}\right)}.$$

It is interesting to find the ratio of the angular frequency of oscillation in θ, to the angular velocity of rotation in φ. This is

$$\frac{\omega_\theta}{\dot{\varphi}} = \sqrt{1 + 3 \cos^2 \theta_0}. \qquad (4.11)$$

We note that this goes from unity when $\theta_0 = \pi/2$ to two when $\theta_0 = \pi$. The reason for this becomes clear when we consider the actual nature of the orbits, as shown in Fig. 14.

In Fig. 14(a) we show the case of a small oscillation, in which θ_0 is nearly π, so that the pendulum is almost at the bottom of the sphere.

In this case, $\cos \theta_0$ is almost equal to -1. The motion is almost simple harmonic, as with a two-dimensional linear oscillator, in which both rectangular coordinates x and y oscillate with simple harmonic

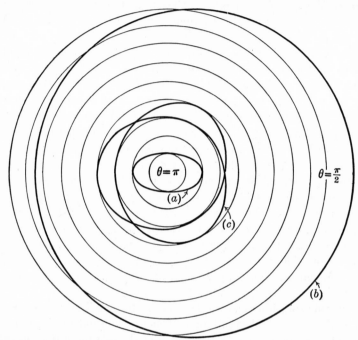

FIG. 14.—Orbits of spherical pendulum, mapped looking up at south pole of sphere. (a) Small orbit around south pole, $\omega/\dot{\varphi} = 2$; (b) orbit around equator, $\omega/\dot{\varphi} = 1$; (c) intermediate case, $\omega/\dot{\varphi} = \frac{3}{2}$.

motion. Two such simple harmonic motions at right angles to each other combine into an elliptical motion, as we can see at once if

$$x = A \cos \omega t, \qquad y = B \sin \omega t.$$

in which case

$$\frac{x^2}{A^2} + \frac{y^2}{B^2} = 1,$$

giving the equation of an ellipse of semiaxes A and B. Since x and y would both execute periodic motion like a simple pendulum, we should have the angular frequency ω equal to $\sqrt{g/R}$, as for a simple pendulum. This would give also the angular frequency of rotation in the elliptical orbit. Now in Fig. 14a, the orbit is approximately an ellipse. The angular frequency of rotation is given by (4.9), which reduces to the value $\sqrt{g/R}$ for the case $\theta_0 = \pi$. Looking at the figure, we see that, for such an elliptical motion, with the center at the origin, the radius (in our case measured by $-R \sin \theta$) oscillates twice from its minimum to its maximum value and back again in one complete period of the motion. That is, the frequency of the motion in θ should be twice that of the frequency in φ, as we have found from (4.11).

The other limiting case is shown in Fig. 14b. Here θ_0 is equal to $\pi/2$. In that case, as we see from Fig. 12, p_φ, and hence $\dot{\varphi}$, must be infinite. That is, the pendulum is rotating so fast that the gravitational force is quite negligible compared with the centrifugal effects. Then the motion must be in a great circle on the sphere. If this great circle is tilted with respect to the equator, the orbit will be as in Fig. 14b, the orbit lying at greater θ than $\pi/2$ on one side of the orbit, smaller θ on the other side, so that θ oscillates once from its maximum to its minimum in one complete period of the motion, again as we have found from (4.11). Finally we may consider an intermediate case, as in Fig. 14c. Here by (4.11) the periods of motion in φ and θ are different, so that the motion is doubly periodic, rather than being periodic as in the two limiting cases. The resulting motion is simply an oscillation of θ, of frequency between once and twice the frequency of the conical motion, superposed on the motion of the conical pendulum.

From this solution that we have found for small oscillations, combined with the general result of the energy method, as brought out in Fig. 11, we can get a very good idea of the complete motion of the spherical pendulum. This is an excellent example of the way in which, without using advanced mathematical methods, it is often possible to go a long way toward solving a rather involved mechanical problem, by the use of Lagrange's equations and the method of the energy. In particular, in many problems we can investigate the behavior of small oscillations about steady motions, such as the conical pendulum case in the present problem. A more complicated, but similar, problem will come up next, when we treat the motion of a symmetrical top. We shall find that its steady precession corresponds to the conical pendulum, and that it is also capable of oscillation about this steady state, the oscillations being called "nutation." Even in that quite complicated case, we can get a good deal of analytical information, without being able to get the complete solution of the problem.

Problems

1. An Atwood's machine is built as follows: A string of length l_1 passes over a light fixed pulley, supporting a mass m_1 on one end and a pulley of mass m_2 (negli-

gible moment of inertia) on the other. Over this second pulley passes a string of length l_2 supporting a mass m_3 on one end and m_4 on the other, where $m_3 \neq m_4$. Set up Lagrange's equations of motion for this system, using two appropriate generalized coordinates. From these show that the mass m_1 remains in equilibrium if

$$m_1 = m_2 + m_3 + m_4 - \frac{(m_4 - m_3)^2}{m_3 + m_4}.$$

2. A particle slides on the inside of a smooth paraboloid of revolution whose axis is vertical. Use the distance from the axis, r, and the azimuth θ as generalized coordinates. Find the equations of motion. Find the angular momentum necessary for the particle to move in a horizontal circle. If the latter motion is disturbed slightly, show that the particle will perform small oscillations about this circular path, and find the period of these oscillations.

3. Set up the problem of a spherical pendulum subject to gravity, and to a resisting force proportional to the velocity and opposite in direction. Derive the Lagrangian and Hamiltonian equations, showing that the damping forces give extra terms in the equations proportional to the momenta. Show that these equations in general cannot be separated. Derive a solution, however, for the special case in which the instantaneous motion would be a rotation about the lowest point of the sphere if damping were absent. Assume small damping, so that the actual motion is a gradual spiraling in toward the lowest point.

4. A particle moves under the action of gravity on the inner surface of a smooth inverted cone of angle 2α. Using the angle about the symmetry axis of the cone and the distance along the cone, measured from the vertex, as generalized coordinates, set up the Lagrangian function for this motion, and obtain the differential equations of motion. Under what conditions can circular motion in a horizontal plane occur? Discuss the stability of such motion.

5. A homogeneous solid right circular cone of mass M, half angle α, and slant height L rolls without slipping on an inclined plane of angle β with the horizontal. Using the angle θ between the contact line of the cone and plane and the line of steepest slope on the plane, set up the Lagrangian function for the motion. Find the equations of motion and the period of small oscillations.

6. The force on a particle of charge e, moving with a velocity $\mathbf{v}$ in an electric field $\mathbf{E}$ and magnetic induction $\mathbf{B}$, is given by $\mathbf{F} = e[\mathbf{E} + (\mathbf{v} \times \mathbf{B})]$, where e is expressed in coulombs, $\mathbf{E}$ in volts per meter, $\mathbf{B}$ in webers per square meter (1 weber/sq m $= 10^4$ gausses), and where mks units are used. The term in $\mathbf{E}$ corresponds to the ordinary electrostatic force, that in $\mathbf{B}$ to the ordinary motor law, in which the force on a circuit is proportional to the current (here ev) and to the field, and at right angles to both. The electric field and magnetic induction can be expressed in terms of a scalar potential φ, and a vector potential $\mathbf{A}$, by the equations $\mathbf{E} = - \operatorname{grad} \varphi - \partial \mathbf{A}/\partial t$, $\mathbf{B} = \operatorname{curl} \mathbf{A}$. Show that the equations of motion of such a particle of mass m can be expressed in terms of Lagrange's equations, with the Lagrangian function $L = \frac{1}{2}mv^2 + e(\mathbf{v} \cdot \mathbf{A}) - e\varphi$, noting that

$$\frac{dA}{dt} = \frac{\partial A}{\partial t} + \frac{\partial A}{\partial x}\frac{dx}{dt} + \frac{\partial A}{\partial y}\frac{dy}{dt} + \frac{\partial A}{\partial z}\frac{dz}{dt}.$$

7. For the particle of Prob. 6, set up the momentum and the Hamiltonian function. Show that the momenta do not equal mass times velocity, and that the Hamiltonian does not have the form $p^2/2m + e\varphi$.

8. In the relativity theory, the equations of motion of a particle are different from what they are in classical mechanics, though they reduce to the same thing for small velocities. In particular, the mass of a particle increases with velocity. If a particle has a mass m_0 when at rest, its mass at speed v is given by

$$m = \frac{m_0}{\sqrt{1 - v^2/c^2}},$$

where c is the velocity of light; reducing to m_0 in the limit $v/c = 0$, but becoming infinite when the particle moves with the speed of light.

Show that the equations of motion are correctly given from the Lagrangian function $L = m_0c^2(1 - \sqrt{1 - v^2/c^2}) + e(\mathbf{v} \cdot \mathbf{A}) - e\varphi$, if the forces are as in Prob. 6.

9. For the case of Prob. 8, derive the momenta, and the Hamiltonian function. Setting the Hamiltonian function equal to $T + V$, where T is the kinetic energy, $V = e\varphi$ is the potential energy, find the value of T, and show that the Lagrangian function is not equal to $T - V$, as is natural from the fact that the kinetic energy is not a homogeneous quadratic function of the velocities. Taking the kinetic energy, expand in power series in the quantity v/c, showing that for low speeds the kinetic energy approaches its ordinary classical value.

10. Using the Hamiltonian function found in Prob. 9, show that it satisfies the equation

$$(H - e\varphi)^2 - c^2(\mathbf{p} - e\mathbf{A})^2 = m_0^2c^4$$

where $\mathbf{p}$ is the momentum. This equation forms the basis of much of the treatment of relativistic quantum mechanics.

11. Consider the motion of an electron in an axially symmetric magnetic field that changes with time (the betatron). Using cylindrical coordinates, r, θ, z, with z the symmetry axis, the magnetic induction $\mathbf{B}$ can be obtained by $\mathbf{B} = \text{curl } \mathbf{A}$, where $A_\theta = A_\theta(r,z,t)$, $A_r = A_z = 0$. The Lagrangian function is as given in Prob. 8, with $\varphi = 0$. Set up the equations of motion for the electron. From these show that circular motion of radius r_0 is possible, provided that the rate of change of magnetic flux linking the circle is twice the area of the circle times the z component of the rate of change of magnetic induction at the orbit. Assuming a linear increase of magnetic induction with time, compute the period of the motion, and show that it tends to a limiting value $2\pi r_0/c$ as time increases.

Investigate the stability of the circular motion with respect to vertical, radial, and angular motion if the magnetic field in the neighborhood of the equilibrium orbit is given by $B_z = B(r_0/r)^n$ and the magnetic field changes quasistatically with time, so that we can neglect curl $\mathbf{B}$. To do this set $r = r_0 + \rho$, $\theta = \omega + \psi$, and treat ρ, z, and ψ as small quantities whose squares and products may be neglected. ω is the angular velocity in the equilibrium orbit. Show that complete stability can occur only if $0 < n < 1$, and prove that for stable motion the sum of the squares of the radial and vertical oscillation frequencies equals the square of the unperturbed rotation frequency.

CHAPTER V

THE MOTION OF RIGID BODIES

All the familiar objects to which we can apply the methods of mechanics are extended bodies, of finite size, rather than the particles of which we have been speaking in the preceding chapters. In most cases these objects are at least approximately rigid bodies; that is, they do not change their shape or size as they move in space. For that reason, a study of the motion of rigid bodies, or more generally of extended bodies of any sort, is necessary if we are to apply mechanics to familiar problems. An extended body may be considered to be a collection of particles, for example, the atoms or molecules of which it is composed, held together by certain forces, as interatomic or intermolecular forces. To handle such a problem completely would be extremely complicated, for there would be three times as many generalized coordinates as there were particles. We have seen in the preceding chapter, however, that the method of generalized coordinates allows us to neglect all those coordinates which remain constant during the motion, on account of constraints. If our body is rigid, all distances between particles remain fixed; only six variables really can change during the motion, three coordinates fixing the position of the body in space, and three fixing the orientation. We shall find in this chapter how to set up these six variables and to find the equations governing their motion.

As a first step, we shall prove several theorems describing the motion of any system of particles, of which a rigid body is a specialized example. These theorems are based on Newton's third law, stating that the action and reaction concerned in the interatomic or intermolecular forces are equal and opposite. They are simple and familiar theorems: the total force acting on a system of particles equals the time rate of change of the total momentum of the system, which in turn equals the mass of the whole system, times the acceleration of the center of mass; the total moment of force, or torque, acting on a system of particles, computed about any fixed point, equals the time rate of change of total angular momentum of the system; likewise the total moment of force computed about the center of mass, which in general is moving, equals the time rate of change of total angular momentum computed about the center of mass. By means of these theorems, we can separate translational and rotational motion of any system of particles, can reduce the translational part to a form similar to the mechanics of a particle, and can lay the foundations for a study of the rotational motion of rigid bodies. We shall now carry out proofs of these theorems, and then shall pass on to their applications.

1. Mechanics of a System of Particles.—Let us assume a number of particles, the ith particle having a mass m_i, and coordinates x_i, y_i, z_i, with respect to some coordinate system fixed in space. (It will be more convenient in this chapter to use x_i, y_i, z_i for the three coordinates of a particle, rather than to set up coordinates all denoted by x_i, as in the preceding chapter.) We shall wish to use vector notation to simplify our calculation. Let us then define the vector $\mathbf{r}_i$, with components x_i, y_i, z_i, representing the vector position of the ith particle. We remind the reader again that vector relations are discussed in Appendix IV, for the benefit of those not familiar with vector analysis. In terms of vector language, the velocity of the ith particle is $\dot{\mathbf{r}}_i$, with components $\dot{x}_i$, $\dot{y}_i$, $\dot{z}_i$, and the acceleration is $\ddot{\mathbf{r}}_i$, with components $\ddot{x}_i$, $\ddot{y}_i$, $\ddot{z}_i$. We shall assume that the force $\mathbf{F}_i$ acting on the ith particle is the sum of two parts. First, there will be a vector force $\mathbf{f}_i$, exerted by actions external to the system of particles. Such a force might arise from gravitation, electric or magnetic forces from outside the system, or other such external influence. Second, there will be forces $\mathbf{f}_{ij}$, exerted on the ith particle by the jth particle. These would be the interatomic or intermolecular forces of which we have already spoken. We shall have to make only one assumption about these forces: that they obey Newton's third law. As a result of that law, since $\mathbf{f}_{ij}$ is the force exerted on the ith particle by the jth, and $\mathbf{f}_{ji}$ is the force exerted on the jth by the ith, we must have

$$\mathbf{f}_{ij} = -\mathbf{f}_{ji}. \tag{1.1}$$

The total force acting on the ith particle will then be $\mathbf{f}_i + \sum_{j \neq i} \mathbf{f}_{ij}$, where the summation excludes the case $j = i$, since that would correspond to the force of the ith particle on itself, which would have no meaning.

Newton's second law for the ith particle, written in vector form, is then

$$m_i \frac{d^2 \mathbf{r}_i}{dt^2} = \mathbf{F}_i = \mathbf{f}_i + \sum_{j \neq i} \mathbf{f}_{ij}. \tag{1.2}$$

Let us add the equations for all particles of the system. Then we have

$$\frac{d^2}{dt^2} \sum_i m_i \mathbf{r}_i = \sum_i \mathbf{f}_i + \sum_i \sum_{j \neq i} \mathbf{f}_{ij}. \qquad (1.3)$$

We now note that, in the double sum of $\mathbf{f}_{ij}$, in (1.3), the term for which i takes on some particular value, and j another value, will be equal and opposite to the term for which i takes on the second value, j the first, on account of (1.1). Thus the double sum vanishes.

We now introduce several definitions. The total mass of the system will be called m: $m = \sum_i m_i$. The coordinates of the center of mass will be described by a vector $\mathbf{R}$, where

$$\mathbf{R} = \frac{\displaystyle\sum_i m_i \mathbf{r}_i}{\displaystyle\sum_i m_i}. \qquad (1.4)$$

Finally, the total external force $\mathbf{F}$ acting on the system is $\mathbf{F} = \sum_i \mathbf{f}_i$. Then (1.3) becomes

$$m \frac{d^2 \mathbf{R}}{dt^2} = \mathbf{F}. \qquad (1.5)$$

This is the first of the theorems we wished to prove: the total force acting on a system of particles equals the total mass times the acceleration of the center of mass. In other words, the center of mass obeys the same equation of motion that we should have for a particle of mass m, acted on by force $\mathbf{F}$. It is really this theorem which makes the dynamics of particles, about which we have so far been speaking, a problem of vital importance to mechanics, not just a mathematical abstraction relating to point masses that do not really exist. An object of complicated shape thrown in the air will execute complicated gyrations; but its center of mass (if we may neglect air resistance) will follow a parabolic path, just like the ideal particle of elementary dynamics. The center of mass of a planet attracted by the sun will move like a particle, following just the orbits that we discussed in Chap. III. Even the center of mass of the whole solar system will move like a particle, and if we can assume that there is no net force acting on the solar system as a whole, it will move with uniform motion in a straight line.

Next we wish to consider the angular momentum of a particle, and the moment of a force, about a fixed point. By definition, the moment of the force $\mathbf{F}_i$, about the origin of coordinates, is $\mathbf{M}_i$, given by $\mathbf{M}_i = \mathbf{r}_i \times \mathbf{F}_i$, or the vector product of $\mathbf{r}_i$ and $\mathbf{F}_i$. That is, the magnitude of the moment equals the magnitude of the force $\mathbf{F}_i$, times the component of $\mathbf{r}_i$ at right angles to $\mathbf{F}_i$ (the lever arm), or alternatively the component of force perpendicular to the radius vector, times the radius vector. The direction of the vector $\mathbf{M}_i$ is at right angles to the force and the lever arm; that is, it is the axis about which the moment would tend to produce rotation. Similarly the moment of momentum of the particle, or the angular momentum, is defined by angular momentum $= \mathbf{r}_i \times (m_i \dot{\mathbf{r}}_i)$. It is equal in magnitude to the mass times the velocity times the lever arm; or to the mass times the radius vector out to the particle times the component of velocity at right angles to the radius vector. The direction of the angular momentum vector is at right angles to the velocity and to the radius vector. To get the sign of the moment and angular momentum vectors clearly in mind, we may consider the simple case in which the particle is located on the x axis, the force along the y direction; then the moment of the force is along z. Similarly if the particle is on the x axis, moving in the y direction, the angular momentum is along z.

We may now prove that the moment of the force acting on a particle equals the time rate of change of its angular momentum. That is, we shall prove

$$\mathbf{M}_i = \mathbf{r}_i \times \mathbf{F}_i = \frac{d}{dt}\,(\mathbf{r}_i \times m_i \dot{\mathbf{r}}_i). \tag{1.6}$$

Carrying out the differentiation on the right, we have

$$\mathbf{r}_i \times \mathbf{F}_i = \dot{\mathbf{r}}_i \times m_i \dot{\mathbf{r}}_i + \mathbf{r}_i \times m_i \ddot{\mathbf{r}}_i. \tag{1.7}$$

Remembering that the vector product of any vector with itself is zero, the first term on the right of (1.7) vanishes, leaving an equation that is just the vector product of $\mathbf{r}_i$ and Newton's second law (1.2). Thus we prove our theorem (1.6). Examples of (1.6) are of course familiar. The simplest example we have met so far is in central motion, where Eq. (3.14) of Chap. III expressed the form that the theorem takes for plane motion, where both moment of force and angular momentum are vectors perpendicular to the plane, and where only their magnitude needs to be considered. In that case, $r\,d\theta/dt$ was the component of velocity at right angles to the radius vector, so that the angular momentum had magnitude $mr(r\,d\theta/dt)$, and F_θ was the component of force at right angles to the radius vector, so that rF_θ

was the torque. In Chap. IV, Sec. 4, dealing with the spherical pendulum, we found a case where torque and angular momentum were vectors. The quantity p_θ of Eq. (4.1), Chap. IV, is the component of angular momentum along a horizontal direction, and p_φ the vertical component of angular momentum. The torque had no vertical component; hence p_φ was independent of time, as in Eq. (4.3), Chap. IV. There was, however, a horizontal component of torque, so that p_θ changed with time, as in Eq. (4.2), Chap. IV. That particular problem, as far as the horizontal component of angular momentum and of torque is concerned, is not so simple as it seems, in that the direction of the component p_θ is not constant, but depends on the position of the particle, so that we cannot apply analysis to it as if it were a component in a fixed direction. The really interesting cases in which we treat the angular momentum and torque as vectors will come when we consider gyroscopic motion a little later.

In (1.6) we have proved that the moment of the force acting on a particle equals the time rate of change of its angular momentum. We may now prove that the total moment of all the external forces acting on a system of particles equals the time rate of change of total angular momentum. This holds only if the internal forces are central; that is, if the force $\mathbf{f}_{ij}$, exerted by the jth particle on the ith, acts along the line connecting the two particles. Let us add Eqs. (1.6), writing $\mathbf{F}_i$ in terms of the internal and external forces by (1.2). Then, if the total moment of forces is $\mathbf{M}$, we have

$$\mathbf{M} = \sum_i \mathbf{M}_i = \sum_i \mathbf{r}_i \times \mathbf{f}_i + \sum_{ij} \mathbf{r}_i \times \mathbf{f}_{ij}$$

$$= \frac{d}{dt} \sum_i \mathbf{r}_i \times m_i \dot{\mathbf{r}}_i. \tag{1.8}$$

In the summation over i and j of $\mathbf{r}_i \times \mathbf{f}_{ij}$, each pair ij of particles appears in two terms, which in consequence of (1.1) may be written $(\mathbf{r}_i - \mathbf{r}_j) \times \mathbf{f}_{ij}$. But the vector $\mathbf{r}_i - \mathbf{r}_j$ is the vector from the jth to the ith particle, which for central forces is in the same direction as $\mathbf{f}_{ij}$, so that the vector product vanishes. Thus (1.8) states that the moment of the external forces equals the time rate of change of the total angular momentum of the system. This theorem holds, as does (1.6), when the angular momentum and the torque are computed with respect to any fixed origin of coordinates; the angular momentum and torque of course depend on the point about which they are computed.

We have a theorem like (1.8), not only about any fixed center of rotation, but also about one particular moving center: the center of mass. Let us prove that the moment of all external forces, taken about the center of mass, equals the time rate of change of angular momentum, also computed about the center of mass. The angular momentum computed about the center of mass is

$$\sum_i (\mathbf{r}_i - \mathbf{R}) \times m_i(\dot{\mathbf{r}}_i - \dot{\mathbf{R}}) = \sum_i (\mathbf{r}_i \times m_i\dot{\mathbf{r}}_i - \mathbf{R} \times m_i\dot{\mathbf{r}}_i - \mathbf{r}_i \times m_i\dot{\mathbf{R}}$$

$$+ \mathbf{R} \times m_i\dot{\mathbf{R}}) = \sum_i \mathbf{r}_i \times m_i\dot{\mathbf{r}}_i - \mathbf{R} \times m\dot{\mathbf{R}}, \quad (1.9)$$

where the last step results from the definition (1.4) of center of mass. Similarly the torque about the center of mass is

$$\sum_i (\mathbf{r}_i - \mathbf{R}) \times \mathbf{f}_i = \sum_i \mathbf{r}_i \times \mathbf{f}_i - \mathbf{R} \times \mathbf{F}. \quad (1.10)$$

We can now prove, by the same method used to prove (1.6), that

$$\mathbf{R} \times \mathbf{F} = \frac{d}{dt} (\mathbf{R} \times m\dot{\mathbf{R}}).$$

Subtracting this from (1.8), assuming as before that the forces $\mathbf{f}_{ij}$ are central forces, and using (1.9) and (1.10), we then have our result

$$\sum_i (\mathbf{r}_i - \mathbf{R}) \times \mathbf{f}_i = \frac{d}{dt} \sum_i (\mathbf{r}_i - \mathbf{R}) \times m_i(\dot{\mathbf{r}}_i - \dot{\mathbf{R}}), \quad (1.11)$$

or the torque about the center of mass equals the time rate of change of angular momentum about the center of mass. Incidentally, Eq. (1.9) provides a useful result in itself: the angular momentum of a system of particles about any arbitrary fixed point equals the angular momentum about the center of mass, plus the angular momentum of a particle whose mass is the mass of the system, located at the center of mass, with respect to the arbitrary fixed point.

2. The Rotation of a Rigid Body.—A rigid body is a special type of system of particles, so that the theorems of the preceding section apply to it: the center of mass moves like a particle whose mass is the mass of the body, acted on by the total external force exerted on the body; and the total torque exerted on the body equals the time rate of change of its angular momentum, both being regarded as vectors, where torque and angular momentum are computed either about an arbitrary fixed point, or about the center of mass. As a corollary, of course we have the familiar relations governing the statics of a rigid body: for equilibrium, the net force, and the net torque or moment about any arbitrary point, must be zero.   Since the torque is a vector, this means that the moments of the external forces about three mutually perpendicular axes passing through the arbitrary point must all vanish.   The results of these theorems are familiar from elementary courses on physics.

Our task in the present section is to consider the rotation of a rigid body.   Two cases may be conveniently considered together. First, we may have a freely moving rigid body.   Then we have seen that its center of mass moves like a particle under the action of the external forces, and that the body rotates around the center of mass under the action of the external torques.   In that case, we take the origin to be at the center of mass, and apply Eq. (1.11), stating that the torque acting about the center of mass equals the time rate of change of angular momentum about that point.   The other case is that of a rigid body constrained by being pivoted at a fixed point, as the pivot of a top, or the center of a gyroscope.   In that case we choose the fixed point as the origin, and apply (1.8), again stating that the torque acting about the origin equals the time rate of change of angular momentum about that point.   Since the dynamical equations are the same in each case, our treatment can be the same for both.

If a body is pivoted at the origin, there must be an instantaneous axis of rotation, passing through the origin.   Let us define an angular velocity vector $\boldsymbol{\omega}$ as a vector passing through the origin along the axis of rotation, whose magnitude equals the magnitude of the angular velocity.   For a body whose axis of rotation is fixed, as a wheel rotating on an axle, the angular velocity vector will keep a fixed direction, changing only its magnitude, but in the general case the direction as well as the magnitude of the angular velocity can change with time.   In terms of the angular velocity vector, we can easily write the linear velocity $\dot{\mathbf{r}}_i$ of the ith particle.   It is equal in magnitude to the product of the angular velocity, and the perpendicular distance from the axis of rotation out to the particle, and is in a direction at right angles to the plane determined by the axis of rotation, and the vector position of the particle.   That is, we have

$$\dot{\mathbf{r}}_i = \boldsymbol{\omega} \times \mathbf{r}_i. \qquad (2.1)$$

In Eq. (2.1) we not only determine the magnitude and direction of the velocity correctly, but we also assume the sense of the angular velocity vector. For instance, if the angular velocity is along the z axis, the radius vector to the particle along the x axis, then the velocity is along the y axis.

In terms of the assumption (2.1) for the velocities of the various points of the body, we can compute the angular momentum, as it occurs in (1.8). Let the angular momentum vector be denoted by **p**. Then we have

$$\mathbf{p} = \sum_i \mathbf{r}_i \times m_i(\boldsymbol{\omega} \times \mathbf{r}_i). \tag{2.2}$$

Let us expand the quantity on the right side of (2.2) in terms of its components. For the x component, for example, we have

$$
\begin{aligned}
p_x &= \sum_i m_i[y_i(\omega_x y_i - \omega_y x_i) - z_i(\omega_z x_i - \omega_x z_i)] \\
&= \sum_i m_i(y_i^2 + z_i^2)\omega_x - \sum_i m_i x_i y_i \omega_y - \sum_i m_i x_i z_i \omega_z \\
&= I_{xx}\omega_x + I_{xy}\omega_y + I_{xz}\omega_z
\end{aligned}
\tag{2.3}
$$

and similarly

$$
\begin{aligned}
p_y &= I_{yx}\omega_x + I_{yy}\omega_y + I_{yz}\omega_z \\
p_z &= I_{zx}\omega_x + I_{zy}\omega_y + I_{zz}\omega_z
\end{aligned}
\tag{2.4}
$$

where

$$
\begin{aligned}
I_{xx} &= \sum_i m_i(y_i^2 + z_i^2), & I_{xy} &= -\sum_i m_i x_i y_i, & I_{xz} &= -\sum_i m_i x_i z_i \\
I_{yx} &= -\sum_i m_i y_i x_i, & I_{yy} &= \sum_i m_i(z_i^2 + x_i^2), & I_{yz} &= -\sum_i m_i y_i z_i \\
I_{zx} &= -\sum_i m_i z_i x_i, & I_{zy} &= -\sum_i m_i z_i y_i, & I_{zz} &= \sum_i m_i(x_i^2 + y_i^2).
\end{aligned}
\tag{2.5}
$$

The nine quantities I_{xx}, I_{xy}, ... I_{zz} form the components of the moment of inertia. A quantity with nine components, and two subscripts, of this sort, is known as a "tensor," and the particular case we have here, in which $I_{ab} = I_{ba}$, where a and b are any two of the indices x, y, z, is called a "symmetric tensor." We may write Eqs. (2.3) and (2.4) in symbolic form

$$p_a = \sum_b I_{ab}\omega_b, \qquad a, b = x, y, z. \tag{2.6}$$

The summation on the right is called a "tensor product" of the tensor I and the vector $\boldsymbol{\omega}$, and results in the vector **p**. The simple properties of tensors are described in Appendix V. The diagonal components I_{xx}, I_{yy}, I_{zz} of the tensor I are often called the "moments of inertia," and the nondiagonal components $I_{xy} = I_{yx}$, $I_{yz} = I_{zy}$, $I_{zx} = I_{xz}$ are called the "products of inertia" (sometimes their negatives are called the products of inertia). It is evident that the components I_{xx}, I_{yy}, I_{zz} are the moments of inertia, in the ordinary elementary sense, computed about the x, y, z axes.

The kinetic energy of the rotating body can be written easily in terms of the angular velocity vector and the moment of inertia tensor. Using (2.1) for the velocity of a particle, the kinetic energy is

$$T = \tfrac{1}{2} \sum_i m_i \dot{\mathbf{r}}_i^2 = \tfrac{1}{2} \sum_i m_i (\boldsymbol{\omega} \times \mathbf{r}_i)^2. \tag{2.7}$$

Expanding in terms of rectangular components, and using (2.5), we find easily that

$$T = \tfrac{1}{2} \sum_{a,b} I_{ab} \omega_a \omega_b, \tag{2.8}$$

where a and b are separately to take on the values x, y, z in the summation. We notice that

$$\sum_a p_a \omega_a = 2T = \mathbf{p} \cdot \boldsymbol{\omega}, \tag{2.9}$$

an equation that has a close analogy to Eq. (2.2) of Chap. IV. We notice that (2.7) can be given an elementary meaning. The magnitude of the vector product $\boldsymbol{\omega} \times \mathbf{r}_i$ in that equation equals the magnitude of $\boldsymbol{\omega}$, times the perpendicular distance from the axis of rotation to the particle. Thus the kinetic energy is half the product of the square of the magnitude of the angular velocity, and the sum over all particles of the product of their masses by the squares of the perpendicular distances from the axis of rotation. This summation is the moment of inertia as calculated in elementary physics. It is easily seen from (2.9) to be $\mathbf{p} \cdot \boldsymbol{\omega}/|\boldsymbol{\omega}|^2$, or the component of angular momentum along the axis of rotation, divided by the magnitude of the angular velocity, so that it is the quantity by which we must multiply the angular velocity to get the component of angular momentum along the axis. However, we note that in general the angular momentum is not in the direction of the axis of rotation. Thus if $\omega_x = \omega_y = 0$, so that the angular velocity is along the z axis, we see from (2.6) that all three components of p are different from zero, unless the products of inertia vanish. This possibility, of having a component of angular momentum at right angles to the axis of rotation, is not ordinarily considered in elementary treatments, and we shall discuss its significance in the next section.

3. Principal Axes of Inertia.—We have just mentioned that it is generally true that the angular momentum has a component at right angles to the axis of rotation. This has a very simple physical meaning. Let us consider a very elementary sort of rigid body, two equal weights on the ends of a weightless rod, rotating as indicated in Fig. 15. The axis of rotation is vertical in Fig. 15. However, the angular momentum is at right angles to the rod, since it is at right angles to the vector velocity, and to the radius vector out to the particles. A little reflection will show, in fact, that the instantaneous velocity of the particles is not enough in this simple case to define the axis of rotation; it might just as well be along the direction of the angular momentum vector. This is a special case resulting from the extreme simplicity of our example, however. Now, if the angular momentum is not along the axis of rotation, this means that the angular momentum vector will be carried around a cone as the body rotates, and that therefore it will be varying with time, and that a torque must be exerted to keep the body rotating about the vertical axis. We can easily find this torque. The time rate of change of the angular momentum vector, in Fig. 15, is the vector in the direction in which the tip of the angular momentum vector is moving, or at right angles to the plane of angular velocity and angular momentum, and equal to the magnitude of the angular velocity, times the projection of the angular momentum perpendicular to the axis of rotation. That is, it is

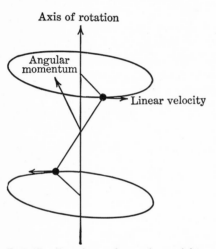

Axis of rotation

Angular momentum

Linear velocity

Fig. 15.—Rotating rod carrying weights.

$$\dot{\mathbf{p}} = \boldsymbol{\omega} \times \mathbf{p}, \tag{3.1}$$

an equation that shows a perfect analogy to (2.1), giving the linear velocity. The torque necessary to keep the body rotating about the vertical axis must then be in this same direction. It is physically clear why this torque must be applied. Centrifugal effects would tend to make the two weights of Fig. 15 fly out so that the rod connecting them would be at right angles to the axis of rotation, and the torque is just such as to counteract this tendency. This would be felt in a simple physical way, if the body were constrained to rotate about its axis of rotation by means of bearings: there would be a sideways thrust on the bearings. Let us consider this question of the thrust on bearings a little more closely.

If a piece of rotating machinery is constrained by bearings to rotate around a given axis, the machine will be unbalanced statically if its center of mass is not located on the axis of rotation. This can be tested easily if its axis is horizontal: the machine will come to rest with its center of mass directly below the axis, and will oscillate about this position like a pendulum. Even if the center of mass is on the axis, however, so that the machine is balanced statically, it will still not necessarily be balanced dynamically, in the sense that it will not exert thrust on its bearings, for as we have just seen the angular momentum in general has a component at right angles to the axis of rotation. A symmetrical body, such as a wheel rotating about its axle, will be balanced dynamically, however. We can see this easily from Eqs. (2.3) and (2.4), or (2.6). Thus for simplicity let the angular velocity be along the x axis, so that $p_y = I_{yx}\omega_x$, $p_z = I_{zx}\omega_x$. If we have dynamic balance, the angular momentum must be along the x axis, or $I_{yx} = I_{zx} = 0$. But this will be the case, as we can see from (2.5), for in computing the products of inertia, as $I_{xy} = -\sum_i m_i x_i y_i$, a mass with a certain value of x_i and y_i will be balanced by symmetry by another mass with the same x_i but a y_i that is the negative of the preceding value. All the elements of mass of the body can be balanced off in this way, and the products of inertia will be zero.

We can readily see that, in a symmetrical body such as a rectangular prism, there must be three separate axes along which the body can rotate with dynamical balance; in that case, the three axes passing through the center of the body, perpendicular to the three pairs of faces. These axes are called the "principal axes of inertia"; if they are chosen as the coordinate axes, the products of inertia all vanish.

We shall now prove a very general and important theorem: any rigid body pivoted about any point, has three principal axes of inertia, in terms of which the products of inertia vanish. If the pivot is at the center of mass, the body will be in dynamic balance if it is rotated about any one of these three principal axes. The practical importance of this theorem is obvious; it means that any statically balanced object can be dynamically balanced, and that to achieve dynamic balance, we need only find its principal axes, and use any one of these three axes as the axis of rotation. Our problem is now not merely to prove the existence of these principal axes, but to set up a procedure for finding them, in case the body is unsymmetrical, so that it is not intuitively obvious how to set them up.

The property of a principal axis is that, if the body rotates around such an axis, the angular momentum is in the same direction as the angular velocity. Thus if $\boldsymbol{\omega}$ is an angular velocity along one of the principal axes, $\mathbf{p}$ the corresponding angular momentum vector, we must have

$$\mathbf{p} = I\boldsymbol{\omega} \qquad (3.2)$$

where I is a scalar, equal to the moment of inertia about the principal axis. If p_x, p_y, p_z are the components of $\mathbf{p}$, ω_x, ω_y, ω_z of $\boldsymbol{\omega}$, then by combination of (2.6) and (3.2) we may write

$$p_x = I\omega_x = I_{xx}\omega_x + I_{xy}\omega_y + I_{xz}\omega_z$$
$$p_y = I\omega_y = I_{yx}\omega_x + I_{yy}\omega_y + I_{yz}\omega_z$$
$$p_z = I\omega_z = I_{zx}\omega_x + I_{zy}\omega_y + I_{zz}\omega_z$$

or

$$(I_{xx} - I)\omega_x + I_{xy}\omega_y + I_{xz}\omega_z = 0$$
$$I_{yx}\omega_x + (I_{yy} - I)\omega_y + I_{yz}\omega_z = 0$$
$$I_{zx}\omega_x + I_{zy}\omega_y + (I_{zz} - I)\omega_z = 0. \qquad (3.3)$$

Equations (3.3) are three simultaneous algebraic linear homogeneous equations for the three unknowns ω_x, ω_y, ω_z. As shown in Appendix V, these equations in general have no solutions other than $\omega_x = 0$, $\omega_y = 0$, $\omega_z = 0$. The reason is that there are really only two independent unknowns. We can, for instance, divide each equation by ω_x, and then we have three equations for ω_y/ω_x and ω_z/ω_x. Two equations, however, would suffice to determine these two unknowns, which fix the direction but not the magnitude of the angular velocity, and which thus fix the direction of the principal axis; the third equation is superfluous, and unless it is consistent with the other two, no solutions are possible, except of course the obvious solution, zero.

In Appendix V we show that the condition that the three equations (3.3) be compatible with each other, so that they have solutions different from zero, is that the determinant of their coefficients should vanish:

$$\begin{vmatrix} I_{xx} - I & I_{xy} & I_{xz} \\ I_{yx} & I_{yy} - I & I_{yz} \\ I_{zx} & I_{zy} & I_{zz} - I \end{vmatrix} = 0. \qquad (3.4)$$

If we expand this determinant, it is a cubic equation for I. Thus, since a cubic equation has three roots, there are three values of I for which we can solve Eqs. (3.3). Using any one of these three values, we can at once solve the first two of Eqs. (3.3) for ω_y/ω_x and ω_z/ω_x, determining thus the direction of the appropriate principal axes, and we can be sure that the third of Eqs. (3.3) will automatically be satisfied by these values. We thus determine three principal axes, one from each of the three values of I determined from (3.4). It is proved in Appendix V that these three axes are at right angles to each other. If we choose, we may label them the x_1, x_2, and x_3 axes. Then in terms of the principal axes the relations between angular momentum and angular velocity are

$$p_1 = I_1\omega_1$$
$$p_2 = I_2\omega_2$$
$$p_3 = I_3\omega_3, \qquad (3.5)$$

where I_1, I_2, I_3 are the three values of I found by solving (3.4). Equations (3.5) are the special form that (2.6) takes on when the products of inertia are zero. Thus we have shown how to set up principal axes of inertia, and to compute the principal moments of inertia, the components of moment of inertia along the principal axes. In terms of the principal axes, the kinetic energy takes on a very simple form: from (2.8) it is

$$T = \tfrac{1}{2}(I_1\omega_1^2 + I_2\omega_2^2 + I_3\omega_3^2). \qquad (3.6)$$

4. Equations of Motion of a Rigid Body.—In elementary physics, the analogy between translational and rotational motion is often stressed. In translational motion in one dimension, the force equals the time rate of change of the momentum, or the mass times the acceleration. Similarly, if a rigid body is rotating on an axle, which, for instance, is along the x axis, the component of torque along the x axis equals the time rate of change of x component of angular momentum, or equals I_{xx}, the moment of inertia about the x axis, times the time rate of change of angular velocity, or the angular acceleration. In each case, the velocity can be written as the time rate of change of a coordinate; in the translational case this coordinate is the distance through which the body has traveled, and in the case of rotation about a fixed axis it is the angle of rotation about the axis. The law that the force equals the mass times acceleration, or that torque equals moment of inertia times angular acceleration, then becomes a second order differential equation for coordinates as a function of time, which can be solved by the methods of Chap. I, including the method of the energy. So far, the analogy between translational and rotational motion is complete.

When we come to three-dimensional motion, at first sight it would seem that the analogy still holds. We have shown, in the present chapter, that the torque, regarded as a vector, equals the time rate of change of angular momentum, also a vector, just as the vector force equals the time rate of change of the vector momentum in translational motion. Here, unfortunately, however, the analogy ends, and it is a result of the breakdown of the analogy that the motion of rigid bodies is a much more complicated subject than the translational motion of a particle. There are two aspects to the breakdown of the analogy, which we shall now go into.

First is the relation (2.6) between angular momentum and angular velocity. An essential part of the ordinary treatment of translational motion is that the momentum equals a constant, the mass, times the velocity. With rotational motion, however, the angular momentum is the tensor product of a tensor, the moment of inertia, and the angular velocity vector. Not only is the tensor product a more complicated concept than the product of a constant, or scalar, like the mass, with a vector; more important is the fact that the moment of inertia tensor itself is not a constant. For from (2.5) we have seen the definition of the moment of inertia, and it depends on the positions of the various particles of the body. As the body rotates, the components I_{ab} of the tensor change, so that in finding the time rate of change of angular momentum, we must consider the time rate of change of the I_{ab}'s as well as of the angular velocity. This situation does not come up in the rotation of a body about a fixed axis, for in that case the component of moment of inertia about that fixed axis, which is the only one concerned in the equation of motion, remains constant. But in the general case, where the I_{ab}'s are functions of time, we simply cannot set up any method of treatment analogous to the translational case.

In addition to this difficulty, there is another equally serious breakdown in the analogy between rotational and translational motion. In translational motion, or in rotation about a fixed axis, there are simple coordinates, whose time derivatives give the velocities. In three-dimensional rotation, however, there are no such coordinates. In particular, it is impossible to set up three angles, whose time derivatives are ω_x, ω_y, and ω_z, respectively. This seems like a surprising fact, when it is first encountered. We might suppose, for instance, that the angle of rotation about the x axis was the coordinate to associate with ω_x, and similarly for ω_y and ω_z.   But we cannot do this, for finite rotations about the axes do not act like vectors, though infinitesimal rotations, such as those we encounter in setting up the angular velocities, do act like vectors.

We can see this by a simple example.   Certainly if finite rotations about the axes acted like vectors, we should get the same final answer if we first rotated through a fixed angle about the x axis, then through a fixed angle about y, or if we rotated first about y, then about x; this is inherent in the definition of vector addition.   But let us see what

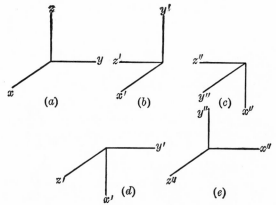

Fig. 16.—Diagram to illustrate finite rotations.

happens.   For simplicity, we take our angle of rotation to be 90°. We then first rotate through 90° about x, so that the y axis rotates to the previous direction of the z axis, and z rotates into $-y$.   This situation is shown in Fig. 16, where (a) shows the original axes, (b) the rotated axes, denoted by x', y', z'.   Next we rotate through 90° about the y axis, rotating the z axis (whose place is now taken by the y' axis) into the original position of the x axis.   Thus, as we see in (c), the final situation after the two rotations is that the original y axis has been rotated into the position of the original x axis, the original z axis is along $-y$, and the original x axis is along $-z$.   Next consider the reverse order, first rotating around the y axis.   As shown in (d), the rotated z axis, or z', is in the direction of the original x axis, while the rotated x axis x' is along $-z$.   Next we rotate about the x axis, resulting, as in (e), in a situation where the rotated x axis x'' is along y, the rotated y axis y'' is along z, and the rotated z axis z'' is along x, a completely different situation from (c).   This simple example should convince one that finite rotations of this sort cannot be used as coordinates. If there are no coordinates to go with the angular velocity components ω_x, ω_y, ω_z, or the angular momentum components p_x, p_y, p_z, we certainly cannot use methods analogous to those used for translation.

Two possibilities are open to us, in solving the general problem of the motion of a rigid body. One is to introduce coordinates that suffice to describe the position of the body, and to proceed by the Lagrangian method to set up and solve the equations of motion, without use of our relations between torque and time rate of change of angular momentum. That is the method that will be used in the next chapter. We introduce certain angles, called "Euler's angles," which have none of the symmetry of rectangular coordinates, but which can be used to solve the problem. The equations of motion that we get can be handled, much as were the equations for the spherical pendulum in the preceding chapter, and we shall get a satisfactory treatment of gyroscopic motion in that way. The results are consistent with our theorems about torque and angular momentum, as we shall show, but we do not make direct use of those theorems. These methods are practical and powerful, but not elegant.

The other approach is to get as far as we can by direct application of the theorems of this chapter; we shall now describe what can be done in this way. The mere statement that the torque equals the time rate of change of angular momentum can often give considerable information. Thus, for instance, a body acted on by no torques must have a constant angular momentum, constant both in magnitude and in orientation in space. This by no means implies a constant angular velocity vector, however; for we have seen that the relation between angular velocity and angular momentum involves the moment of inertia tensor, which is continually changing. We shall actually find in the next chapter that a body on which no torques are exerted carries out a complicated precessional motion. One simplification we have not taken advantage of, however, so far, is the use of the principal axes as coordinates. In terms of the principal axes, the moment of inertia tensor has a simple form, and furthermore it is independent of time. We shall show that, by expressing the equations of motion in principal axes, we can get a simple and symmetrical set of equations, which have considerable usefulness.

The principal axes, of course, are moving; in fact, since they are rigidly attached to the body, they are rotating with an instantaneous angular velocity $\boldsymbol{\omega}$. If we express the angular momentum in terms of its components with respect to the principal axes, or the quantities

p_1, p_2, p_3 of Eq. (3.5), then the time rate of change of this angular momentum will have two terms.   First there will be the time rate of change with respect to principal axes, and secondly there will be the rate at which the angular momentum would change on account of the rotation of the axes, if its components in principal axes remained constant.   This time rate of change is simply $\omega \times \mathbf{p}$, as in Eq. (3.1). Using (3.5), and denoting the components of the external torque with respect to the principal axes by M_1, M_2, M_3, we have for the equations of motion

$$M_1 = I_1\dot{\omega}_1 + (\omega \times \mathbf{p})_1 = I_1\dot{\omega}_1 + (I_3 - I_2)\omega_3\omega_2$$
$$M_2 = I_2\dot{\omega}_2 + (\omega \times \mathbf{p})_2 = I_2\dot{\omega}_2 + (I_1 - I_3)\omega_1\omega_3$$
$$M_3 = I_3\dot{\omega}_3 + (\omega \times \mathbf{p})_3 = I_3\dot{\omega}_3 + (I_2 - I_1)\omega_2\omega_1. \tag{4.1}$$

The equations (4.1) are called "Euler's equations."   They serve, as we see, to determine the time rate of change of the angular velocity vector in terms of principal axes, if we know the torque in terms of principal axes.   Then from (3.5) we can find the angular momentum vector in principal axes.   That is, we can find how the body moves with respect to the angular momentum vector, so that if we can also find directly how the angular momentum vector moves in space, we can derive fairly complete information about the motion of the body from Euler's equations.   They do not form, however, a really convenient way to attack a problem in the motion of rigid bodies, and we shall not give any examples of their use until the next chapter.   There, where we shall solve problems by direct solution of the equations of motion in terms of Euler's angles, we shall show that the solutions so derived satisfy Euler's equations, and shall understand their interpretation and physical significance.

Problems

1. Prove that, if a body is pivoted about a fixed axis of rotation making direction cosines λ, μ, ν with the coordinate axes, the moment of inertia I for rotation about that axis, equal to the summation of the masses of all volume elements, times the squares of the perpendicular distances of the elements from the axis, is equal to $\lambda^2 I_{xx} + \mu^2 I_{yy} + \nu^2 I_{zz} + 2\lambda\mu I_{xy} + 2\mu\nu I_{yz} + 2\nu\lambda I_{zx}$.

2. Find the principal moments of inertia of a solid homogeneous right circular cone of density ρ, altitude h, and vertex angle 2α, pivoted about its apex, using spherical coordinates.   What are the principal axes?   Find the moment of inertia of the cone about its slant height.

3. A thin piece of metal of mass 80 g has the cross section shown in Fig. 17. Find the moment and products of inertia for the axes Ox and Oy.   Through what angles must these axes be rotated to coincide with the principal axes?   Suppose the body is rotating at a given instant about the Ox axis with an angular velocity of 10 radians/sec.   Find the direction of the angular momentum vector at this instant.

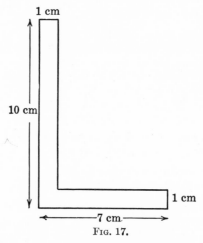

1 cm

10 cm

1 cm

7 cm

Fig. 17.

4. A rigid body rotates freely about a principal axis.   From the Euler equations of motion show that this motion is stable in general when it is about an axis of largest or smallest moment of inertia, but unstable about the axis of intermediate moment of inertia.

5. A solid homogeneous sphere of radius r, at rest on the top of another fixed sphere of radius R, is displaced slightly and begins to roll.   If the coefficient of friction between the two surfaces is μ, find where slipping starts.   Under what conditions will the rolling sphere leave the surface of the other before slipping starts?

6. A hollow cylinder of inner radius 10 in. is held fixed with its axis horizontal, and a solid sphere of radius 3 in. rests inside it in equilibrium.   The sphere is displaced in a plane perpendicular to the cylinder axis and, released from rest, rolls without slipping.   Set up the potential and kinetic energy for the motion, and find the frequency of small oscillations.   Discuss the change in period as a function of the amplitude of the motion.

7. The ends of a uniform rod of length $2a$ can slide on the inside of a smooth circular vertical track of inner radius b.   Find the period of small oscillations of the rod about its equilibrium position.

8. A solid disk rotating about its horizontal axis with a rim speed of 32 ft/sec is placed on an inclined plane of base 12 ft and altitude 5 ft.   The coefficient of friction between disk and plane is $\frac{1}{2}$, and the disk rotates so that it tends to roll up the plane.   How far up the plane does the disk move?   During what fraction of this distance does the disk roll without slipping?   How much energy is dissipated during this motion?

CHAPTER VI

THE MOTION OF A SYMMETRICAL RIGID BODY

In the preceding chapter we found a number of properties relating to the motion of rigid bodies. We have not, however, been able to solve any specific problems. We shall now take up a particular and important problem: the motion of a symmetrical rigid body. By this, we mean a body two of whose principal moments of inertia are equal to each other, as they would be for a body with rotational symmetry about an axis, such as a top. Many of the most important rigid-body motions are examples of this problem. The most obvious one is the gyroscope, a device with many practical applications. Another, less familiar example is that of the rotation of the earth about its axis. The earth is flattened at the poles, and thus is not a perfect sphere. Furthermore, it does not rotate precisely about its axis of figure, and the resulting motion shows interesting precession. Still another, quite different example comes from atomic and molecular structure. An atom is a structure of electrons rotating about a nucleus. Although it is not strictly a rigid body, it acts like one in many respects, and furthermore acts in many cases like a symmetrical body. Some symmetrical molecules also have rotations that follow the laws of motion of rigid bodies. All these cases can be handled by the methods we shall develop in this chapter.

We have seen in Chap. V that the vector law that the torque acting on a body equals the time rate of change of its angular momentum is not so useful in practice as we should think at first sight, since there are no generalized coordinates of which the three rectangular components of angular momentum are the generalized momenta. Thus we must introduce less symmetrical coordinates, and we shall use the angles known as Euler's angles. We shall follow through the details of the motion, as described in terms of Euler's angles, and shall see how this motion is consistent with the laws of the preceding chapter.

1. Euler's Angles.—In Fig. 18 we show Euler's angles. The axis of the top has its orientation specified by two angles θ and φ, which are similar to the angles of a conventional set of spherical polar coordinates. One of the principal axes of inertia is along the axis

of the top, by definition.   This will be called axis 3, and the moment
of inertia along it will be I_3.   The other two principal axes, 1 and 2,
are shown in Fig. 18.   The plane perpendicular to axis 3 intersects
the xy plane in a line called the "line of nodes."   The angle φ is
the angle, in the xy plane, between the x axis and the line of nodes; the
angle ψ, which describes the rotation of the top around its own axis,

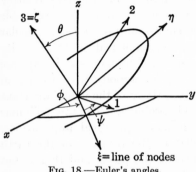

ξ=line of nodes

FIG. 18.—Euler's angles.

is measured in the plane perpendicular to axis 3, and is the angle
between the line of nodes and axis
1.   We shall find it convenient to
introduce a rotated set of rectan-
gular axes ξ, η, ζ, as shown, ξ being
along the line of nodes, η in the
plane of axes 1 and 2 at right
angles to ξ, and ζ coinciding with
axis 3.

The axes as we have shown can
be used for a nonsymmetrical

rigid body as well as for a symmetrical one; we should still have the
principal axes 1, 2, 3 in the directions shown.   For the symmetrical
body, two simplifications result.   In the first place, the two principal
moments of inertia I_1 and I_2 become equal to each other; we may call
each one I_1.   In the second place, it is no longer possible to fix uniquely
the directions of axes 1 and 2.   All that we can do is to say that they
are two axes, perpendicular to each other, in the $\xi\eta$ plane.   This is
obvious without proof for a solid that is really a figure of revolution;
there is no unique axis perpendicular to the axis of figure.   For a solid
that merely has I_1 and I_2 equal to each other, and yet is not a figure
of revolution, a more formal proof is perhaps worth while.   In that
case, we should like to show that any direction in the 1-2 plane has the
property of a principal axis, that the angular velocity and the angular
momentum are parallel.   Let us consider Eq. (2.6) of Chap. V:

$$p_a = \sum_b I_{ab}\omega_b. \qquad (1.1)$$

Consider an angular velocity in the 1-2 plane, with components ω_1, ω_2
along axes 1 and 2, and with $\omega_3 = 0$.   Remembering that $I_1 = I_2$, and
that 1, 2, 3 are principal axes, (1.1) then gives $p_1 = I_1\omega_1$, $p_2 = I_1\omega_2$,
showing that the angular momentum is parallel to the angular velocity,
so that the arbitrary direction in the 1-2 plane forms a principal axis.

It is interesting to see the physical interpretation of the time rates of change of the various angles, θ, φ, and ψ. First we assume that only ψ is different from zero, all other generalized velocities being zero. Then clearly the body is rotating about its axis 3, or axis of figure, if it is a symmetrical body. It has an angular velocity of ψ in the ζ direction. Secondly, we assume that only $\dot{\varphi}$ is different from zero. The axis of the body is then tracing out a cone around the z axis. This type of motion is called "precession." The angular velocity around the z axis is $\dot{\varphi}$. Finally, we suppose that only $\dot{\theta}$ is different from zero. Then the inclination of the axis of figure with respect to the z axis is changing with time. If at the same time there is precessional motion, the resulting motion of the axis of figure is called "nutation." This type of motion is similar to the general motion of the spherical pendulum, as decribed in Chap. IV, Sec. 4. A motion in which only $\dot{\theta}$ is different from zero is clearly a rotation with angular velocity $\dot{\theta}$ about the ξ axis.

We have just seen that $\dot{\theta}$, $\dot{\varphi}$, $\dot{\psi}$, represent angular velocities about the ξ, z, and ζ axes, respectively. The asymmetry of Euler's angles is apparent from this: the three axes are not perpendicular to each other. We may, however, resolve $\dot{\varphi}$ along the η and ζ axes: $\dot{\varphi}$ has a component $\dot{\varphi} \sin \theta$ along the η axis, $\dot{\varphi} \cos \theta$ along the ζ axis. If we now superpose all three types of rotation, remembering that angular velocities add like vectors, we have

$$\omega_\xi = \dot{\theta}, \qquad \omega_\eta = \dot{\varphi} \sin \theta, \qquad \omega_\zeta = \dot{\psi} + \dot{\varphi} \cos \theta. \qquad (1.2)$$

Furthermore, we may resolve along the axes 1, 2, 3:

$$\omega_1 = \dot{\theta} \cos \psi + \dot{\varphi} \sin \theta \sin \psi$$
$$\omega_2 = -\dot{\theta} \sin \psi + \dot{\varphi} \sin \theta \cos \psi$$
$$\omega_3 = \dot{\psi} + \dot{\varphi} \cos \theta. \qquad (1.3)$$

2. Lagrange's Equations in Terms of Euler's Angles.—To derive Lagrange's equations, we first need to set up the kinetic energy in terms of the coordinates and velocities. We may do this most conveniently from Eq. (3.6) of Chap. V,

$$T = \tfrac{1}{2}(I_1\omega_1^2 + I_2\omega_2^2 + I_3\omega_3^2)$$

taken in connection with (1.3). Setting $I_1 = I_2$ for the symmetrical solid, we have

$$T = \tfrac{1}{2}[I_1(\dot{\theta}^2 + \sin^2\theta \; \dot{\varphi}^2) + I_3(\dot{\psi} + \dot{\varphi} \cos \theta)^2].$$

The generalized momenta are now the derivatives of T with respect to the generalized velocities. Thus we have

$$p_\theta = \frac{\partial T}{\partial \dot\theta} = I_1 \dot\theta$$

$$p_\varphi = \frac{\partial T}{\partial \dot\varphi} = I_1 \sin^2\theta \, \dot\varphi + I_3 \cos\,\theta(\dot\psi + \dot\varphi \cos\,\theta)$$

$$p_\psi = \frac{\partial T}{\partial \dot\psi} = I_3(\dot\psi + \dot\varphi \cos\,\theta). \tag{2.1}$$

To get the significance of these results, it is interesting to rewrite in terms of the angular velocity components ω_ξ, ω_η, ω_ζ, of (1.2). We have

$$p_\theta = I_1\omega_\xi$$
$$p_\varphi = I_1\omega_\eta \sin\,\theta + I_3\omega_\zeta \cos\,\theta$$
$$p_\psi = I_3\omega_\zeta. \tag{2.2}$$

We may set up components p_ξ, p_η, p_ζ of the angular momentum vector in the ξ, η, ζ axes, using Eq. (1.1). We have

$$p_\xi = I_1\omega_\xi, \qquad p_\eta = I_1\omega_\eta, \qquad p_\zeta = I_3\omega_\zeta.$$

In terms of these,

$$p_\theta = p_\xi, \qquad p_\varphi = p_\eta \sin\,\theta + p_\zeta \cos\,\theta, \qquad p_\psi = p_\zeta. \tag{2.3}$$

That is, referring to Fig. 18, p_θ, p_φ, and p_ψ are, respectively, the components of the angular momentum vector along the ξ, z, and ζ directions, just as we found earlier that $\dot\theta$, $\dot\varphi$, and $\dot\psi$ are the components of the angular velocity along these same axes.

The next step in setting up Lagrange's equations is to find the meaning of the generalized forces associated with the angles θ, φ, ψ. The rate of working of the external forces on a rigid body is the product of the forces times the velocities of the various particles, or is $dW/dt = \sum_i \mathbf{f}_i \cdot \dot{\mathbf{r}}_i$. Using $\dot{\mathbf{r}}_i = \boldsymbol\omega \times \mathbf{r}_i$ from Eq. (2.1), Chap. V, this is $dW/dt = \sum_i \mathbf{f}_i \cdot (\boldsymbol\omega \times \mathbf{r}_i)$. Using the vector theorem

$$[\mathbf{A} \cdot (\mathbf{B} \times \mathbf{C})] = [\mathbf{B} \cdot (\mathbf{C} \times \mathbf{A})] = [\mathbf{C} \cdot (\mathbf{A} \times \mathbf{B})],$$

proved in one of the problems of Appendix IV, this equals $\boldsymbol\omega \cdot \sum_i \mathbf{r}_i \times \mathbf{f}_i$. Using Eq. (1.8) Chap. V, $\sum_i \mathbf{r}_i \times \mathbf{f}_i = \mathbf{M}$, the moment of the external forces. Thus we find that the rate of working of the external forces is

$$\frac{dW}{dt} = \mathbf{M} \cdot \boldsymbol\omega \tag{2.4}$$

where $\mathbf{M}$ is the vector moment of the external forces, $\boldsymbol{\omega}$ is the vector angular velocity. Using (1.2) for the components of angular velocity in terms of ξ, η, and ζ axes, and M_ξ, M_η, M_ζ for components of the moment of external forces in the same axes, we have

$$dW = M_\xi\, d\theta + M_\eta \sin\theta\, d\varphi + M_\zeta(d\psi + \cos\theta\, d\varphi)$$
$$= M_\xi\, d\theta + (M_\eta \sin\theta + M_\zeta \cos\theta)\, d\varphi + M_\zeta\, d\psi$$
$$= M_\theta\, d\theta + M_\varphi\, d\varphi + M_\psi\, d\psi,$$

where

$$M_\theta = M_\xi, \qquad M_\varphi = M_\eta \sin\theta + M_\zeta \cos\theta, \qquad M_\psi = M_\zeta,$$

so that M_θ, M_φ, and M_ψ are the generalized forces associated with θ, φ, and ψ, and are at the same time the components of the moment of external force along ξ, z, and ζ, respectively. In terms of them, we may if we choose find the components M_1, M_2, M_3 of the moment along the principal axes. We have

$$M_\theta = M_1 \cos\psi - M_2 \sin\psi$$
$$M_\varphi = (M_1 \sin\psi + M_2 \cos\psi) \sin\theta + M_3 \cos\theta$$
$$M_\psi = M_3 \tag{2.5}$$

from which M_1, M_2, M_3 can at once be found.

We may now at once set up Lagrange's equations. They are

$$\frac{dp_\theta}{dt} = I_1\ddot\theta = \frac{\partial T}{\partial\theta} + M_\theta$$
$$= I_1\dot\varphi^2 \sin\theta \cos\theta - I_3\dot\varphi \sin\theta(\dot\psi + \dot\varphi \cos\theta) + M_\theta$$
$$\frac{dp_\varphi}{dt} = \frac{d}{dt}[I_1 \sin^2\theta\, \dot\varphi + I_3 \cos\theta\, (\dot\psi + \dot\varphi \cos\theta)] = M_\varphi$$
$$\frac{dp_\psi}{dt} = \frac{d}{dt}[I_3(\dot\psi + \dot\varphi \cos\theta)] = M_\psi. \tag{2.6}$$

These are at first sight rather complicated equations. They should, of course, be essentially equivalent to Euler's equations, (4.1), of Chap. V, and they are. To prove this, we may start with Euler's equations, which are expressed in terms of M_1, M_2, M_3, and ω_1, ω_2, ω_3; express the angular velocities by (1.3), and the components of the moments by (2.5). Writing everything in terms of θ, φ, and ψ, then, we find that Lagrange's equations (2.6) follow as a consequence of Euler's equations. This is a complicated way of deriving them, but it shows that Lagrange's equations essentially express simply the fact that the torque equals the time rate of change of angular momentum. The only one of Euler's equations that transforms simply is the one for axis 3. Since the body is symmetrical, and $I_1 = I_2$, Eq. (4.1) of Chap. V states that $M_3 = I_3\dot{\omega}_3$, which by (1.3), (2.5), is just the third equation of (2.6). Though Lagrange's equations are at first sight complicated, we shall see by examples that they can lead to simple results in important special cases.

3. The Free Motion of a Symmetrical Rigid Body.—The first example we shall take up is that of the motion of a symmetrical rigid body under the action of no torques. In that case, we may simplify the problem by choosing our axes properly at the outset. We know that, since no torques act on the body, its angular momentum is constant. Let the angular momentum then be along the z axis of our coordinates, and be a constant value p_z. In this case we shall have

$$p_\xi = 0, \qquad p_\eta = p_z \sin\theta, \qquad p_\zeta = p_z \cos\theta$$
$$p_\theta = 0, \qquad p_\varphi = p_z, \qquad p_\psi = p_z \cos\theta. \tag{3.1}$$

Since $p_\theta = I_1\dot{\theta}$, we see at once that θ must be constant, or the angle between the axis of figure and the total angular momentum is constant. Lagrange's equations (2.6) then become

$$0 = \dot{\varphi}\sin\theta[I_1\dot{\varphi}\cos\theta - I_3(\dot{\psi} + \dot{\varphi}\cos\theta)]$$
$$p_z = \text{constant} = I_1\sin^2\theta\,\dot{\varphi} + I_3\cos\theta(\dot{\psi} + \dot{\varphi}\cos\theta)$$
$$p_z\cos\theta = \text{constant} = I_3(\dot{\psi} + \dot{\varphi}\cos\theta). \tag{3.2}$$

It is convenient to express p_z, $\dot{\varphi}$, and $\dot{\psi}$, from (3.2), in terms of the angle θ, and the component of angular velocity about the axis of figure, which by (1.3) is $\omega_3 = \dot{\psi} + \dot{\varphi}\cos\theta$, and hence by (3.2) remains constant during the motion. From the third of Eqs. (3.2) we have

$$p_z\cos\theta = I_3\omega_3, \tag{3.3}$$

which is also obvious from (3.1), (2.2), and (1.2). From the first of (3.2) we have

$$\dot{\varphi}\cos\theta = \frac{I_3}{I_1}\omega_3 \tag{3.4}$$

which also follows from the second of (3.2) together with (3.3). Finally we have

$$\dot{\psi} = \omega_3 - \dot{\varphi}\cos\theta = \frac{(I_1 - I_3)}{I_1}\omega_3. \tag{3.5}$$

Thus we find that $\dot{\psi}$ and $\dot{\varphi}$ are constants, and find their values.

The physical nature of the motion may be seen from Fig. 19. For definiteness we show the case $I_3 > I_1$, which would be the case for an oblate spheroid, as for instance the rotating earth, which is flattened at the poles. The z axis is the axis of angular momentum, and the

ζ axis the axis of figure.   The angular velocity vector, as shown, lies in the plane of z and ζ, but is not in the same direction as the angular momentum.   We may see this from the fundamental relationship that $p_\eta = I_1\omega_\eta$, $p_\zeta = I_3\omega_\zeta$, so that, since I_3 is greater than I_1, the angular momentum is more nearly parallel to the axis of figure than is the angular velocity.

We show in Fig. 19 the way in which the angular velocity is made up of a vector $\dot\varphi$ along the z axis, given by (3.4), and a vector ψ along the ζ axis, given by (3.5), and hence negative in the present case.   The motion becomes easy to understand when we consider the two cones shown in Fig. 19.   One of these cones is fixed in space, and has the z axis as its axis of symmetry, while the other is fixed in the body, and has the ζ axis as its axis of symmetry; both cones pass through the axis of angular velocity.   The motion of the body may now be considered to be a rolling of the body cone on the space cone.   In such a rolling motion, the angular velocity vector will move around the space cone, rotating about the angular momentum vector.   At the same

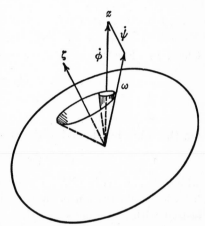

Fig. 19.—Space cone and body cone, for rotation of a symmetrical rigid body.

time, with respect to the body, it will move around the body cone. The time required for the angular velocity to move once around the space cone is the period associated with the angular velocity $\dot\varphi$; after one such period, the axis of figure will have returned to its original orientation in space.   In this time, however, the body cone will have rolled around the space cone in such a way that the line of tangency of the two cones, which is the angular velocity vector, will have rotated a certain distance around the body cone.   Thus in this time axes 1 and 2 will have rotated with respect to axes ζ and η, and it is this rotation which is described by the angular velocity ψ.   If ψ is small compared with $\dot\varphi$, as it will be according to (3.4) and (3.5) if the body is almost symmetrical, this means that the body cone has a much wider aperture than the space cone, as shown in Fig. 19, so that it requires many periods of φ for the orientation of the angular velocity vector with respect to the body to describe the body cone.

If we consider the angular velocity vector with respect to coordinates fixed in the body, we see that it describes the body cone, with angular velocity $-\dot{\psi}$. To see this analytically, let us set up the components ω_1, ω_2, ω_3 of angular velocity with respect to axes fixed in the body, from (1.3). We have

$$\omega_1 = \dot{\varphi} \sin \theta \sin \psi, \qquad \omega_2 = \dot{\varphi} \sin \theta \cos \psi. \qquad (3.6)$$

Since $\dot{\varphi} \sin \theta$ is a constant, this means that ω_1 and ω_2 are two components of a vector making an angle ψ with axis 2, measured down toward axis 1, so that this vector rotates with an angular velocity $-\dot{\psi}$. This rotation is given immediately by Euler's equations, (4.1) of Chap. V. For this case, those equations become

$$I_1\dot{\omega}_1 + (I_3 - I_1)\omega_2\omega_3 = 0$$
$$I_1\dot{\omega}_2 + (I_1 - I_3)\omega_1\omega_3 = 0$$
$$I_3\dot{\omega}_3 = 0. \qquad (3.7)$$

On the other hand, taking the time rates of change of (3.6), we have

$$\dot{\omega}_1 = \dot{\psi}\omega_2, \qquad \dot{\omega}_2 = -\dot{\psi}\omega_1,$$

which, taken with (3.5), leads at once to Euler's equations (3.7). This is an illustration of the way in which Euler's equations are consistent with Lagrange's equations, but give much less information.

The general motion of the freely rotating symmetric body is then as follows: it consists of a rotation about an axis that rotates rapidly in space about a cone, the space cone, whose axis is the fixed axis of total angular momentum; at the same time, the axis rotates more slowly with respect to the body, about a cone, the body cone, whose axis is the axis of figure. The inclination of the axis of figure to the fixed axis of angular momentum is constant. The motion is thus a type of precessional motion of the axis of figure about the axis of angular momentum. Of course, it is evident that there is a special case in which the axis of angular momentum coincides with the axis of figure; then the axis of angular velocity is also along this direction, and the motion becomes a simple rotation about the axis of figure, as around an axle. Similarly there is a special case in which the rotation is about any axis in the 1-2 plane; in any such case the axis of rotation is a principal axis, so that the angular velocity is parallel to the angular momentum, and stays fixed in space. For this case $\theta = \pi/2$, so that $\omega_3 = 0$, and, using (3.7), $\dot{\omega}_1$ and $\dot{\omega}_2$ are zero, showing that the angular velocity vector, which is in the 1-2 plane, is fixed with respect to the body.

We have described the motion of the freely rotating symmetrical rigid body in the simplest possible way in terms of Euler's angles: we have taken the constant direction of the angular momentum to be that of the z axis.   This is by no means necessary, however; we could have taken the angular momentum in any direction.   If we had done this, we should have a much more complicated solution, which we can describe, since we know the nature of the motion.   Let us imagine Fig. 19 tipped at an angle.   Then the axis of figure, instead of describing a cone with constant angle θ, will describe a cone in space for which θ will change with time.   The orientation will come back to its original value periodically, the frequency of this motion being $\dot{\varphi}$, so that θ must oscillate between maximum and minimum values with this angular frequency.   Simultaneously φ and ψ will execute much more complicated motions than when the angular momentum is along z.   We shall see an example of this general situation in the next section, when we take up a more general case of motion, and treat the free rotation as a limiting case when the torque goes to zero.

4. The Top Spinning under Gravity.—One of the most important types of rigid-body problem is that of the symmetrical body such as a top moving under the type of torque produced by gravity.   Suppose the body is pivoted at a point on its axis of figure.   Then gravity will exert a torque tending to make the top fall, or to increase θ, if the z axis is taken vertically upward.   If the mass is m, acceleration of gravity is g, and the distance from the pivot to the center of mass is L, the gravitational torque will be

$$M_\theta = mgL \sin \theta, \qquad M_\varphi = M_\psi = 0. \tag{4.1}$$

Lagrange's equations are then

$$M_\theta = I_1\ddot{\theta} - I_1\dot{\varphi}^2 \sin \theta \cos \theta + I_3\dot{\varphi} \sin \theta(\dot{\psi} + \dot{\varphi} \cos \theta)$$

$$0 = \frac{dp_\varphi}{dt} = \frac{d}{dt}[I_1 \sin^2\theta \, \dot{\varphi} + I_3 \cos \theta(\dot{\psi} + \dot{\varphi} \cos \theta)]$$

$$0 = \frac{dp_\psi}{dt} = \frac{d}{dt}[I_3(\dot{\psi} + \dot{\varphi} \cos \theta)]. \tag{4.2}$$

We may use the constancy of p_φ and p_ψ to eliminate $\dot{\varphi}$ and $\dot{\psi}$ from the first equation above.   We then find

$$I_1\ddot{\theta} = M_\theta + \frac{(p_\varphi - p_\psi \cos \theta)(p_\varphi \cos \theta - p_\psi)}{I_1 \sin^3 \theta}. \tag{4.3}$$

In Eq. (4.3) we have reduced our problem to that of the motion of a single variable, θ, which we can handle as if we had a problem of the motion of a particle in one dimension. Having found how θ varies with time, we can then find φ and ψ from the equations

$$\dot{\varphi} = \frac{p_\varphi - p_\psi \cos \theta}{I_1 \sin^2 \theta}$$

$$\dot{\psi} = \frac{p_\psi}{I_3} - \frac{(p_\varphi - p_\psi \cos \theta) \cos \theta}{I_1 \sin^2 \theta} \tag{4.4}$$

which follow from (4.2), and which can be integrated directly once θ is known.

First let us consider the case of no torque, so as to make connections with the preceding section. In that case (4.3) becomes

$$I_1 \ddot{\theta} = \frac{(p_\varphi - p_\psi \cos \theta)(p_\varphi \cos \theta - p_\psi)}{I_1 \sin^3 \theta}. \tag{4.5}$$

The case of Sec. 3 was that in which $p_\psi = p_\varphi \cos \theta$, as we see from (3.1), so that (4.5) leads at once to $\ddot{\theta} = 0$. As we mentioned at the

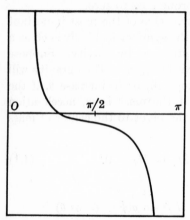

end of the last section, however, we can handle the same problem with different orientations of the angular momentum vector, and (4.5) includes this general case. To understand it, we must consider the function of θ on the right side of (4.5). This function plays the part of a fictitious torque, arising from the coordinate system, producing an acceleration of θ. The general form of this torque is shown in Fig. 20. For $\theta = 0$, it approaches $(p_\varphi - p_\psi)^2 / I_1 \sin^3 \theta$, or is positively infinite; and for $\theta = \pi$, it approaches $-(p_\varphi + p_\psi)^2 / I_1 \sin^3 \theta$, or is negatively infinite. It is zero just once

Fig. 20.—Effective force acting to increase θ, for rigid body with no torque.

between, when one or the other of the two factors in the numerator becomes zero, and decreases monotonically over the whole range. The torque vanishes when

$$\cos \theta = \frac{p_\varphi}{p_\psi} \text{ or } \frac{p_\psi}{p_\varphi}. \tag{4.6}$$

At this point there is equilibrium, and θ can remain constant.

Only one of these two conditions can be fulfilled with any prescribed values of p_φ and p_ψ, since $\cos \theta$ must be less than unity. If the second case holds, we have the situation taken up in Sec. 3, where the angular momentum is along the z axis.   If the first holds, the angular momentum is along the axis of figure, so that the angular velocity is also in that direction, and remains independent of time, but the axes are set up so that the axis of figure is not along the z axis.   These are the only two cases in which θ can remain constant, even in the absence of torques.

If we denote by θ_0 the value of θ defined by (4.6), at which the right side of (4.5) vanishes, we can then expand the right side in power series in $(\theta - \theta_0)$.   The expansion can be carried out straightforwardly, and the result is

$$I_1\ddot{\theta} = -\frac{p_\psi^2}{I_1}(\theta - \theta_0) \qquad \text{if } \cos\theta_0 = \frac{p_\varphi}{p_\psi}$$

$$I_1\ddot{\theta} = -\frac{p_\varphi^2}{I_1}(\theta - \theta_0) \qquad \text{if } \cos\theta_0 = \frac{p_\psi}{p_\varphi}, \qquad (4.7)$$

where we retain only the linear term of the expansion.   That is, by (4.7), θ can execute simple harmonic oscillations of small amplitude about θ_0, with an angular frequency which is p_ψ/I_1 in the first case, p_φ/I_1 in the second.   We can now see by comparison with Sec. 3 that this is just what we should expect.   The first case is that in which the angular momentum is almost exactly along the axis of figure, so that the space and body cones both have very small angular apertures.   If we were to set this motion up, as in Sec. 3, with the angular momentum vector along the z axis, we should have θ nearly zero. Then, using (3.1), (3.3), and (3.4), we should have approximately $\dot{\varphi} = p_\psi/I_1$.   This would give the rate of precession of the axis of figure, and hence the angular frequency of oscillation of θ in our present axes, in which θ is inclined to the z axis.   Since p_ψ has the same meaning in both sets of coordinates, representing the component of angular momentum along the axis of figure, we justify our result in the first case.   In the second case, the angular momentum is almost, but not quite, along the z axis.   In that case, again by (3.1), (3.3), and (3.4), we have approximately $\dot{\varphi} = p_\varphi/I_1$, and this should be the angular frequency of oscillation of θ in our present coordinates, in which the angular momentum is slightly inclined to the z axis, so that θ oscillates with small amplitude with the same frequency as the rotation of the axis of figure.

Now that we have considered the limiting case of no torque, in the general set of coordinates that lead to Eq. (4.3), we may go to the general case in which there is an external torque M_θ, which in particular may have the value $mgL \sin \theta$ of (4.1). Adding this function to the fictitious force on the right side of (4.5), shown in Fig. 20, the resulting function still has the same general form: it is positively infinite for $\theta = 0$, negatively infinite for $\theta = \pi$, and vanishes once between, but for a larger value of θ than that given by (4.6), for given values of p_φ and p_ψ. Just as in the case with no torque, there is still a precessional motion possible, in which θ remains constant, at this particular value for which the total apparent force is zero; for in that case, by (4.3), $\ddot{\theta} = 0$. Let us first consider the case of this precession. If θ is constant, by (4.4), both $\dot{\varphi}$ and $\dot{\psi}$ are constant, so that the axis of figure precesses with uniform angular velocity $\dot{\varphi}$ about a cone making an angle θ with the vertical, while the top spins with angular velocity $\dot{\psi}$ about its axis. This is the conventional type of motion of a spinning top.

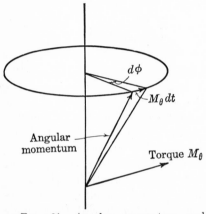

There is a familiar elementary treatment of the precession of a top, which we can easily adapt to give the exact solution for this case. The angular momentum vector is in the plane of the axis of figure and the vertical axis, making a constant angle with the vertical, and precessing about a cone with an angular velocity $\dot{\varphi}$. The time rate of change of this vector is the torque M_θ, which as we see from Fig. 21 is a vector at right angles to the angular momentum. Thus in time dt the change of angular momentum is $M_\theta\, dt$. If we take the horizontal component of angular momentum, we then see that $d\varphi$, the change in angle φ in time dt, must be the change of angular momentum, $M_\theta\, dt$, divided by the horizontal component of angular momentum; that is, $\dot{\varphi}$ equals M_θ divided by the horizontal component of angular momentum. In the elementary treatment, it is assumed that the angular momentum is along the axis of figure; thus, if the total angular momentum vector has a magnitude p, the horizontal component is $p \sin \theta$, so that, using (4.1),

$$\dot{\varphi} = \frac{M_\theta}{p \sin \theta} = \frac{mgL \sin \theta}{p \sin \theta} = \frac{mgL}{p}. \qquad (4.8)$$

That is, the rate of precession is inversely proportional to the angular

Fig. 21.—Angular momentum and torque for precessing motion of symmetrical rigid body.

momentum, and is independent of the inclination of the axis of figure to the vertical. This treatment is inaccurate only in that the total angular momentum vector is not exactly along the axis of figure. This is a result of the fact that the angular velocity consists of two parts: $\dot{\psi}$, an angular velocity along the axis of figure, whose angular momentum p_ψ is along the axis of figure; but also the precessional angular velocity $\dot{\varphi}$ along the vertical axis, involving angular momentum in other directions. It is only for a slow precession, in which $\dot{\varphi}$ can be neglected compared with $\dot{\psi}$, that the elementary treatment is correct.

To improve on this elementary treatment, we may use the notation of Fig. 18. Then the component of angular momentum in the plane perpendicular to the axis is $p_\xi \sin \theta - p_\eta \cos \theta$. Using (2.3), this in turn is $p_\psi \sin \theta - (p_\varphi - p_\psi \cos \theta) \cos \theta / \sin \theta$. By (2.1), this is $(p_\psi - I_1\dot{\varphi} \cos \theta) \sin \theta$, so that, remembering that p_ψ is the angular momentum associated with the spin around the axis, we see that we have agreement with our previous value $p \sin \theta$, if $\dot{\varphi}$ is so small that it can be neglected. Taking the general case, however, we have in place of (4.8)

$$\dot{\varphi} = \frac{M_\theta}{p_\psi \sin \theta - (p_\varphi - p_\psi \cos \theta) \cos \theta / \sin \theta}. \tag{4.9}$$

Writing $\dot{\varphi} = (p_\varphi - p_\psi \cos \theta)/I_1 \sin^2 \theta$, which follows from (2.1), this equation becomes

$$M_\theta = \frac{(p_\varphi - p_\psi \cos \theta)(p_\psi - p_\varphi \cos \theta)}{I_1 \sin^3 \theta} \tag{4.10}$$

which is just the form that (4.3) takes when θ is independent of time, or for precessional motion. Thus that general case can be explained in terms of a simple geometrical discussion. The ordinary case of the top is the case of small $\dot{\varphi}$, or large p_ψ, but our present discussion is perfectly general, and holds for any arbitrary values of the momenta and angular velocities.

Finally, not only can we have uniform precession, as in Fig. 21, and in Eq. (4.9) or (4.10), but also we can have an oscillation of θ about the angle at which precession occurs, as determined from (4.10). Referring to (4.3), we could in the general case find the value of θ for which the right side of (4.3), or the effective torque, is zero [this is the value of θ determined by (4.10)], and then we could expand the effective torque in power series about this value, just as we did in (4.7) for the case of no external torque. The expansion is not so simple as in that case, but nevertheless if we keep only the linear term we shall still find that θ is governed by the equation of simple harmonic motion, so that θ will still oscillate about the fixed value given by (4.10). The general motion, combining an oscillation of θ with a precession of the axis of figure, is called "nutation." Here as before, when we have solved for θ as a function of time, we can determine φ and ψ by (4.4). Thus we have in effect a general solution of the problem of the top spinning under gravity, and a general description of its motion.

Problems

1. Discuss the motion of a symmetrical top under gravity by the energy method, showing that the effective potential energy can be written in the alternative forms

$$V' = mgL \cos\theta + \frac{(p_\varphi^2 + p_\psi^2 - 2p_\varphi p_\psi \cos\theta)}{2I_1 \sin^2\theta} + \text{constant}$$

$$= mgL \cos\theta + \frac{1}{2} I_3\omega_3^2 + \frac{(p_z - I_3\omega_3 \cos\theta)^2}{2I_1 \sin^2\theta}.$$

2. A top is started spinning vertically, with no other motion, so that initially $\theta = 0$, $d\theta/dt = 0$. Show that $p_z = I_3\omega_3$, $E = \text{energy} = \frac{1}{2}I_3\omega_3^2 + mgL$. Substituting these expressions in the energy equation $E = \frac{1}{2}I_1\dot\theta^2 + V'$, show that, if $\omega_3 > \omega'$, where $(\omega')^2 = 4mgL(I_1/I_3^2)$, the angle θ must remain equal to zero, but that if ω_3 falls below ω', θ will oscillate between 0 and the angle $\cos^{-1}[2(\omega_3/\omega')^2 - 1]$. Experimentally, if a top is started as we have described, with $\omega_3 > \omega'$, there will be a frictional torque decreasing ω_3, and as soon as the torque reduces ω_3 below ω', the top will begin to wobble.

3. For a nutation of small amplitude about the steady precessional motion of a top, the angle θ oscillates sinusoidally about the equilibrium angle. Find the frequency of the nutation, by expanding the potential V' in power series in $\theta - \theta_0$, where θ_0 is the angle of steady precession with the same angular momentum. Retain only the constant and the term in $(\theta - \theta_0)^2$, and get the frequency by comparing with the corresponding expression for the linear oscillator.

4. In Fig. 19, show that the tangent of the angle between ω and the axis of figure is a/ω_3, and the tangent of the angle between the z axis and the ζ axis is $(I_1/I_3)(a/\omega_3)$, where a, ω_3 represent the components of the angular velocity at right angles to and along the figure axis. Knowing from (3.5) that the time required for the axis of angular velocity to perform a complete rotation with respect to the body is $\tau = (2\pi/\omega_3)[I_1/(I_1 - I_3)]$, show that the time for it to perform a complete rotation in space is approximately $(2\pi/\omega_3)(I_1/I_3)$, if the angles mentioned above are small. Hence show that for the earth the axis of angular velocity is not fixed, but rotates about a fixed direction approximately once a day.

5. The earth is acted on by torques exerted by the sun and moon, and as a consequence its angular momentum precesses about a fixed direction in space. This is entirely separate from the effect of Fig. 19 and Prob. 4, which we now neglect. This precession has a period of 25,800 years, and carries the angular momentum about a cone of semivertical angle 23°27', so that the pole in succession points to different parts of the heavens, resulting in the precession of the equinoxes, and in the fact that different stars act as pole star at different periods of history. Show that the motion can be represented by the rolling of a cone fixed in the earth, of diameter 21 in. at the north pole, on a cone of angle 23°27' fixed in the heavens.

6. A system of electrons moving about a center of attraction has a certain angular momentum, equal to $\Sigma m(\mathbf{r} \times \mathbf{v})$, and also a magnetic moment, equal to $\frac{1}{2}\Sigma e(\mathbf{r} \times \mathbf{v})$, where e is the charge and m the mass of an electron. This magnetic effect results because the electrons in rotation act like little currents, which in turn have magnetic fields like bar magnets. An external magnetic induction $\mathbf{B}$ exerts a torque on the system, equal to the vector product of the magnetic moment and $\mathbf{B}$. Show that, under the action of the field, the system of electrons precesses with angular velocity $eB/2m$ about the direction of the field. This precession, which, as we see, is independent of the velocities of the electrons, is called "Larmor's precession."

CHAPTER VII

COUPLED SYSTEMS AND NORMAL COORDINATES

In Chap. V we laid the foundation for discussing the mechanics of a system of particles, showing that the system as a whole moved in much the same way that a single particle would: its center of mass was governed by Newton's second law, the external force acting on the system as a whole equaling the time rate of change of the total momentum; and the external torque acting on the system as a whole equaled the time rate of change of the angular momentum. Now we shall take up the converse problem, the internal motions of the particles of the system. A first and obvious example of the general problem is a solid body itself; we may regard it as a collection of molecules or atoms, and may investigate the relative motions of the atoms. Somewhat simpler would be the motions of the atoms in a molecule. The particles in these examples are held to positions of equilibrium by linear restoring forces, which, acting between the individual atoms, add together to make up the elastic forces that result in Hooke's law for a solid body. Our problem in this chapter will be to consider the general mechanical motion of a set of particles held together, or coupled, by linear restoring forces.

Many other mechanical problems lead to the same mathematical problem. For example, on a larger scale, we may have rigid bodies, coupled together by ordinary springs. Ordinary elastic vibrations, then, involving several particles, come under our general problem. More generally, we shall find our methods underlying our later discussions of the large-scale vibrations of elastic bodies such as strings, plates, and membranes. In musical instruments, such bodies are set into harmonic vibration as sources of sound, and the various overtones in which they can vibrate are of just the sort that we shall come across in the present chapter. Our methods are important not only in mechanics, but in electricity as well. Just as a single resonant circuit has the same mathematical treatment as a single particle held by a linear restoring force, so a set of coupled circuits acts like a set of coupled oscillators. We shall set up this analogy, and show how our methods can be applied to circuit problems. At higher frequencies, where ordinary electric-circuit theory cannot be used, it is usual to excite electromagnetic oscillations in cavity resonators, and the theory of these resonators again is similar to the theory of vibrations that we shall set up. We could name many other applications of the same methods, but this should be enough to show the widespread importance of the problem that we shall now treat in its most fundamental form.

We shall not, however, by any means be handling all problems of coupled particles. We limit ourselves explicitly to linear restoring forces, just as we did for the single particle in Chap. II. Thus we cannot include one of the most obvious examples of coupled systems, the solar system, with the planets held together by inverse square gravitational forces; or another equally obvious case, an atom, with the electrons likewise held by inverse square forces, and at the same time with the complication that their motion is governed by wave mechanics, rather than classical mechanics. Furthermore, even for the case of vibrations, it is often the case that for small oscillations the restoring force is proportional to the displacement, so that we can treat the problem, but for larger amplitudes the proportionality no longer holds.

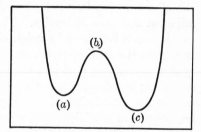

FIG. 22.—Hypothetical potential energy curve for an atom with two potential minima.

Thus our treatment is essentially one of small oscillations. We may get a simple illustration of this in the vibrations of the atoms of a solid. At ordinary temperatures, the atoms are in continuous oscillation; we refer to this motion as "temperature agitation." The energy of a particle, proportional to the square of its amplitude, is proportional to the absolute temperature (provided that we can neglect the fact that the atomic motions really obey quantum mechanics, not classical mechanics). This holds, however, only at low enough temperatures so that the amplitude of oscillation is small, and the restoring force is linear. At higher temperatures, the situation may be quite different. For instance, the potential energy curve for an atom may be as shown in Fig. 22, with a minimum (a) in the neighborhood of which the potential energy can be approximated by a parabola, or the restoring force by a constant times the displacement. So long as the amplitude is small, the atom will oscillate about this point with simple harmonic motion. At larger temperatures, and hence larger amplitudes, however, the atom can pass over the maximum (b)

and start oscillating around a quite different minimum (c).   If then
the amplitude again decreases, as by reducing the temperature again
the atom may stay oscillating around (c).   In this case the process of
heating and subsequent cooling has brought about a permanent change
in the system.   A physical example of this might be the heat-treat-
ment of a metal.   Such phenomena clearly lie outside the range of our
present theory, in which all restoring forces are assumed to be linear.
It is well at the outset to recognize the limitations of our treatment.

The problem of a single particle executing simple harmonic motion
is of course simple, and we have discussed it completely in Chap. II.
The present complication is that the forces acting in a collection of
particles are not simply forces pushing a particle to a fixed position of
equilibrium, but are rather forces of interaction between particles, as
the elastic forces in a solid are really forces of short range between
adjacent atoms or molecules.   Thus, if a single particle starts oscillating, it exerts forces on its neighbors and sets them going, and they in
turn pass the motion along, so that in general all the particles of the
system are taking part in the oscillation.   This means a complicated
situation; but fortunately there is a method of simplifying it, which
will be the foundation of our treatment.   It proves to be possible, in
any system of particles held by linear restoring forces, to set up certain
vibrations, called "normal vibrations," or "normal modes," in which
all particles oscillate, with prescribed amplitudes, but with the same
frequency.   There are a definite number of these normal modes
possible, each with its own frequency, and each differing from the
others in the way the particles vibrate.

Perhaps the most familiar example of these normal modes is
found in the vibrating string: each of the modes corresponds to one
of the overtone vibrations of the string, in which the string takes the
form of a sine curve, with an integral number of half wave lengths
included in the length of the string.   We can then prove that the most
general motion of the system, provided that it is acted on by no
external forces, is a superposition of vibrations in all these normal
modes, each with its appropriate amplitude and phase.   The possibility
of superposing the vibrations, the so-called "principle of superposition," is a result of the linear nature of the problem.   Furthermore, we can prove that, if external forces act on the particles of the
system, in addition to the linear restoring forces, the individual normal
modes act very much like individual oscillators; if the external forces
vary sinusoidally with time, for example, there will be a resonance
phenomenon at the resonant frequency of each of the normal modes.

Mathematically we can use the existence of the normal modes to carry out a transformation of coordinates, one for each of the normal modes.   When we express Lagrange's equations in terms of the normal coordinates, we find that we have a separation of variables: the equation for each of the normal coordinates involves only that coordinate, and furthermore it has just the form of the equation for the oscillation of a single particle held by a linear restoring force, so that we can handle it by the methods of Chap. II.   Thus the introduction of the normal coordinates provides a simple and complete solution of the problem of the coupled oscillations.   Our problem then forms a very general and important one for which a complete solution is possible. We shall now proceed with the formulation of the problem, and show how to introduce normal coordinates, and to use them.

1. The Equation of Motion of a Coupled System.—As in Chap. IV, Sec. 1, we shall assume that we have a system consisting of a number of particles, each with x, y, and z coordinates, and shall name the rectangular coordinates of the particles $x_1, x_2, \ldots x_n$, where x_1, x_2, x_3 are the x, y, z coordinates of the first particle, x_4, x_5, x_6 of the second, and so on; n is then three times the number of particles.   Since we are assuming that the particles can be in equilibrium with particular values of the coordinates, it is a convenience to measure the displacement of each particle from its position of equilibrium.   Thus there is a different origin in space for each set of x, y, z's; but when all the x's are zero, no forces act on any particle of the system.   We may now consider the potential energy V as a function of the x_i's, and see what conditions are imposed on it by our assumptions.

We may expand the potential energy in a Taylor's series in the x_i's.   Using the formula for a Taylor's expansion of a function of several variables, we have

$$V(x_1 \cdots x_n) = V_0 + \sum_{i=1\cdots n} \left(\frac{\partial V}{\partial x_i}\right)_0 x_i$$
$$+ \sum_{i,j=1\cdots n} \frac{1}{2}\left(\frac{\partial^2 V}{\partial x_i\, \partial x_j}\right)_0 x_i x_j + \cdots . \quad (1.1)$$

Here V_0, $(\partial V/\partial x_i)_0$, $(\partial^2 V/\partial x_i\, \partial x_j)_0$ are values of V and of the derivatives for the case where all x_i's are zero.   Terms higher than the second are not written out explicitly in (1.1).   The force acting on the coordinate x_i is then

$$F_i = -\frac{\partial V}{\partial x_i} = -\left(\frac{\partial V}{\partial x_i}\right)_0 - \sum_{j=1\cdots n}\left(\frac{\partial^2 V}{\partial x_i\, \partial x_j}\right)_0 x_j \cdots \quad (1.2)$$

where in the last term of (1.2) we note that the $\frac{1}{2}$ present in the corresponding term of (1.1) drops out since in carrying out the differentiation of (1.1) we can have the i that appears in (1.2) equal to the index of either the first or the second factor x in (1.1).

We may now apply our condition that no force acts on any particle when all the x_i's are zero. That results immediately from (1.2) in the relation $(\partial V/\partial x_i)_0 = 0$, or the potential energy has a minimum (or maximum) when all x_i's are zero. Since we wish to consider only stable oscillations, we must assume that the potential energy has a minimum, not a maximum, at this position. We may furthermore take the value V_0 of potential energy at the position of equilibrium to be zero. Then (1.1) and (1.2) simplify to the forms

$$V(x_1 \cdots x_n) = \frac{1}{2} \sum_{i,j} A_{ij} x_i x_j,$$

$$F_i = - \sum_j A_{ij} x_j, \qquad (1.3)$$

where

$$A_{ij} = A_{ji} = \left(\frac{\partial^2 V}{\partial x_i \, \partial x_j} \right)_0.$$

In these equations we have the general expression for potential energy for the small oscillations of any system of particles. We note that the force on the ith particle is a linear function not only of the displacement of that particle, but of the displacement of every other particle; the motion of any particle perturbs all other particles, and tends to make them oscillate. The quantities A_{ij} measure the interaction between the particles, and of course can be zero if two particles really exert no forces on each other. The A_{ij}'s form a symmetric tensor, of the type discussed in Appendix V, and already encountered in Chap. V, in discussing the moments and products of inertia. The diagonal components A_{ii} represent the force constants of the restoring force acting on a single particle, when that particle alone is displaced.

The kinetic energy of the system of particles is of course

$$T = \sum_i \frac{1}{2} m_i \dot{x}_i^2 \qquad (1.4)$$

where m_i is appropriate to the coordinate x_i, as in Sec. 1, Chap. IV. The equations of motion, in the original coordinates, are then

$$\frac{d}{dt} (m_i \dot{x}_i) = m_i \ddot{x}_i = F_i = - \sum_j A_{ij} x_j. \qquad (1.5)$$

We see at once that each of the equations (1.5) involves all n coordinates, so that we cannot proceed to a direct solution. It is to separate the variables, and obtain n equations each involving a single unknown, that we introduce the normal coordinates.

2. Normal Modes of Oscillation.—Our first step in discussing Eqs. (1.5) will be to prove that normal modes exist: modes of oscillation in which all coordinates oscillate sinusoidally with a common frequency. To do this, we shall assume that x_i depends on time through a factor $e^{j\omega t}$, as in Chap. II. Then $\ddot{x}_i$ will equal $-\omega^2 x_i$, so that (1.5) becomes

$$\sum_j A_{ij} x_j - m_i \omega^2 x_i = 0, \qquad i = 1 \cdots n. \tag{2.1}$$

To make the situation a little clearer, let us write out the equations (2.1). They are

$$(A_{11} - m_1 \omega^2) x_1 + A_{12} x_2 + \cdots + A_{1n} x_n = 0$$
$$A_{21} x_1 + (A_{22} - m_2 \omega^2) x_2 + \cdots + A_{2n} x_n = 0$$
$$\cdots \cdots \cdots \cdots \cdots \cdots \cdots \cdots \cdots \cdots$$
$$A_{n1} x_1 + A_{n2} x_2 + \cdots + (A_{nn} - m_n \omega^2) x_n = 0. \tag{2.2}$$

These are n simultaneous algebraic linear homogeneous equations for the n unknowns $x_1 \ldots x_n$. They are mathematically equivalent to the equations (3.3) of Chap. V which we met in introducing principal axes of inertia, and which we discuss in Appendix V. As before, the equations in general have no solutions except

$$x_1 = x_2 = \cdots = x_n = 0,$$

for they can determine only the $(n - 1)$ ratios of x_i's, not the absolute values of the x_i's, and we have one equation too many to determine $(n - 1)$ variables. As shown in Appendix V, the condition that the n equations (2.2) be compatible with each other is that the determinant of their coefficients should vanish:

$$\begin{vmatrix} A_{11} - m_1 \omega^2 & A_{12} \cdots \cdots \cdots A_{1n} \\ A_{21} & A_{22} - m_2 \omega^2 \cdots A_{2n} \\ \cdots \cdots \cdots \cdots \cdots \cdots \\ A_{n1} & A_{n2} \cdots A_{nn} - m_n \omega^2 \end{vmatrix} = 0. \tag{2.3}$$

The determinantal equation (2.3) is an equation of the nth degree for ω^2, which will thus have n roots for ω^2. It can be proved that these roots are all real; this follows from the fact that $A_{ij} = A_{ji}$. The corresponding values of ω will then be either real (if ω^2 is positive) or pure imaginary (if ω^2 is negative). If an ω is real, then we have solutions corresponding to either $e^{j\omega t}$ or $e^{-j\omega t}$, where these correspond to the positive and negative values of the square root, and ω is chosen to be positive; this is the case of a simple harmonic oscillation, as in Chap. II. If an ω is pure imaginary, equal to $-j\omega'$, where ω' is positive, then the two solutions will correspond to $e^{\omega' t}$ or $e^{-\omega' t}$. These are the solutions of the problem of the motion of a particle repelled from a point by a force proportional to the displacement from that point, a problem that we did not consider in Chap. II, but that in general leads to motion in which the particle goes more and more rapidly away from the center of repulsion. We shall assume that we are dealing only with the oscillational case.

Equation (2.3) is often called the "secular equation," for the following reason: In celestial mechanics, one can calculate certain simple periodic orbits, and can prove that other orbits are possible in their neighborhood, corresponding to oscillations about the periodic orbits. The situation is similar to that which we met in discussing the spinning top, in which the nutational motion was an oscillation about the precessional motion. The problem of vibrations about the periodic orbits can be shown to lead to an equation like (2.3) for determining the frequencies of vibration. It can then happen that some of the ω's are real, others imaginary, as in this case. The real ω's lead to periodic oscillations about the orbits; the orbits are then called "stable," just as a point about which oscillations can occur is a point of stable equilibrium. Our case of nutation was a stable oscillation. On the other hand, imaginary ω's lead to a departure from the original orbit which becomes greater and greater as time goes on, so that the particle never returns to the orbit. Such a continually increasing perturbation is called a "secular perturbation," and the corresponding orbit is unstable. Equation (2.3), then, allows us to distinguish between stable and unstable orbits, or between periodic oscillations and secular perturbations, and for that reason is called the "secular equation."

We shall now assume that the secular equation (2.3) has been solved for ω^2, and that the corresponding frequencies are real. The actual solution of (2.3) can be very difficult, and may have to be carried out numerically. We shall later work out the simple illustration of the case $n = 2$, in which (2.3) is a quadratic, and we can solve it immediately. We shall label the n roots $\omega_1, \omega_2, \ldots \omega_n$, numbering the frequencies in any order we please, such as the order of increasing frequency, ω_1 being the smallest. Then, substituting any of the n frequencies in (2.2), we can solve for the ratios of the x_i's. We shall get a different set of x_i's for each frequency ω_j; let us call the x_i associated with the jth frequency x_{ij}. We then have found as a possible solution of the problem

$$x_i = A_j x_{ij} e^{i\omega_j t}, \tag{2.4}$$

where A_j is an arbitrary amplitude factor. This, however, is not the general solution; for, because of the linear nature of the equations of motion (1.5), we can add solutions and still get a solution. That is, the general solution is

$$x_i = \sum_j A_j x_{ij} e^{i\omega_j t} \tag{2.5}$$

showing that the motion is a superposition of n simple harmonic oscillations. Of course, it should be understood that the real x_i is the real part of (2.5), and that the A_j's can be complex numbers, determining both phase and amplitude as in Eq. (1.7), Chap. II. By a normal mode of oscillation we then mean the motion described in Eq. (2.4), in which all particles oscillate with the same frequencies, and amplitudes proportional to the x_{ij}'s; Eq. (2.5) is then an expression of the principle of superposition, showing that the general motion is a superposition of normal modes. Since there are n A_j's, each with an amplitude and phase, we see from (2.5) that there are $2n$ arbitrary constants in our solution, so that we can satisfy an initial condition at $t = 0$, determining the initial amplitudes and velocities of the particles.

There is an important theorem regarding the x_{ij}'s, which is proved in Appendix V. This is contained in the statement

$$\sum_{i=1}^n m_i x_{ij} x_{ik} = 0 \qquad \text{if } j \neq k. \tag{2.6}$$

This is called the "orthogonality condition," for the following reason: Suppose we postulated an n-dimensional space, in which we could have n-dimensional vectors. Suppose then that $\sqrt{m_i}\, x_{ij}$ represented the ith component of a vector $\mathbf{X}_j$, and that $\sqrt{m_i}\, x_{ik}$ represented the ith component of another vector $\mathbf{X}_k$. Then the scalar product of the vectors $\mathbf{X}_j$ and $\mathbf{X}_k$ would, by analogy with three dimensions, be

$$\mathbf{X}_j \cdot \mathbf{X}_k = \sum_i m_i x_{ij} x_{ik}. \tag{2.7}$$

Equation (2.6) then states that the scalar product of any two of the vectors X_j and X_k is zero. This, however, is the statement that these vectors are at right angles, or orthogonal, to each other. We have already seen an example of the same situation in Chap. V, Sec. 3, where we were determining the principal axes of inertia by Eqs. (3.3) and (3.4) of that chapter. They were mathematically equivalent to our present problem, and we determined as a result of them three angular velocity vectors, whose directions were the three principal axes of inertia. We then used the result of Appendix V to show that these axes were at right angles to each other. Here our vector with n components $\sqrt{m_i}\, x_{ij}$, where i goes from 1 to n, is the analogue of the three-dimensional angular velocity vector in the rigid-body problem.

We have so far not given any way of determining the absolute magnitudes of the x_{ij}'s; the solution of Eqs. (2.2) determines only their ratios. We may, however, use our vector analogy to lead to a reasonable choice of magnitudes. The vectors $X_1 \ldots X_n$ form n orthogonal vectors in the n-dimensional space in which the components of X_j are $\sqrt{m_i}\, x_{ij}$. If these vectors were of unit length, they could form the n unit vectors of a new set of coordinates, rotated with respect to the original ones. Let us then assume that the x_{ij}'s are so chosen that the X_j's do have unit length. That is, pursuing our analogy of (2.7), we wish the scalar product of one of the X_j's with itself to be unity, or

$$1 = \sum_i m_i x_{ij}^2. \tag{2.8}$$

The condition (2.8) is generally called the "normalization condition." If it is satisfied, the x_{ij}'s are then uniquely determined, so that the amplitudes A_j of (2.4) are definite quantities. The orthogonality conditions (2.6) and normalization conditions (2.8) are often combined into one statement by the use of the symbol δ_{ij}, sometimes called the "Kronecker symbol," from its introducer, defined by the relation

$$\begin{aligned} \delta_{ij} &= 1 & &\text{if } i = j \\ &= 0 & &\text{if } i \neq j. \end{aligned} \tag{2.9}$$

In terms of this symbol, the conditions are

$$\sum_{i=1}^{n} m_i x_{ij} x_{ik} = \delta_{jk}. \tag{2.10}$$

The orthogonality and normalization conditions (2.10) are of more than academic importance, for they allow us to determine the amplitudes A_j in terms of arbitrary initial conditions, in a simple and direct way. Thus suppose we take care of the phase and amplitude part of A_j in (2.5) by writing A_j in terms of real and imaginary parts, as in Eq. (1.9), Chap. II. Then we have as the real solution

$$x_i = \sum_j x_{ij}(C_j \cos \omega_j t + D_j \sin \omega_j t)$$

where the C_j's and D_j's are real constants. The displacement at $t = 0$ is

$$x_i(0) = \sum_j C_j x_{ij} \tag{2.11}$$

and the velocity

$$\dot{x}_i(0) = \sum_j \omega_j D_j x_{ij}. \tag{2.12}$$

If the initial displacements and velocities $x_i(0)$ and $\dot{x}_i(0)$ are given as initial conditions, we then wish to solve (2.11) for the C_j's, (2.12) for the D_j's. Either set of equations is a set of n simultaneous linear equations, which of course can be solved straightforwardly, but the orthogonality conditions (2.10) furnish a simple way of going about the solution. Thus multiply each side of (2.11) by $m_i x_{ik}$, and sum over i. We have

$$\sum_i m_i x_i(0) x_{ik} = \sum_{i,j} C_j m_i x_{ij} x_{ik}$$
$$= \sum_j C_j \sum_i m_i x_{ij} x_{ik} = \sum_j C_j \delta_{jk}$$
$$= C_k \tag{2.13}$$

where we have used (2.9) and (2.10). Thus we have a direct solution for C_k, in terms of the $x_i(0)$'s. In a similar way we can solve (2.12) for the D_k's.

3. Normal Coordinates.—In Eq. (2.5) we have found a general solution of the problem of the free vibrations of our system of n degrees of freedom, determined by the n coordinates x_i. This is a superposition of the n normal modes (2.4), with arbitrary amplitudes and phases. We may now use the insight into the problem which we have gained by discussing the normal modes, to set up n coordinates, called the "normal coordinates," in terms of which the equations of motion are separated, so that any one of the normal coordinates can be excited to oscillation independently of the others. The solution in terms of normal coordinates gives us no new information as far as the problem of free vibration is concerned, but it allows us to solve the problem of forced vibration in a simple and complete manner.

We have introduced an n-dimensional space, in which the quantities $\sqrt{m_i}\, x_i$, proportional to the various coordinates of the problem, are considered to be the rectangular coordinates of an n-dimensional point. The motion of this point, which we may call the "representative point," describes the complete motion of the system, for it determines all the x_i's as functions of time. The problem of coupled oscillation is, in fact, completely equivalent to the fictitious problem of the motion of a single particle in this n-dimensional space. The potential energy of this particle, given by (1.3), is a general quadratic function of the x_i's. Thus it must be a generalization of a conic, and the case we have chosen, in which our oscillations are stable and all frequencies are real, is that in which the equipotential "surfaces" in our n-dimensional space are generalized ellipsoids. These ellipsoidal energy surfaces will have a set of principal axes, just as an ellipse has principal axes at right angles to each other; and we shall now show that the n unit vectors $\mathbf{X}_j$ which we introduced in the last section are in fact unit vectors pointing along the n principal axes of the energy ellipsoid. To do this, let us set up a new set of axes, with the vectors $\mathbf{X}_j$ as unit vectors, and let us express the potential energy in terms of these new axes, showing then that the equation is that of an ellipsoid expressed in terms of its principal axes.

Let the coordinates of the representative point, with respect to the new set of axes, be q_j. That is, the vector $\sum\limits_{j} q_j \mathbf{X}_j$, the vector sum of the unit vectors $\mathbf{X}_j$, each multiplied by the appropriate q_j, is the vector displacement of the representative point. In this case, the component of that vector along the $\sqrt{m_i}\, x_i$ axis must be simply $\sqrt{m_i}\, x_i$. We can express this condition in the following form:

$$\sqrt{m_i}\, x_i = \sum_{j} q_j \sqrt{m_i}\, x_{ij}, \qquad (3.1)$$

since the component of $\mathbf{X}_j$ along the x_i axis is $\sqrt{m_i}\, x_{ij}$. We may solve very simply for q_k by multiplying (3.1) by $\sqrt{m_i}\, x_{ik}$, summing over i, and using (2.6). In this way we find the relations

$$q_k = \sum_{i} m_i x_i x_{ik}, \qquad x_i = \sum_{j} q_j x_{ij} \qquad (3.2)$$

where the second equation of (3.2) is merely (3.1) rewritten.   Now we shall write the potential energy (1.3) in terms of the q's.   It is

$$V = \tfrac{1}{2} \sum_{ij} A_{ij} x_i x_j$$

$$= \tfrac{1}{2} \sum_{ijkl} A_{ij} q_k x_{ik} q_l x_{jl}. \qquad (3.3)$$

We note that (2.1) may be written

$$\sum_j A_{ij} x_{jl} - m_i \omega_l^2 x_{il} = 0$$

where x_{il}, x_{jl}, are the x's corresponding to the lth mode, and ω_l^2 is the square of the corresponding frequency; for (2.1) referred to any one of the normal modes.   Thus (3.3) may be rewritten

$$V = \tfrac{1}{2} \sum_{ikl} q_k q_l m_i \omega_l^2 x_{ik} x_{il}$$

$$= \tfrac{1}{2} \sum_{kl} q_k q_l \omega_l^2 \sum_i m_i x_{ik} x_{il}$$

$$= \tfrac{1}{2} \sum_{kl} q_k q_l \omega_l^2 \delta_{kl}$$

$$= \tfrac{1}{2} \sum_k \omega_k^2 q_k^2. \qquad (3.4)$$

From (3.4), the equation of an equipotential surface $V = $ constant, in the rotated axes in which the q's are the coordinates, is the equation of an n-dimensional ellipsoid referred to its principal axes, just as the equation of an ellipsoid in three dimensions, with semiaxes a, b, c, along the x, y, z directions, is $(x/a)^2 + (y/b)^2 + (z/c)^2 = 1$. Thus we have verified our statement that the vectors $\mathbf{X}_j$ are vectors along the principal axes of the ellipsoid.

We have not only verified our statement about the ellipsoid; we have also expressed the potential energy as a function of the quantities q_k.   These quantities may be used as generalized coordinates, for by (3.2) they suffice to determine the coordinates x_i of the problem; and they are in fact just the normal coordinates about which we have spoken.   Let us now express Lagrange's equations in terms of the normal coordinates, and show that they allow us to solve the equations of motion in a very simple way.   To set up the Lagrangian function, we need not only the potential energy V of (3.4), but also the kinetic energy, in terms of the velocities $\dot{q}_k$. We have at once, from (1.4),

$$T = \sum_i \tfrac{1}{2}\, m_i \dot{x}_i^2$$

$$= \tfrac{1}{2} \sum_{ijk} m_i \dot{q}_j x_{ij} \dot{q}_k x_{ik}$$

$$= \tfrac{1}{2} \sum_{jk} \dot{q}_j \dot{q}_k \sum_i m_i x_{ij} x_{ik} = \tfrac{1}{2} \sum_{jk} \dot{q}_j \dot{q}_k \delta_{jk}$$

$$= \tfrac{1}{2} \sum_k \dot{q}_k^2. \tag{3.5}$$

Then, from (3.4) and (3.5), we have for the Lagrangian function

$$L = \tfrac{1}{2} \sum_k (\dot{q}_k^2 - \omega_k^2 q_k^2)$$

and Lagrange's equation for the coordinate q_j is

$$\frac{d}{dt}\left(\frac{\partial L}{\partial \dot{q}_j}\right) - \frac{\partial L}{\partial q_j} = \ddot{q}_j + \omega_j^2 q_j = 0. \tag{3.6}$$

The solution of (3.6) is immediately

$$q_j = A_j e^{j\omega_j t}$$

so that, using (3.2), the solution of the problem is

$$x_i = \sum_j q_j x_{ij} = \sum_j A_j x_{ij} e^{j\omega_j t} \tag{3.7}$$

in agreement with our previous solution (2.5).

We have found the formal solution of our problem, and the mathematical relations of the normal coordinates; let us see if we can gain a better insight into their meaning. If just one of the normal coordinates, say the jth, is different from zero, then by (3.2) the coordinates x_i are all proportional to the quantities x_{ij}, the displacements corresponding to the jth normal mode. Thus the excitation of one of the normal coordinates, without the others, is just equivalent to the excitation of a normal mode. The value of the normal coordinate measures the amplitude of that normal mode. It is clear then why a single normal coordinate has the simple equation of motion (3.6), representing simple harmonic oscillation with the appropriate frequency of the normal mode. Mathematically, the fact that the motions of the various normal coordinates are independent of each other, so that the equation (3.6) for the jth normal coordinate involves only that coordinate, and the variables are separated, is a result of the fact that the generalized force $-\partial V/\partial q_k = -\omega_k^2 q_k$ appropriate to the kth normal coordinate, from (3.4), is a constant times the value of that coordinate.   In other words, when expressed in terms of the normal coordinates, the problem is no longer one of coupled oscillations, but is one of independent oscillations.   It is what we should have found in the first place, in (1.3), if all the nondiagonal components of the tensor A_{ij} had vanished, so that there would have been no coupling between oscillators.

4. Example of Two Coupled Oscillators.—The simplest example of coupled oscillations comes for the case $n = 2$, where there are two oscillators.   The secular equation (2.3) then becomes

$$\begin{vmatrix} A_{11} - m_1\omega^2 & A_{12} \\ A_{12} & A_{22} - m_2\omega^2 \end{vmatrix} = 0.$$

Expanding the determinant, this is

$$(A_{11} - m_1\omega^2)(A_{22} - m_2\omega^2) - A_{12}^2 = 0,$$

a quadratic in ω^2, whose solution, with a little manipulation, can be put in the form

$$\omega^2 = \frac{1}{2}\left(\frac{A_{11}}{m_1} + \frac{A_{22}}{m_2}\right) \pm \sqrt{\left[\frac{1}{2}\left(\frac{A_{11}}{m_1} - \frac{A_{22}}{m_2}\right)\right]^2 + \frac{A_{12}^2}{m_1 m_2}}. \quad (4.1)$$

Two values of ω^2 are given by (4.1), corresponding to two normal modes.   If A_{12} is zero, so that there is really no coupling between the coordinates x_1 and x_2, (4.1) gives at once $\omega^2 = A_{11}/m_1$ or A_{22}/m_2, as it should.   For a small value of A_{12}, the two solutions of (4.1) differ from these values by small quantities proportional to A_{12}^2, as we could see by expanding the square root in (4.1) by binomial expansion.   It is not hard to see, by considering this expansion, that one of the values of ω^2 from (4.1) is greater than the larger of the two values A_{11}/m_1 or A_{22}/m_2, and the other is less than the smaller of the two; that is, the interaction between the two oscillators, resulting from the term A_{12}, pushes apart the two resonant frequencies.   If A_{12} is large enough, the value of ω^2 given by the negative sign in front of the square root in (4.1) can be negative, and the frequency imaginary, resulting in a secular perturbation of the type discussed in Sec. 2, but the positive sign will always give oscillatory motion.   It is interesting to look at the special case in which the two frequencies are the same in the absence of interaction, or where $A_{11}/m_1 = A_{22}/m_2$; then the values of ω^2 from (4.1) are $A_{11}/m_1 \pm A_{12}/\sqrt{m_1 m_2}$, so that, even in this case, which is sometimes called the "case of degeneracy," the two resonant frequencies will be different, the amount of separation between them depending on A_{12}, measuring the interaction between the two oscillators.

From Eq. (2.2) we can find the relations between x_1 and x_2 in the two normal modes. We may write the relations in either of the forms

$$x_1 = -\frac{(A_{12}/m_1)x_2}{(A_{11}/m_1) - \omega^2}, \qquad x_2 = -\frac{(A_{12}/m_2)x_1}{(A_{22}/m_2) - \omega^2} \qquad (4.2)$$

in which we are to insert one or the other value of ω^2 from (4.1). The expressions (4.2) have a form that is easy to interpret. Considering the first, we may consider that the second coordinate, oscillating with a time dependence given by $e^{j\omega t}$, results in a sinusoidal force $-A_{12}x_2$ on the first coordinate. This force produces a forced motion of the first particle, as indicated by (4.2), the denominator being a resonance denominator of the usual form, as was seen, for instance, in Eq. (3.4), Chap. II. Similarly the second form of (4.2), which must be equivalent to the first as a result of (4.1), indicates the forced motion of the second coordinate under the action of the first. We may notice one interesting special case. If the two resonant frequencies without the interaction A_{12} were equal, that is, if $A_{11}/m_1 = A_{22}/m_2$, and if at the same time $m_1 = m_2$, then we find at once from (4.2) that

$$x_1 = \pm x_2 \qquad \text{if } \omega^2 = \frac{A_{11}}{m_1} \pm \frac{A_{12}}{m_1}. \qquad (4.3)$$

That is, in this case, the two coordinates oscillate with equal amplitudes, and either with the same or with opposite phase, in the two modes.

The nature of the motion of two coupled oscillators is made easy to understand by plotting the path of the representative point, in a space in which $\sqrt{m_1}\, x_1$ and $\sqrt{m_2}\, x_2$ are plotted as coordinates, as we have discussed earlier. Such a plot is shown in Fig. 23. In the first place, we show an equipotential line, given by the equation

$$\tfrac{1}{2}(A_{11}x_1^2 + 2A_{12}x_1x_2 + A_{22}x_2^2) = V \qquad (4.4)$$

or the equation of an ellipse. The rotated axes, coincident with the axes of the ellipse, are the axes of the system of normal coordinates; that is, the normal coordinates are the coordinates of a representative point, referred to these rotated axes. In an arbitrary oscillation, each of the normal coordinates oscillates with a fixed amplitude, and with one or the other of the two frequencies (4.1), which in general are incommensurable with each other. The resulting oscillation is shown in Fig. 23. An oscillation of this type, in which two coordinates at right angles to each other oscillate sinusoidally with different frequencies, is called a "Lissajous figure." The rectangle in the $x_1 x_2$ plane in which the Lissajous figure is inscribed must touch the equipotential, for if the particle happens to strike one corner of the rectangle, its kinetic energy is zero, so that its total energy is potential, and it is located on the equipotential; otherwise it has kinetic energy, and must lie within the equipotential. We may use the methods of energy, as in Chap. III, for discussing this problem qualitatively. Clearly the problem is the same as that of the vibration of a single particle in two dimensions, with a potential energy (4.4); we may then plot potential energy as a function of x_1 and x_2, obtaining a bowl-

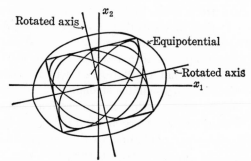

FIG. 23.—Lissajous figure.

shaped surface, and may discuss the motion by analogy with a ball rolling on this surface, as in Chap. III, Sec. 2. The resulting motion is that given in Fig. 23.

5. Coupled Oscillators with External Forces and Damping.—Let us suppose that, in addition to the linear restoring forces that we have already considered, the coordinate x_i is subject to an additional force f_i, which may be a function of time, coordinates, or velocities. Then we may most conveniently handle the resulting forced motion in terms of the normal coordinates. We must first find the generalized force F_j associated with the jth normal coordinate. We remember, from Chap. IV, that we do this by setting up the work done, dW, in the form $\sum_j F_j\, dq_j$. In our case, we have, using (3.2),

$$dW = \sum_i f_i\, dx_i = \sum_{ij} f_i \frac{\partial x_i}{\partial q_j}\, dq_j$$

$$= \sum_{ij} f_i x_{ij}\, dq_j,$$

so that

$$F_j = \sum_i f_i x_{ij}.$$ (5.1)

In terms of this generalized force, Lagrange's equation (3.6) becomes

$$\ddot{q}_j + \omega_j^2 q_j = F_j,$$ (5.2)

or an equation analogous to the forced motion of a linear oscillator according to Chap. II. Thus we can use all the methods learned in that chapter in discussing the motion of each of the normal coordinates. We notice from (5.1) that a force f_i acting on one of the coordinates is effective in exciting a normal mode j in proportion to the amplitude x_{ij} which that coordinate would have in the jth mode. Thus a force applied to a particle cannot excite a mode in which that particle does not oscillate, but will be very effective in exciting a mode in which it oscillates strongly.

As a first example, suppose that the forces f_i all vary sinusoidally with the time, according to the exponential $e^{j\omega t}$, where ω is arbitrary. Then F_j will likewise vary according to this exponential, so that to solve (5.2) we assume that q_j varies in the same way. Then, as in Chap. II, we find

$$q_j = \frac{F_j}{\omega_j^2 - \omega^2}$$

$$x_i = \sum_j \frac{F_j x_{ij}}{\omega_j^2 - \omega^2}.$$ (5.3)

That is, in the response curve of x_i as a function of frequency, there will now be n separate resonance points, corresponding to the frequencies ω_j of the normal modes, rather than just one resonance as with a single oscillator.

Another example of an impressed force is a damping force, proportional to the velocity. Thus let there be a force $-c_i \dot{x}_i$ acting on the coordinate x_i, as a result of friction. Then there will be a generalized force

$$F_j' = - \sum_i c_i \dot{x}_i x_{ij} = - \sum_i c_i x_{ij} \sum_k \dot{q}_k x_{ik}$$

$$= - \sum_k \gamma_{jk} \dot{q}_k, \qquad \text{where } \gamma_{jk} = \sum_i c_i x_{ij} x_{ik}.$$ (5.4)

If this force acts on the oscillators, we have instead of (5.2)

$$\ddot{q}_j + \omega_j^2 q_j = -\sum_k \gamma_{jk}\dot{q}_k. \tag{5.5}$$

These equations have a simple solution, if only one overtone is excited, as for instance the jth; for then all the q's except q_j are zero, and (5.5) becomes merely

$$\ddot{q}_j + \gamma_{jj}\dot{q}_j + \omega_j^2 q_j = 0,$$

which is an equation for a damped oscillator, as in Eq. (2.8), Chap. II, from which we see that the Q of the resonance, which we may call Q_j, is defined by

$$\gamma_{jj} = \frac{\omega_j}{Q_j}. \tag{5.6}$$

On the other hand, if all the overtones are excited, Eq. (5.5) will not be separated, and we cannot get a general solution. There is a special case in which we do have separation: that in which the non-diagonal terms γ_{jk}, for $j \neq k$, are zero. From the orthogonality relation (2.10) we see that this is the case only if c_i is proportional to m_i, for then the summation of (5.4) would have the properties of the orthogonality summation (2.10). Furthermore, in this case, the γ_{jj}'s of (5.6) would all be equal, or the Q's of the various overtones would be proportional to the corresponding frequencies, which would lead to an equal rate of damping of all modes, as we see from Eq. (2.5), Chap. II. This is a special and unusual case, but nevertheless we shall see an example in the next chapter in which it is important.

Finally let us consider the superposition of damping, as in (5.5), with a sinusoidal force, as in (5.2). We may then write the equations of motion

$$\ddot{q}_j + \frac{\omega_j}{Q_j}\dot{q}_j + \omega_j^2 q_j = F_j - \sum_{k \neq j} \gamma_{jk}\dot{q}_k. \tag{5.7}$$

If we neglect the summation on the right, and assume that the F_j's are sinusoidal functions of time with frequency ω, as before, we then have

$$q_j = \frac{F_j}{-\omega^2 + \omega_j^2 + (j\omega\omega_j/Q_k)}$$

$$x_i = \sum_j \frac{F_j x_{ij}}{-\omega^2 + \omega_j^2 + (j\omega\omega_j/Q_j)} \tag{5.8}$$

as in Eq. (3.3), Chap. II.   Thus the effect of the damping is to introduce an imaginary term into the denominator of each resonance term
of (5.3), preventing the amplitude from going infinite at resonance, and
resulting in a change of phase, so that power is absorbed by the
oscillators at each resonance.   In this solution, we have neglected
the nondiagonal terms of the γ_{jk} matrix.   We can easily show, however, that this neglect is justified to a high approximation, so long
as the Q_j's are large, and the frequencies of the modes are well separated from each other.   For in the first place, if the frequency ω is
far from any of the resonances, the amplitudes will be small, the
damping small, and all the damping terms can be approximately
neglected; whereas in the second place, if the frequency is near one
of the resonant frequencies, the corresponding term in the summation
in (5.8) will be large, all the others small, so that in (5.7) all the $\dot{q}_k$'s
will be small compared with the term in $\dot{q}_j$.   For small Q_j's, this situation no longer holds.   In that case, the various resonances effectively
overlap, and the resistive effect of one resonance is felt even at the
next resonance frequency.   Such cases cannot be treated accurately
in any simple way.   In fact, even with the simple case of two coupled
oscillators, with large damping and small separation between the
resonant modes, an exact treatment is very difficult.

The problems we have been taking up in this chapter have related
to coupled mechanical oscillations.   However, exactly similar methods apply to coupled electric circuits.   For any number of purely
reactive circuits, coupled in any arbitrary way, as by mutual inductance, or capacity, we can introduce normal coordinates, which are
linear combinations of the currents or charges in the various circuits,
in close analogy to Eq. (3.2).   The equations of motion of these
normal coordinates are like (3.6), and result in a separate oscillation
of each normal coordinate, so that the general oscillation of the coupled
circuits is a superposition of normal vibrations, as in (3.7).   If the
circuits contain resistance, then we meet the situation we have just
taken up in the present section.   If the nondiagonal components of
the damping matrix are zero, we can get the general solution in this
case too, but that is a special case resulting only from particular
choices of circuit parameters.   In general, if the losses in the circuits
are small, we can introduce an approximate solution like (5.8); but, if
the losses are high, the exact solution is impossible, and even with two
coupled circuits it is very difficult.   Some of these circuit examples
are taken up in the problems at the end of the chapter.

Problems

1. Two balls, each of mass m, and three weightless springs, one of length $2d$, the others of length d, are connected together in the arrangement spring d—ball—spring $2d$—ball—spring d, and the whole thing is stretched in a straight line between two points, with a given tension in the springs. Gravity is neglected. Investigate the small vibrations of the balls at right angles to the straight line, assuming motion in only one plane. Show in general that there are two modes of vibration, one having the lower frequency, in which both balls oscillate to the same side at one time, then to the other, and the second mode, with higher frequency, where they oscillate to opposite sides. [*Hint:* If the first is displaced x_1, and the second x_2, and if these displacements are so small that the tension T is unchanged, then there will be two forces acting on the first ball: a force T toward the point of support, making an angle whose tangent is x_1/d, and another directed toward the second ball, at an angle whose tangent is $(x_2 - x_1)/d$. The component at right angles to the straight line, and thus producing the motion, is then $-x_1(T/d) + (x_2 - x_1)(T/2d)$. Similarly the force on the second is $-x_2(T/d) + (x_1 - x_2)(T/2d)$.]

2. Two identical pendulums hang from a support that is slightly yielding, so that they can interchange energy. Assume that coupling is linear. Now suppose one pendulum is set into motion, the other being at rest. Show that gradually the first pendulum will come to rest, the second taking up the motion, and that there is a periodic pulsation of the energy from one pendulum to the other. Show that the frequency of this pulsation gets smaller as the coupling becomes smaller, until with an infinitely rigid support the energy remains always in the first pendulum (this is all without damping forces).

3. One simple pendulum is hung from another; that is, the string of the lower pendulum is tied to the bob of the upper one. Discuss the small oscillations of the resulting system, assuming arbitrary lengths and masses. Use the angles that each string makes with the vertical as generalized coordinates. In the special case of equal masses and equal lengths of strings, show that the frequencies of the motion are given by $\sqrt{g(2 \pm \sqrt{2})/L}$.

4. Show that, if the mass of the upper pendulum becomes very great compared with the lower one, the solution of Prob. 3 approaches that of Prob. 13, Chap. II. Show in the other limiting case, where the upper mass is small compared with the lower one, that the motion consists approximately of an oscillation of the large mass with a period derived from the combined length of both pendulums, and a more rapid oscillation of the small mass back and forth with respect to the line connecting point of support and the large mass.

5. A rigid uniform bar of mass M, length L, is supported in equilibrium in a horizontal position by two springs attached one to each end. The springs have the same force constant. Find the normal modes and frequencies of vibration of the system, if the motion is constrained to a vertical plane. If initially one end of the bar is displaced, the other remaining in its equilibrium position, and the system released from rest, find the motion.

6. A uniform horizontal rectangular plate is supported by four identical springs, one at each corner. Find the normal frequencies, and describe the normal modes of vibration.

7. A mass M hangs on a spring of stiffness coefficient K. From M is suspended a second mass m by means of a second spring of stiffness coefficient k. The mass M is subject to an external vertical force $F = A \sin \omega t$. Calculate the amplitude of the steady motion of each mass.

8. Two series circuits I and II contain inductances L_1, L_2, and capacities C_1, C_2, respectively. They are coupled by the mutual inductance $M = k \sqrt{L_1 L_2}$. Find the natural frequencies of the system and the normal coordinates. If at time $t = 0$ an emf $E \sin (\omega t - \delta)$ is applied to circuit I, find the currents in both circuits as functions of time.

9. In Prob. 8, assume that the circuits have small resistances R_1 and R_2, respectively, so small that the Q's of the separate circuits are large. Discuss the damped oscillations, showing that the solution can be carried out if squares of resistances are small enough to be neglected, but that it leads to a biquadratic equation for the frequency for large R. (*Hint:* Write the frequency as the sum of a real and an imaginary part.)

10. Given an ellipse $ax^2 + bxy + cy^2 = d$, perform a rotation of axes so that the new coordinates will lie along the major and minor axes of the ellipse. From this rotation, find the angle between the major axis and the x axis, in terms of the coefficients a, b, c, d. It is simplest to write the transformation directly in terms of the angle θ: $x' = x \cos \theta + y \sin \theta$, etc.

CHAPTER VIII

THE VIBRATING STRING

Up to now we have been treating the motions of single particles, of systems of particles, or of rigid bodies. In most of the rest of the book we shall be considering continuous bodies, solids and liquids and gases and their motions. Of course, a physical body is always made up of molecules, and so is really only a very large system of particles, and on occasion we shall bring out this aspect of our problems. Nevertheless continuous bodies show some properties that are less obvious with systems of particles. Foremost among these properties is that of transmitting wave motion. If an oscillatory motion is impressed on one part of a body, waves are propagated out to all parts of the body. The simplest example is the one we take up in the present chapter: a uniform string, stretched between two fixed supports. More complicated examples, which we take up in later chapters, are stretched membranes, sections of elastic solids, and liquids and gases. All these bodies have many properties in common, and we shall take them up in most detail in our simple example of the stretched string.

In the first place, if an elastic body is held rigidly around its boundary, as a string is held at its two ends or a drumhead around its circumference, any wave striking the boundary is reflected without loss of energy, and a standing wave is set up. There is an infinite set of standing waves, each with its own frequency. For instance, with the string, the various standing waves are determined by the condition that the length of the string must be n half wave lengths, where n is an integer, and the corresponding frequencies, being inversely proportional to the wave lengths, are whole multiples of a fundamental frequency. They are called "harmonics," or "resonant modes." We shall see that they are closely analogous to the normal modes of coupled systems, as discussed in the preceding chapter. In fact, if we consider the continuous body as being really made up of a finite set of molecules, the harmonics become identical with the normal modes, and we can set up normal coordinates, and use all the methods that we have been discussing, in handling the oscillations. The main difference is that, on account of the very large number of molecules,

143

the number of normal modes is very large; in fact, the conventional theory of the resonant modes of a continuous body is the limit in which we consider the number of normal modes to be infinite. The property of orthogonality of the normal modes, which we found for coupled systems, holds here also, and leads to an important branch of mathematical physics, that of orthogonal functions, and their use in solving partial differential equations (for the equations of motion of the vibrating system prove to be partial differential equations), and in satisfying the initial conditions for the vibration. One special case, which we shall encounter in this chapter, is the Fourier series; it forms the simplest example of orthogonal functions.

In the general vibration of a continuous body, we can introduce normal coordinates, and that means that we can handle the problem of forced motion. Furthermore it means that the system will show the same sort of resonance about each of the resonant modes which we have met in treating coupled systems. We can get approximate treatments of damping, as we have done, and can find the Q's of the various resonances. There is one respect in which the problem is different from that of coupled systems, however: the edge, or boundary, of the continuous body has a special significance, which we do not meet so plainly with coupled systems. We may, for instance, have the end of a string held by a support which, rather than being rigid, is yielding, as for instance a stiff spring, or a spring with a resisting force proportional to its velocity. We see at once that, if there is a resistance depending on the velocity, the support will absorb energy, so that the reflected wave will have less intensity than the incident wave. In the limiting case the support might absorb all the energy, and there would be no reflected wave at all. Or, to take another case, one end of the string might be held by a tuning fork or other device that could impose a sinusoidal motion on it, setting the string into forced vibration.

These examples are really only special cases of the general problem, which we have taken up in the preceding chapter, of impressed forces, and damping forces, and we can handle them by our general methods. We shall see, however, that we can also give simpler and more elementary treatments of them, and for the string in particular that is worth doing. We shall in fact consider arbitrary terminations at the two ends of the string, and shall take up the case where power is fed into one end of the string, by a tuning fork or other device, and is taken out at the other end by a resistive termination, so that in effect the string is transmitting power from one end to the other. This problem is mathematically entirely analogous to the transmission of electrical power down a transmission line, such as a pair of parallel wires, a coaxial line, or a wave guide, and the mathematical treatment that we shall give is practically identical with the corresponding electrical case. Furthermore, if we take account of the molecular nature of the string, or if we consider a string with its mass concentrated at discrete points, the problem becomes equivalent to the artificial electric line, a network made up of discrete circuits coupled together. In such a case, we shall see that the line shows the properties of a filter, in that it transmits some frequencies, but attenuates others without transmitting them.

Finally, if the continuous body is not limited at all, it propagates waves to an infinite distance. Such propagation is really the simplest form of wave motion. For a string, waves are possible that travel either to the left or the right along the string. For the membrane, the waves spread out from a point of origin with circular wave fronts, and for the three-dimensional body, as the solid or liquid or gas, they spread as spheres. At a large enough distance from the source, the circular or spherical wave fronts become approximately straight lines or planes, and we speak of " plane waves." Such waves in air or water are waves of sound, and we shall investigate their velocity, and show how it depends on the properties of the medium. In fact, in our chapters on vibrations and wave motion we shall be covering all the essential points of the theory of sound. Ordinary musical and acoustical instruments are vibrating systems: vibrating strings, membranes, plates, and more complicated objects. They are set into motion, by being struck, bowed, or otherwise acted on, and then set the air or other medium into oscillation, starting the wave which, traveling to far distances, becomes the wave of sound. All these matters we shall discuss to some extent in succeeding chapters.

We shall now start the discussion of the vibrations of a string stretched between two rigid supports. Our first step will be to set up the differential equation governing the motions of the string. This equation is nothing more than Newton's second law, stated in appropriate form. It is, in the first place, a partial differential equation: it describes the displacement u of the element of the string at distance x from the end, at time t. Thus u is a function of x and of t, and hence any derivative we take must be a partial derivative, and the differential equation must be a partial differential equation. And the form of our differential equation is important: it is what is called the " wave equation," and it underlies all study of wave motion, of every type.

We shall now proceed to the simplest form of the wave equation, and its solution.

1. The Wave Equation for the Stretched String.—Assume that at a given time the string is displaced so that its shape is given by $u(x)$. We consider how this curve will change with time. We assume that the string has a mass μ per unit length (a constant, for the uniform string), and that it has a tension T. Take a short element of the string of length dx and mass $\mu\,dx$. Its acceleration is $\partial^2 u/\partial t^2$, so that the mass times acceleration is $\mu\,dx\,\partial^2 u/\partial t^2$. This must be equal to the force acting on the element, which arises from the tensions. In

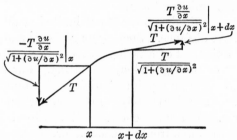

Fig. 24.—Tensions in an element of string.

Fig. 24 we show the element dx, with the tensions T acting on each end of it. These tensions will be of the same magnitude, and if the element is straight they will be in opposite directions and they will balance, resulting in no net force on the element. However, if the element is curved, there will be a resultant force. The component of T at right angles to the x axis is $T(\partial u/\partial x)/\sqrt{1 + (\partial u/\partial x)^2}$, and the component along the x axis is $T/\sqrt{1 + (\partial u/\partial x)^2}$. We shall assume that $\partial u/\partial x$ is small enough so that its square can be neglected; that is, we assume that the string is not distorted very much. Then the x component of force is approximately T, so that the x components on the two ends of the element dx balance. The component of force at right angles to x, however, arising from the tensions at the two ends of the element dx, will be

$$T\left.\frac{\partial u}{\partial x}\right|_{x+dx} - T\left.\frac{\partial u}{\partial x}\right|_{x} = T\frac{\partial^2 u}{\partial x^2}\,dx.$$

The equation of motion is then obtained by setting the force equal to the mass times the acceleration, or is

$$T\frac{\partial^2 u}{\partial x^2} = \mu\frac{\partial^2 u}{\partial t^2}, \qquad \frac{\partial^2 u}{\partial x^2} = \frac{\mu}{T}\frac{\partial^2 u}{\partial t^2}. \tag{1.1}$$

This is the one-dimensional form of the wave equation.

One of the simplest and most straightforward methods of solving a partial differential equation like (1.1) is to seek a solution that is a product of functions of each of the independent variables.   Often such a solution can be found, and if it can, the problem can be reduced to one in ordinary differential equations.   In this case, we assume

$$u(x,t) = X(x)\Theta(t)$$

where X is a function of x only, Θ a function of t only.   Substituting, (1.1) becomes

$$\Theta \frac{d^2X}{dx^2} = \frac{\mu}{T} X \frac{d^2\Theta}{dt^2}.$$

Let us divide by the product $X\Theta$.   Then we have

$$\frac{1}{X} \frac{d^2X}{dx^2} = \frac{\mu}{T} \frac{1}{\Theta} \frac{d^2\Theta}{dt^2}. \tag{1.2}$$

We now observe that the left side of (1.2) is a function of x alone, whereas the right side is a function of t alone.   This is manifestly impossible unless each side is a constant.   For reasons that will be at once obvious we let this constant be $-\omega^2\mu/T$, where ω is so far undetermined.   Then we have

$$\frac{1}{X} \frac{d^2X}{dx^2} = \frac{\mu}{T} \frac{1}{\Theta} \frac{d^2\Theta}{dt^2} = -\omega^2 \frac{\mu}{T}.$$

This is equivalent to two equations,

$$\frac{d^2\Theta}{dt^2} = -\omega^2\Theta, \qquad \frac{d^2X}{dx^2} = -\omega^2 \frac{\mu}{T} X. \tag{1.3}$$

The process we have just used, by which we have obtained two ordinary differential equations (1.3) which are equivalent to a partial differential equation (1.1), is called "separation of variables."   The solutions of (1.3) are

$$\Theta = e^{\pm j\omega t}, \qquad X = e^{\pm j\omega\sqrt{\mu/T}\, x}. \tag{1.4}$$

By multiplying Θ by X, using any of the four possible combinations of sign, we have a solution of (1.1); obviously we may multiply this solution by an arbitrary complex constant, giving it an arbitrary phase and amplitude, and may take the real part, or may add the solution and its conjugate, as in Chap. II, to get a real solution.

The solution we have just found is of the form

$$u = \frac{\sin}{\cos} \omega \left(t \pm \frac{x}{v} \right) = \frac{\sin}{\cos} \left(\omega t \pm \frac{2\pi x}{\lambda} \right) \tag{1.5}$$

where

$$v = \sqrt{\frac{T}{\mu}}, \qquad \frac{\omega}{2\pi} \lambda = v.$$

This function represents a wave, of angular frequency ω, traveling along the $-x$ axis [if we have the $+$ sign in (1.5)] or the $+x$ axis (if we have the $-$ sign) with the velocity v. To verify this last fact, we need only notice that u is a function of $t \pm x/v$, so that u stays constant, representing a definite feature of the wave, as a wave crest, when $x = \mp vt +$ constant, the equation of a point traveling along the x axis with velocity $\mp v$. The wave length, or distance along the x axis in which the wave repeats itself, is λ. We shall give more discussion later of traveling waves of this type. They are clearly not, however, the type that we need to solve our problem, for we must find a solution for which u is zero for all values of t at the extremities of our string, where it is held. To set up such a solution, we may rewrite the solutions (1.4) in the form

$$\theta = \frac{\sin}{\cos} \omega t, \qquad X = \frac{\sin}{\cos} \omega \frac{x}{v}$$

which are equally good solutions of (1.3). Multiplying them, we have

$$u = \frac{\sin}{\cos} \omega t \frac{\sin}{\cos} \omega \frac{x}{v}. \tag{1.6}$$

If the two rigid supports at which the string is held are at $x = 0$, $x = L$, we must have $u = 0$ always at these points. If we use the sine solution for the function of x, the condition at $x = 0$ will be automatically satisfied. To satisfy the condition at $x = L$, we must then have

$$\sin \omega \frac{L}{v} = 0, \qquad \omega \frac{L}{v} = n\pi, \quad \text{where } n = 1, 2, 3, \cdots. \tag{1.7}$$

This condition can be satisfied by choosing ω properly; we notice that up to this point our equations would be satisfied by any value of ω. If we define ω_n, the nth frequency, by the equation

$$\omega_n \frac{L}{v} = n\pi \tag{1.8}$$

we may rewrite (1.6) in the form

$$u = \frac{\sin}{\cos} \omega_n t \sin \frac{n\pi x}{L}. \tag{1.9}$$

The solution (1.9) is a standing wave; that is, at any instant of time the function of x has the same form, so that some points, the nodes, at which the factor $\sin n\pi x/L$ is zero, are always at rest, and other points, the antinodes, where $\sin n\pi x/L$ equals unity, oscillate with maximum amplitude.

2. The General Solution for the Stretched String.—A standing wave of the form (1.9) is a particular solution of the problem of the stretched string. It is an oscillation in which the length of the string is divided into n segments, with nodes between, and in which the frequency of oscillation is n times a fundamental frequency, defined by (1.8) with $n = 1$. These various types of oscillation are called "normal modes," or "resonant modes," or "harmonics," or "overtones"; we shall find them to be almost exactly analogous to the normal modes of coupled systems, which we took up in the preceding chapter. Each of the normal modes (1.9) can be excited with an arbitrary amplitude and phase. But it is now clear, from the linear nature of the differential equation, that a sum of solutions is itself a solution, so that we can build up a general solution by superposing all the normal modes, each with an arbitrary amplitude and phase. That is, we build up the solution

$$u = \sum_{n=1}^{\infty} (A_n \cos \omega_n t + B_n \sin \omega_n t) \sin \frac{n\pi x}{L}. \tag{2.1}$$

This general solution of our problem has an infinite number of arbitrary constants. This is a characteristic of the solution of partial differential equations; instead of having a small number of arbitrary constants, as with the solution of an ordinary differential equation, we have an infinite number, or alternatively we have arbitrary functions.

We may now consider how to determine the A_n's and B_n's in a practical case. Usually we should have to determine these constants from initial conditions, at $t = 0$: we may know, for instance, that the displacement is a given function of x, $u_0(x)$, at $t = 0$, and that the velocity is another given function, $\dot{u}_0(x)$. The problem then becomes similar to that which we met in Chap. VII, Sec. 2, where we found the corresponding coefficients for a system of coupled oscillators. Here, as there, we have a form of orthogonality conditions. These conditions take the form of the equation

$$\frac{2}{L} \int_0^L \sin \frac{n\pi x}{L} \sin \frac{m\pi x}{L} \, dx = \delta_{nm} \tag{2.2}$$

where n and m are two integers, each different from zero. Equation (2.2) can be proved at once from elementary integration; we shall later see that in principle it is really closely analogous to the orthogonality condition (2.10) of Chap. VII. We are now trying to satisfy the equations

$$u_0(x) = \sum_{n=1}^{\infty} A_n \sin \frac{n\pi x}{L}, \qquad \dot{u}_0(x) = \sum_{n=1}^{\infty} \omega_n B_n \sin \frac{n\pi x}{L} \tag{2.3}$$

which we get by writing the position and velocity of the string at $t = 0$ from (2.1). To satisfy the first of the equations, let us multiply both sides of (2.3) by $(2/L) \sin m\pi x/L$, and integrate from 0 to L. We then have

$$\frac{2}{L} \int_0^L u_0(x) \sin \frac{m\pi x}{L} \, dx = \sum_n A_n \frac{2}{L} \int_0^L \sin \frac{n\pi x}{L} \sin \frac{m\pi x}{L} \, dx$$

$$= \sum_n A_n \delta_{nm} = A_m.$$

This is closely equivalent to Eq. (2.13) of Chap. VII, and it gives us the coefficients A_m in terms of integrals that can be computed, once u_0 is known. In a similar way we can find the B_m's.

The series (2.3) for $u_0(x)$ and $\dot{u}_0(x)$ are Fourier series of a simple form. The general Fourier series is a sum of both sine and cosine functions, such as a series

$$\frac{C_0}{2} + \sum_{n=1}^{\infty} C_n \cos \frac{2n\pi x}{X} + D_n \sin \frac{2n\pi x}{X}.$$

We discuss some of the properties of such a series in Appendix VI. It represents a function that is periodic with period X, for each of the terms of the series has this periodicity. If the series includes only the sine terms, the series is odd in x (that is, changing the sign of x changes the sign of the series); whereas, if it includes only the cosine terms and the constant term, it is even (that is, changing the sign of x leaves the series unchanged). In our particular case, we wish to represent a function that is always zero when $x = 0$. It is thus reasonable to take a series of sines, each of which has this property. We then choose the fundamental period X equal to $2L$, extending from $x = -L$ to $x = L$, and define $u_0(-x) = -u_0(x)$, so as to make an odd function out of it. The series (2.3) is then the representation of this odd function, which in particular represents the actual $u_0(x)$ in the range between $x = 0$ and $x = L$, which alone is of physical significance.

3. The String as a Limiting Case of the Vibration of Particles.— The vibrating string has a very close relationship to the problems of vibrating particles, and coupled oscillators, which we took up in the preceding chapter, and we wish to show this relationship in the present section. To do this, we might consider the problem as it really is: the string is really a set of vibrating atoms or molecules, each held to its neighbors by approximately linear restoring forces. A complete treatment of this problem would be difficult, however, and we shall instead set up a simpler problem that we can handle easily, and that nevertheless points out clearly the relationships between the continuous problem of the vibrating string and the problem of vibrating particles. This is the weighted string: a string whose mass is all concentrated in a set of equally spaced equal masses, or weights, held together by weightless springs with the tension T. This is a perfect example of the sort of analysis used in the preceding chapter, and yet in the limit when the masses become infinitesimal and spaced infinitely closely, it approaches the continuous string. We take up the weighted string in this section, and show how its solutions pass into those of the continuous string in the limit. At the same time, the problem itself has considerable importance, for mathematically it is equivalent to electric filters or artificial lines, and to certain acoustic filters. We shall find that, if we do not pass to the limit, but instead consider the problem with finite weights, the string has filtering properties, in that oscillations of some frequencies can be propagated down it, while other frequencies cannot, a property that becomes lost when we go to the limit of the continuous string.

Let us assume N weights, each of mass m, spaced a distance d apart along the x axis, so that they are located at $x = d, 2d, \cdots Nd$. Between each pair of weights is a spring with tension T, and similar springs connect the end weights to the points $x = 0$, $x = (N + 1)d$, which are held fixed. We may denote the displacement of the ith weight (that is, the one located at $x = id$) at right angles to the x axis as u_i. We may now find the force on the ith weight by an argument almost exactly like that used in Sec. 1. Corresponding to the derivative $\partial u/\partial x$ which we met in that section, we have $(u_{i+1} - u_i)/d$. The vertical component of force on the ith weight is then

$$T\left[\frac{(u_{i+1} - u_i)}{d} - \frac{(u_i - u_{i-1})}{d}\right] = \frac{T}{d}\,(u_{i+1} - 2u_i + u_{i-1}). \quad (3.1)$$

Thus the equation of motion of the ith weight is

$$m\,\frac{d^2u_i}{dt^2} = \frac{T}{d}\,(u_{i+1} - 2u_i + u_{i-1}). \quad (3.2)$$

The force that appears on the right side of (3.2) has the form given by Eq. (1.3), Chap. VII, with

$$A_{ii} = 2\,\frac{T}{d}, \qquad A_{i,i+1} = A_{i,i-1} = -\frac{T}{d}, \quad \text{all other } A\text{'s} = 0. \quad (3.3)$$

The end particles, $i = 1$ and $i = N$, are a special case, for they have only one neighbor each. We may bring them into agreement with Eq. (3.2), however, by defining

$$u_0 = u_{N+1} = 0. \quad (3.4)$$

That is, we might assume that we had a weighted string of indefinite length, with equally spaced weights, but that the weights at $x = 0$ and $x = (N + 1)d$ were rigidly held; the problem would then obviously be exactly equivalent to the real case.

We may now proceed to find the normal modes of the weighted string, as in Sec. 2, Chap. VII. Assuming a sinusoidal oscillation of angular frequency ω, the equations of motion, analogous to (2.2) of Chap. VII, are

$$-\frac{T}{d}\,u_0 + \left(2\,\frac{T}{d} - m\omega^2\right)u_1 - \frac{T}{d}\,u_2 = 0$$

$$-\frac{T}{d}\,u_1 + \left(2\,\frac{T}{d} - m\omega^2\right)u_2 - \frac{T}{d}\,u_3 = 0$$

$$\cdot\ \cdot$$

$$-\frac{T}{d}\,u_{N-1} + \left(2\,\frac{T}{d} - m\omega^2\right)u_N - \frac{T}{d}\,u_{N+1} = 0 \quad (3.5)$$

taken together with (3.4). This leads to a secular determinant, like (2.3), Chap. VII. The secular equation can be solved without too much difficulty, on account of its simple form. However, the problem is simple enough so that we can solve Eqs. (3.5) directly, and this direct solution shows a close resemblance to the method we have used for the continuous string. Equations (3.5) form what is called a "linear difference equation":

$$-\frac{T}{d}u_{i-1} + \left(2\frac{T}{d} - m\omega^2\right)u_i - \frac{T}{d}u_{i+1} = 0. \qquad (3.6)$$

It is in many ways similar to a linear differential equation, and it is a very simple one, in that it has constant coefficients.

As with the corresponding differential equation, we can find exponential solutions: we assume

$$u_i = e^{j\omega t}e^{jik} \qquad (3.7)$$

where $j = \sqrt{-1}$, as usual, and where k is to be determined. Equation (3.6) then becomes

$$-\frac{T}{d}e^{jk(i-1)} + \left(2\frac{T}{d} - m\omega^2\right)e^{jki} - \frac{T}{d}e^{jk(i+1)} = 0$$

or

$$-2\frac{T}{d}\cos k + 2\frac{T}{d} - m\omega^2 = 0$$

from which

$$m\omega^2 = 2\frac{T}{d}(1 - \cos k). \qquad (3.8)$$

That is, for any value of k, we can find an appropriate frequency, from (3.8). So far, however, we have not imposed conditions (3.4), so that as far as our solution is concerned we have an infinitely long string, which would therefore be expected to have an infinite number of resonant modes.

When we consider (3.4), we see that the solution (3.7) cannot be used as it stands, for it does not satisfy the conditions. We must instead build up the equally legitimate solution

$$u_i = e^{j\omega t}\sin ik \qquad (3.9)$$

which we construct from (3.7) and its conjugate, either of which is a solution of (3.5). The solution (3.9) automatically satisfies the condition $u_0 = 0$; to satisfy the other condition, $u_{N+1} = 0$, we must have

$$\sin (N+1)k = 0, \qquad (N+1)k = n\pi, \qquad n = 1, 2, \cdots .$$

We have, then, a discrete set of k's which alone are allowed, when we consider the restriction that the ends of the weighted string are fixed. These conditions are entirely analogous to the corresponding relations for the continuous string, as found in (1.7). For the nth mode, the solution is

$$u_{in} = e^{j\omega_n t} \sin \frac{in\pi}{N+1} \qquad (3.10)$$

where

$$m\omega_n^2 = 2\frac{T}{d}\left(1 - \cos\frac{n\pi}{N+1}\right). \qquad (3.11)$$

We notice immediately that our weighted string has only a finite

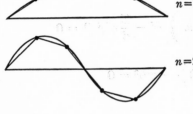

$n=1$

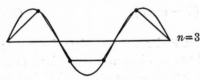

$n=2$

$n=3$

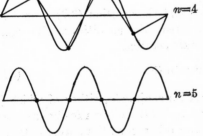

$n=4$

$n=5$

Fig. 25(a).

number of resonant modes, corresponding to $n = 1, 2, \cdots N$. For if we allow n to increase beyond N, we repeat solutions that we have already considered. Thus for $n = N + 1$, $u_{in} = \sin i\pi = 0$, and there is no real mode. For $n = N + 2$,

$$\sin \frac{in\pi}{(N+1)} = \sin\left[i\pi + \frac{i\pi}{(N+1)}\right]$$

$$= -\sin\left[i\pi - \frac{i\pi}{(N+1)}\right]$$

$$= -\sin\frac{iN\pi}{(N+1)},$$

so that the solution (except for the minus sign, which is trivial) is the same as for $n = N$. We satisfy ourselves immediately from (3.11) that the frequency is also the same as for $n = N$. Continuing, we see that the solution for $n = N + 3$ is the same as for $n = N - 1$, and so on, and in fact we get no new solutions, no matter how far we go.

Thus we are limited to the N modes, which we should expect from our general theory of Chap. VII. For instance, if there are only two particles, we should expect two modes. Thus if $N = 2$, we have from (3.10)

$$u_{11} = e^{j\omega_1 t} \sin\frac{\pi}{3}, \qquad u_{21} = e^{j\omega_1 t} \sin\frac{2\pi}{3} = u_{11}$$

$$u_{12} = e^{j\omega_2 t} \sin\frac{2\pi}{3}, \qquad u_{22} = e^{j\omega_2 t} \sin\frac{4\pi}{3} = -u_{12} \qquad (3.12)$$

and

$$m\omega_1^2 = 2\frac{T}{d}\left(1 - \cos\frac{\pi}{3}\right) = \frac{T}{d}$$

$$m\omega_2^2 = 2\frac{T}{d}\left(1 - \cos\frac{2\pi}{3}\right) = \frac{3T}{d}. \qquad (3.13)$$

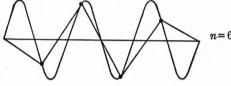

$n = 6$

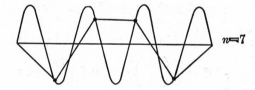

$n = 7$

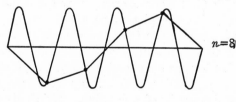

$n = 8$

$n = 9$

FIG. 25(b).—Modes of weighted vibrating string, $N = 4$. Note that $n = 6, 7, 8, 9$ repeat patterns of $n = 4, 3, 2, 1$, with opposite sign.

This solution is in entire agreement with the solution for two coupled particles which we found in Sec. 4, Chap. VII.   There, in Eq. (4.3), we found that, if $A_{11}/m_1 = A_{22}/m_2$, which is the case here, we had

$x_1 = \pm x_2$ if $\omega^2 = A_{11}/m_1 \pm A_{12}/m_2$. Comparing with (3.3), we see that (3.12) and (3.13) lead to just these solutions for the two modes. To show the nature of the modes for a more complicated case, we plot the forms of the various modes for $N = 4$ in Fig. 25. Here we see clearly how it is that values of n greater than 4 lead to modes already considered.

It is easy to show that our solution (3.10) and (3.11) for the weighted string reduces to our previous solution for the continuous string. The displacement u_{in} of the ith particle in the nth mode, as given in (3.10), should agree with the displacement $u_n(id)$, as given in (1.9), for a particle with $x = id$, in a string of length $L = (N + 1)d$. It is clear by comparison of (1.9) and (3.10) that it does. The frequency, as given by (3.11), agrees only asymptotically, when N becomes infinite, with the value given by (1.7) for the continuous string. Thus let N become infinite, d simultaneously vanishing, in such a way that the length $L = (N + 1)d$ stays constant. At the same time let the mass m of the particles decrease in such a way that m/d, the mass per unit length, approaches μ. For a finite value of n, the cosine in (3.11) becomes the cosine of a vanishingly small quantity, so that it can be expanded in power series, and (3.11) becomes

$$\mu d\omega_n^2 = \frac{T}{d}\left(\frac{n\pi d}{L}\right)^2, \qquad \omega_n L \sqrt{\frac{\mu}{T}} = n\pi \qquad (3.14)$$

which agrees with (1.7) when we remember the definition (1.5) of v. For a weighted string, we plot ω_n as a function of n, from (3.11), in Fig. 26. We see that the frequencies of the lowest modes agree well with those of the continuous string, but that the higher modes of the weighted string are bunched together, approaching the limiting value $\omega = 2\sqrt{T/md}$. For a frequency greater than this limit, there is no possible mode of oscillation. We shall see in the next chapter that this corresponds to a wave that cannot be propagated through the weighted string, so that the string acts like a low pass filter, all frequencies above this limit being cut off.

4. Normal Coordinates and the Vibrating String.—In the problem of the weighted string, we can introduce normal coordinates, according to the methods of Sec. 3, Chap. VII, as we can in any problem of coupled oscillators. We shall investigate these normal coordinates in the limiting case where N, the number of particles, is very large, so that we can carry out a passage to the limit of the continuous string. In the first place, we need the quantities x_{ij} of Chap. VII, satisfying the orthogonality condition (2.10) of that chapter,

$$\sum_{i=1}^{N} m_i x_{ij} x_{ik} = \delta_{jk}. \qquad (4.1)$$

The x_{ij}'s represented the displacements of the ith particle in the jth mode. The corresponding quantity u_{ij} in the present case is given in (3.10) of the present chapter, and is proportional to $\sin ij\pi/(N + 1)$. To carry out the normalization implied in (4.1), we must multiply these quantities by a constant factor, independent of i. If we let this factor be C_j, we then must have

$$mC_j C_k \sum_{i=1}^{N} \sin \frac{ij\pi}{N + 1} \sin \frac{ik\pi}{N + 1} = \delta_{jk}. \qquad (4.2)$$

For the case $j \neq k$, (4.2) is the expression of a trigonometric theorem, which could be independently proved by direct methods. For $j = k$, (4.2) leads to

$$mC_j^2 \sum_{i=1}^{N} \sin^2 \frac{ij\pi}{N + 1} = 1 \qquad (4.3)$$

which serves to define C_j, in such a way that we have

$$u_{ij} = C_j \sin \frac{ij\pi}{N + 1}.$$

If N is large, we can easily get an approximate value for the summation in (4.3). We have N terms, and the average value of each is $\frac{1}{2}$, the average value of the square of a sine, averaged over the angle. Thus in this case we have

$$mC_j^2 \frac{N}{2} = 1.$$

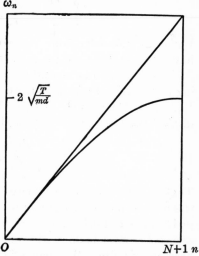

Fig. 26.—Resonant frequency ω_n as function of mode number n, for weighted string. Straight line, corresponding curve for continuous string.

The product mN is the total mass of the N particles; for the continuous string we may replace this by μL, the mass per unit length times the length, which also equals the total mass. Thus in this limit we have

$$C_j = \sqrt{\frac{2}{\mu L}}.$$

In the limit, the orthogonality condition (4.2) takes on a simple form. The ith particle will be found at the position $x = id$ along the string; thus we may rewrite the factor $\sin ij\pi/(N + 1)$ in the form

$$\sin \frac{ij\pi}{N + 1} = \sin \frac{j\pi x}{L}$$

so that

$$u_{ij} = \sqrt{\frac{2}{\mu L}} \sin \frac{j\pi x}{L}, \quad \text{with } x = id. \quad (4.4)$$

In the summation in (4.2), we may multiply and divide by d, and replace d in the numerator by dx, so that the summation will pass in the limit of large N's into an integration. Thus (4.2) becomes

$$\mu \int_0^L \frac{2}{\mu L} \sin \frac{j\pi x}{L} \sin \frac{k\pi x}{L} \, dx = \delta_{jk}$$

or

$$\frac{2}{L} \int_0^L \sin \frac{j\pi x}{L} \sin \frac{k\pi x}{L} \, dx = \delta_{jk}. \quad (4.5)$$

Equation (4.5) is the same as the orthogonality relation (2.2), which we have already discussed for the continuous string.

Now that we have found the normalized quantities u_{ij}, corresponding to the x_{ij}'s of Chap. VII, we can set up normal coordinates, as in Eq. (3.2), Chap. VII. Using (4.4), this means that we write the displacement of the ith particle, located at $x = id$, in the form

$$u(x) = \sum_j q_j \sqrt{\frac{2}{\mu L}} \sin \frac{j\pi x}{L}. \quad (4.6)$$

That is, the normal coordinates q_j are essentially the amplitudes of the normal modes of the vibrating string, as they are in an ordinary problem of coupled vibrations; only here, as the number of normal modes becomes infinite, the number of normal coordinates likewise becomes infinite. We may still, if we choose, use the geometrical interpretation of normal coordinates that we gave in Chap. VII. That is, we take an N-dimensional space, and rotate axes in such a way that the rotated axes point along the principal axes of the surfaces of constant potential energy, which are many-dimensional ellipsoids. Here, however, N becomes infinite, so that we must speak of a space of an infinite number of dimensions. By this we mean simply the limit of the N-dimensional space that we encounter with N coupled particles, as N becomes infinite. In such a space, if the representative point is displaced along one of the original coordinate axes, only one mass particle of the weighted string is displaced, the others all being at their undisturbed positions; whereas, if the representative point is displaced along one of the axes representing the normal coordinates, it means that the particles are displaced as they would be in one of the normal modes of the string.   With an arbitrary displacement of the representative point, the N particles are displaced in arbitrary ways.   In the limit as N becomes infinite, an arbitrary position of the representative point corresponds to an arbitrary displacement of each point of the string, or to an arbitrary function $u(x)$ representing its shape.   For this reason, the space of an infinite number of dimensions is sometimes called a "function space," since each point of it represents a complete function.

It is easy to follow the model of Chap. VII and set up the Lagrangian equations of motion of the string in terms of the normal coordinates.   We first set up the kinetic and potential energies, the latter arising from the stretching of the springs, and from them set up the Lagrangian function.   The kinetic energy is

$$T_1 = \frac{\mu}{2} \int_0^L \dot{u}^2\, dx = \frac{\mu}{2} \int_0^L \left(\sum_k \dot{q}_k \sqrt{\frac{2}{\mu L}} \sin \frac{k\pi x}{L} \right)^2 dx$$

$$= \frac{1}{2} \sum_k \dot{q}_k^2 \tag{4.7}$$

in which we have used the orthogonality relations.   The potential energy V of the weighted string is

$$V = \frac{T}{2d} [(u_1 - u_0)^2 + (u_2 - u_1)^2 + \cdots + (u_{N+1} - u_N)^2] \tag{4.8}$$

where u_0, u_{N+1} are zero.   To prove this, we need only find $-\partial V/\partial u_i$, which is $(T/d)[(u_{i+1} - u_i) - (u_i - u_{i-1})]$, in agreement with (3.1).   Passing to the limit of the continuous string, this becomes

$$V = \frac{T}{2} \int_0^L \left(\frac{\partial u}{\partial x} \right)^2 dx. \tag{4.9}$$

This is then

$$V = \frac{T}{2} \int_0^L \left(\sum_k q_k \sqrt{\frac{2}{\mu L}} \frac{k\pi}{L} \cos \frac{k\pi x}{L} \right)^2 dx$$

$$= \sum_k \frac{T}{2} \frac{2}{\mu L} \frac{k^2 \pi^2}{L^2} \frac{L}{2} q_k^2 = \frac{1}{2} \sum_k \omega_k^2 q_k^2 \tag{4.10}$$

where we have used the fact that the functions $\cos k\pi x/L$ have orthogonality properties like those of sin $k\pi x/L$.   We then have

$$\text{Lagrangian function} = \tfrac{1}{2} \sum_k (\dot{q}_k^2 - \omega_k^2 q_k^2). \tag{4.11}$$

This derivation of the Lagrangian function is not really necessary since the weighted string is a special case of the problem worked out in Chap. VII.   We may be quite sure directly from that derivation that we have (4.11), where ω_k is given by (3.11) for the weighted string, or (3.14) for the continuous string.

We may next use Lagrange's equations to investigate forced and damped motion of the string, as we did in Sec. 5, Chap. VII.   Suppose there is a force $f(x,t)$ per unit length acting on the string at point x at time t.   Then we must use (5.1), Chap. VII, to find the generalized force F_j associated with f.   In that equation $F_j = \sum_i f_i x_{ij}$, we shall replace x_{ij} by u_{ij}, as in (4.4), and shall convert the summation into an integration.   Multiplying and dividing by d, f_i/d becomes the force per unit length, or our $f(x,t)$, and the summation times d goes into an integration.   Thus we have

$$F_j = \int_0^L f(x,t) \sqrt{\frac{2}{\mu L}} \sin \frac{j\pi x}{L} \, dx. \tag{4.12}$$

In terms of this force, we have the Lagrange equations of (5.2), Chap. VII,

$$\ddot{q}_i + \omega_j^2 q_i = F_j. \tag{4.13}$$

If for instance $f(x,t)$ varies sinusoidally with a frequency ω, then we have for the forced motion of the string, as in (5.3), Chap. VII,

$$u(x,t) = \sqrt{\frac{2}{\mu L}} \sum_j \frac{F_j \sin (j\pi x/L)}{\omega_j^2 - \omega^2},$$

showing the familiar phenomenon of resonance if the external force approaches the natural frequencies of vibration of the string.

A damping force proportional to the velocity takes a particularly simple form with the vibrating string.   Thus suppose, for instance, that the string is immersed in a fluid, as air or a liquid, which exerts on each unit length a resisting force proportional to the velocity. We may, for instance, have

$$f(x,t) = -k\dot{u}(x,t).$$

To find the generalized force associated with this resistance, we substitute into (4.12), writing $u(x,t)$ from (4.6).   Using the normalization conditions (4.5), we find at once

$$F_i = -\frac{k}{\mu}\,\dot{q}_i.$$

This corresponds to the special case of Eq. (5.4), Chap. VII, in which the quantity γ_{jk} has only diagonal terms.   We have then the special case mentioned in the discussion of Eq. (5.6), Chap. VII, in which the equations of motion have the variables separated, even in the presence of damping: the equation (4.13) becomes

$$\ddot{q}_i + \frac{k}{\mu}\,\dot{q}_i + \omega_i^2 q_i = F_i', \qquad (4.14)$$

where F_i' represents any additional force, as for instance an external force varying sinusoidally with the time.   Equation (4.14) is of the standard form for a damped harmonic oscillator, with a Q given by

$$\frac{k}{\mu} = \frac{\omega_j}{Q_j}$$

showing that the Q's of the various modes of a string are proportional to the corresponding frequencies, so that the rate of damping is the same for all modes.   Solving (4.14) for a sinusoidal impressed force F_i', we then have the general solution of the damped string,

$$u(x,t) = \sqrt{\frac{2}{\mu L}} \sum_j \frac{F_j' \sin\,(j\pi x/L)}{\omega_j^2 - \omega^2 + j\omega(k/\mu)}. \qquad (4.15)$$

Equation (4.15), of course, represents the steady-state forced motion; to satisfy arbitrary initial conditions, we must superpose a general free oscillation or transient, or solution of (4.14) for the case $F_i' = 0$.

Problems

1. Taking the case of four particles on a string, derive their displacements in the four possible normal vibrations, and compute their frequencies.   Compare these frequencies with the first four frequencies of the corresponding continuous string.   Put in $n = N + 1$, and so on, and show how the solution reduces to one already found.

2. An actual string is composed of atoms, rather than being continuous, so that it has only a finite number of possible overtones.   Assume that it consists of a single string of atoms, spaced 10^{-8} cm apart.   Let the string be 1 m long, and at such tension that its fundamental is 100 cycles/sec.   Find the frequency of the highest possible harmonic, and show that it is in the infrared region of the spectrum. Show that, in this highest harmonic, successive atoms vibrate in opposite phases. Substances actually have such natural frequencies in the infrared, and they are important in connection with their specific heat.

3. A string of length L is pulled aside at a point a distance D from the end, and then released. Thus its initial shape is given by a curve made of two straight lines, and its initial velocity is zero. Find the solution for its motion, and find the amplitude of the nth harmonic.

4. Taking the solution of Prob. 3, for the special case where $D = L/2$, compute the first five terms of the Fourier series, when $t = 0$. Add them and plot the sum, showing how good an approximation they make to the correct curve.

5. A string initially at rest is struck at a distance D from the end, at $t = 0$. Find the intensity in each overtone. Approximate the initial conditions as follows: the initial displacement is zero, and the initial velocity is a constant in a small region of length d about the point D, zero elsewhere.

6. Write down the Hamiltonian function for a vibrating string, using normal coordinates. Set up Hamilton's equations, and show that they are satisfied for the solution we have found.

7. A sinusoidal force of constant amplitude but adjustable frequency acts on an arbitrary point of a string. The string is in addition damped by a frictional force proportional to the velocity. Discuss the resonance of the string to the force, computing the total energy of the string as a function of the applied frequency, and showing that the resulting resonance curve goes through maxima corresponding to the various overtone frequencies. Find approximate heights and breadths of the maxima. Neglect the transient vibrations.

8. Prove directly by trigonometry the orthogonality relations for the normal functions for the weighted string; that is, prove Eq. (4.2).

9. Using the orthogonality relations of Prob. 8, and the analogy of the continuous string, set up a method for finding the amplitudes of the various overtones of the weighted string, in terms of the initial displacements and velocities of the particles.

10. Apply the method of Prob. 9 to the special case of two coupled particles.

11. Apply Prob. 9 to the case of four particles, as in Prob. 1.

12. What sort of force must be applied to a string in order that the forced motion will be a pure vibration of the nth harmonic?

13. Consider the case of two identical coupled particles. Show that, if equal external forces act on both, the overtone in which they vibrate in opposite directions can never be excited.

14. In the case of two coupled particles, assume that at $t = 0$ both particles are at rest, but that one particle is displaced a distance a, the other not being displaced at all. Find the amplitudes of the two overtones, writing down the formulas for the displacements of each particle as functions of time.

15. A particle of mass M hangs on one end of a uniform string of mass m and length L, the other end of the string being fixed. The particle is given a small lateral displacement and released from rest. Set up the differential equation and boundary conditions to determine the motion of the string. Solve for the case $m \ll M$, and determine the natural frequencies.

CHAPTER IX

WAVE PROPAGATION IN THE STRING

In the preceding chapter, we took up one aspect of the vibration of the stretched string: the normal modes, the types of vibration which the string possesses when it is held rigidly at both ends. We have not brought out the quite different aspects of the problem which we encounter with an infinite string, in which wave propagation of any form of wave is possible, or with the string held at a single point, at which the waves are reflected. Furthermore, we have not considered the case in which the string is held by a yielding support capable of absorbing power, rather than by a perfectly rigid support. We shall consider a number of problems of this general type in the present chapter. As we have pointed out in the introduction to Chap. VIII, part of the importance of these problems lies in their resemblance to electrical and acoustical transmission lines, and in their connection with the three-dimensional propagation of mechanical and electromagnetic waves.

1. General Wave Propagation in the Continuous String.—In Eq. (1.1), Chap. VIII, we set up the wave equation for the string. Using the definition (1.5) of that chapter for the velocity of propagation, this wave equation is

$$\frac{\partial^2 u}{\partial x^2} = \frac{1}{v^2}\frac{\partial^2 u}{\partial t^2}. \tag{1.1}$$

We solved this equation by the method of separation of variables, writing u as a product of a function of x and a function of t, and that is the most convenient method of solution for the problem of standing waves. For considering propagation, however, there is a very simple and straightforward solution. This is

$$u = f(x - vt) + g(x + vt) \tag{1.2}$$

where f and g are two perfectly arbitrary functions. To prove this, we need only consider $f(x - vt)$ to be a function $f(w)$, where $w = x - vt$. Then we have

$$\frac{\partial f}{\partial x} = \frac{df}{dw}, \qquad \frac{\partial^2 f}{\partial x^2} = \frac{d^2 f}{dw^2}, \qquad \frac{df}{dt} = -v\frac{df}{dw}, \qquad \frac{\partial^2 f}{\partial t^2} = v^2\frac{d^2 f}{dw^2}$$

163

from which (1.1) follows immediately, with a similar proof for g. The function $f(x - vt)$ represents a wave of arbitrary form, traveling along the x axis with velocity v, and $g(x + vt)$ represents a similar arbitrary wave traveling with velocity $-v$, or along the negative x axis. From (1.2), then, we see that a wave of any arbitrary form can be propagated in either direction along a stretched string, without distortion, and with the constant velocity v. The solutions (1.5) of Chap. VIII, $u = \dfrac{\sin}{\cos} \omega(t \pm x/v)$, were obviously special cases of the general solution (1.2), the special cases in which the disturbance at a fixed position is a sinusoidal function of time, or the disturbance at a given instant of time is a sinusoidal function of position. The general case, however, requires no assumption that the wave should have sinusoidal form.

We can easily find the functions f and g required to satisfy given initial conditions at $t = 0$. Thus suppose the shape of the string is given by $u_0(x)$ at $t = 0$, and its velocity by $v_0(x)$. Then we have

$$u_0 = f(x) + g(x), \qquad v_0 = v\left[-\frac{df(x)}{dx} + \frac{dg(x)}{dx} \right] \tag{1.3}$$

and

$$\frac{du_0}{dx} = \frac{df(x)}{dx} + \frac{dg(x)}{dx}. \tag{1.4}$$

From (1.3) and (1.4) we have

$$\frac{df(x)}{dx} = \frac{1}{2}\left(\frac{du_0}{dx} - \frac{v_0}{v} \right), \qquad \frac{dg(x)}{dx} = \frac{1}{2}\left(\frac{du_0}{dx} + \frac{v_0}{v} \right)$$

or, integrating with respect to x,

$$f(x) = \frac{1}{2}\left[u_0(x) - \frac{1}{v} \int_{x_0}^{x} v_0(x)\, dx \right]$$

$$g(x) = \frac{1}{2}\left[u_0(x) + \frac{1}{v} \int_{x_0}^{x} v_0(x)\, dx \right] \tag{1.5}$$

from which the functions f and g are determined, except for the constant of integration implied in the arbitrary limit x_0, which cancels out of the final answer. We see from (1.5) that, if the initial velocity of the string is zero, f and g are equal; whereas, if the initial displacement is zero, f and g are equal in magnitude but opposite in sign.

If a string is held rigidly at a fixed point, the wave approaching it from the left will be reflected with change of phase, and will travel back toward the left again. In this way, the character of the wave $g(x + vt)$ traveling to the left is uniquely determined from the wave $f(x - vt)$ traveling to the right. Expressed analytically, if the fixed point is at $x = 0$, we must have

$$g(x + vt) = -f[-(x + vt)], \tag{1.6}$$

or, if the fixed point is at $x = x_1$, we must have

$$g(x + vt) = -f[2x_1 - (x + vt)] \tag{1.7}$$

since as we see immediately the function $f(x - vt) + g(x + vt)$ will be zero for all values of time when $x = 0$ in (1.6), or when $x = x_1$ in (1.7). If furthermore the function f is periodic with a period $2L$, the function g will be periodic with the same period, and we can show at once that the displacement u will be zero not only at $x = x_1$, but at $x_1 \pm nL$, where n is any integer. For at such a point the displacement is

$$f(x_1 \pm nL - vt) - f[2x_1 - (x_1 \pm nL + vt)] = f(x_1 \pm nL - vt)$$
$$- f(x_1 \mp nL - vt) = 0$$

on account of the periodicity of f. Thus such a solution satisfies the conditions for the vibration of a string held at x_1 and $x_1 + L$, or the problem of the preceding chapter.

Examples of such a solution are given in Fig. 27, for the cases in which the initial velocity and the initial displacement of the string are zero. The waves f and g, traveling to the right and left, form the direct and reflected waves at each of the two points where the string is held. The period of the wave is the time required for the wave to travel a distance $2L$, making a round trip after reflections from both ends of the string. By comparison with Eq. (1.8), Chap. VIII, we see that this period is the fundamental period found there; setting $n = 1$ in that equation, we had $\omega(L/v) = \pi$, period $= 2\pi/\omega = 2L/v$. The harmonics all have periods that are integral submultiples of this fundamental, so that after the time $2L/v$ the whole motion repeats itself. The solution of the type we have just set up, consisting of an arbitrary direct wave with its reflected wave, is no more and no less general than the solution in terms of sine functions which we found in Eq. (2.1), Chap. VIII. If we were to take the solution in terms of the direct and reflected waves, remembering that the function f must in that case be periodic, and were to analyze f in Fourier series, we should be led back to exactly the solution of the preceding chapter. When we are interested in the overtones, the solution in terms of normal modes is to be preferred, but when we are interested in the actual shape of the string, as for instance in the case of Fig. 27, the present method is much more direct.

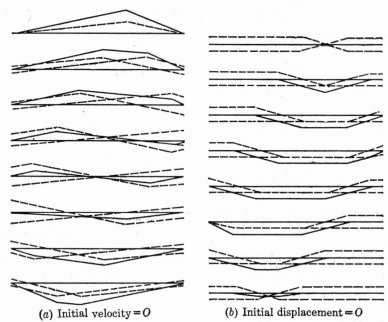

(a) Initial velocity $= 0$ (b) Initial displacement $= 0$

Fig. 27.—Successive shapes of a string, held at both ends. Dotted lines show functions f, g. Case (a), initial velocity $= 0$, string pulled aside at one point; case (b), initial displacement $= 0$, string struck and given impact over narrow region. Motion followed over approximately a half cycle, each case.

2. Wave Propagation in the Weighted String.

—The reason we can get the beautifully simple solution (1.2), expressing the general motion of the string as a superposition of two arbitrary waves traveling to the right and left with velocity v, is that the velocity of propagation of a sinusoidal wave, of definite frequency and wave length, is independent of the frequency, for the continuous string. For this reason, if at a given instant we build up the general solution as a superposition of sinusoidal solutions, the sinusoidal waves will all travel along with the same speed, and the complicated phase relations between them which are necessary to make them add up to the general solution will be preserved as the wave travels along, and it will not change its form. On the other hand, this is a special case; in many cases, a sinusoidal wave can travel without change of form, but different waves of different wave lengths or frequencies travel with different velocities. This phenomenon is called "dispersion," from the optical case, in which light waves of different wave lengths travel with different speeds through glass or other material media, though they travel with the same speed in empty space. When there is dispersion, it is only a sinusoidal wave which is propagated without change of form; for, if we build up any other wave by superposing sine waves, the different velocities of the various waves will rapidly destroy the interaction between them, and will distort the form. Since dispersion often occurs in wave motion, and since we must use sinusoidal waves to get a simple solution in a dispersive medium, it is customary to use sinusoidal solutions of the wave equation generally, even in nondispersive media (as the uniform continuous string, or as sound in the air, or light in empty space). We do not lose in generality thereby, for we have seen in the preceding chapter that the most general solution can be built up by superposing sinusoidal waves. From now on, then, we shall use sinusoidal solutions of the wave equation.

The weighted string, which we discussed from the standpoint of normal modes of vibration in the preceding chapter, forms a simple example of a dispersive medium. To prove this, let us write down the solution for traveling sinusoidal waves in such a weighted string, and show that the velocity of propagation depends on the frequency. Such a solution is

$$u_i = e^{j(\omega t - ik)} = e^{j[\omega t - (k/d)x]}$$

where $x = id$, using the notation of Sec. 3, Chap. VIII. The velocity is then

$$v = \omega \frac{d}{k} = \sqrt{\frac{2Td}{m} \frac{(1 - \cos k)}{k^2}} \tag{2.1}$$

where we have used the expression (3.8) of Chap. VIII to write ω in terms of k. Thus we have a velocity that depends on k, or on ω. For low frequencies, k is small, we may expand the cosine in power series and use the quadratic term, and we find the limiting value of $v = \sqrt{Td/m} = \sqrt{T/\mu}$, as for the continuous string. On the other hand, as we saw in Chap. VIII, all possible types of waves are included in values of k up to a maximum of π; for this value, we have

$$v = \left(\frac{2}{\pi}\right) \sqrt{\frac{T}{\mu}},$$

showing that the velocity decreases to this value as the frequency increases.

The change of velocity with frequency can be seen graphically from Fig. 26, which may be interpreted as a plot of ω as a function of $\gamma = k/d$, from Eq. (3.8), Chap. VIII. The velocity is ω/γ, or the slope of the line drawn from the origin to a point with the appropriate frequency. A graph of ω vs. γ, for any wave $e^{j(\omega t - \gamma x)}$, is an instructive way to plot its propagation characteristics. If the velocity is constant, the wave can be written $e^{j\omega[t-(x/v)]}$, so that $\gamma = \omega/v$, and the line is straight. We shall now show that the slope of the curve of Fig. 26, or $d\omega/d\gamma$, has a physical significance, as well as the slope of the chord ω/γ. The quantity ω/γ is called the "phase velocity"; to distinguish it, the quantity $d\omega/d\gamma$ is called the "group velocity." We shall now show that the group velocity has this significance: if we build up a superposition of waves of almost the same frequency, the resultant pattern will travel forward with the group velocity. We shall prove this result only for the superposition of two waves of nearly the same frequency, in which case the pattern they form is the familiar one of beats; but, since the group velocity is independent of the particular waves superposed, the result holds in general.

Let us superpose waves $e^{j[(\omega+\delta\omega)t-(\gamma+\delta\gamma)x]}$ and $e^{j[(\omega-\delta\omega)t-(\gamma-\delta\gamma)x]}$, having slightly different values of the angular frequency ω and propagation constant γ. The sum of the two waves is

$$e^{j(\omega t-\gamma x)}\left(e^{j[(\delta\omega)t-(\delta\gamma)x]} + e^{-j[(\delta\omega)t-(\delta\gamma)x]}\right)$$
$$= e^{j(\omega t-\gamma x)}2\cos\left[(\delta\omega)t - (\delta\gamma)x\right]. \quad (2.2)$$

The first term is a wave with the average frequency and propagation constant of the two superposed waves; it is multiplied by the factor $\cos\left[(\delta\omega)t - (\delta\gamma)x\right]$, which may be regarded as an amplitude, varying

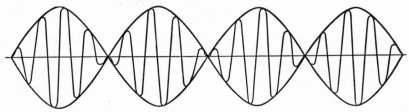

Fig. 28.—Beats between two sinusoidal oscillations.

slowly with time and position. Regarded as a function of x, at a fixed time, the real part of (2.2) has the form shown in Fig. 28. We should find a similar curve for the function as a function of time, at a fixed position x. This is the phenomenon known as "beats": the amplitude gradually decreases from a maximum (when the cosine function is unity) to zero, and back again.   The frequency of pulsation is 2 $\delta\omega$, or the difference between the frequencies of the two oscillations. When we now consider the variation of the beats in both space and time, we note that the cosine function stays constant when

$$x = \left(\frac{\delta\omega}{\delta\gamma}\right) t,$$

so that the beats travel forward with the velocity $\delta\omega/\delta\gamma$, which we have already defined as the group velocity.

We note from Fig. 26 that the group velocity, or slope of the curve, is less than the phase velocity, or slope of the chord.   The time variation of the beats, as in Fig. 28, is then as follows: the envelope of the oscillations moves forward with the group velocity, but the individual waves travel forward with the phase velocity, which is greater.   Thus the form of the disturbance changes as the time goes on.   This is an example of our statement that the only form of wave that travels without change of form, in a dispersive medium, is a sinusoidal wave.   The only case in which any type of wave can be propagated without change of form is in a medium in which the group velocity equals the phase velocity.   In such a medium, in the curve analogous to Fig. 26, the slope of the curve must equal the slope of its chord, which demands that the curve be a straight line, or that the velocity be independent of frequency; that is, it must be a medium without dispersion.

In our discussion so far of wave propagation in the weighted string, we have tacitly taken the case in which the frequency ω in Eq. (3.8) of Chap. VIII, or Eq. (2.1) of the present chapter, was small enough so that cos k was less numerically than unity.   The maximum such value is obviously $\omega = 2\sqrt{T/md}$, corresponding to the case where cos $k = -1$, $k = \pi$, so that the phase of the oscillation differs by π in going from one particle to the next, or so that the distance between particles is a half wave length.   If we tried to find the solution of our problem for a higher frequency, we should have to have cos k greater numerically than unity, and negative.   The meaning of this is simple: k must be a pure imaginary, plus π.   We may see this most easily from the equation

$$\cos(jk + \pi) = -\cos jk = -\cosh k.$$

For any real value of k, we see that cos jk, the cosine of a pure imaginary number, is real, and furthermore is greater than unity, since the hyperbolic cosine is greater than unity for all real values of its argument. Thus, in place of (3.8), Chap. VIII, we have

$$m\omega^2 = 2\frac{T}{d}(1 + \cosh k) \tag{2.3}$$

and in place of (3.7), Chap. VIII, expressing the displacement of the ith particle, we have

$$u_i = e^{ji(jk+\pi)} = e^{-ik}e^{\pi ji} = (-1)^i e^{-ik},$$

showing that the displacements decrease exponentially as we go along the string, and change sign from one weight to the next; an equally legitimate solution with the positive sign in the exponent would represent exponentially increasing displacements. In other words, for frequencies greater than the critical value, waves are not propagated along the weighted string, but instead we have an attenuated disturbance. We find, in other words, as we have mentioned earlier, that the weighted string acts like a low pass filter, allowing frequencies below a cutoff frequency to be propagated sinusoidally, but cutting off higher frequencies, in the sense that, if the string is long enough, no disturbance will be felt at the far end. The rate of attenuation is given by (2.3), solving for k in terms of ω.

3. Reflection and Standing Waves.—A sinusoidal wave, traveling along the $+x$ direction, may be written as the real part of $Ae^{j\omega(t-x/v)}$. A reflected wave, traveling along the $-x$ direction, may be written as the real part of $Be^{j\omega(t+x/v)}$. The simplest case of reflection is that in which the string is held at a certain point, as at $x = 0$, so that the displacement must always be zero at that point. In that case we must have $B = -A$, so that the total disturbance is

$$u = Ae^{j\omega t}(e^{-j\omega x/v} - e^{j\omega x/v}) = -2jAe^{j\omega t}\sin\omega\frac{x}{v} \tag{3.1}$$

whose real part is like the solution of Eq. (1.6), Chap. VIII. Thus the superposition of a direct wave, and a reflected wave with equal amplitude but opposite phase, produces a standing wave. This is the simplest case of reflection, but many more complicated cases exist. For instance, the string, instead of being held fast at a given point, may be held by a yielding support, which may have both inertia and friction. In this case there is still a reflected wave, but its phase will not be exactly opposite to that of the incident wave, so that the point of support will not be motionless, and its amplitude will be less than that of the incident wave, since some of the energy of the incident wave must be lost in the friction of the support, and only the remainder is left over for the reflected wave.

Another similar case is that in which there is a discontinuity in properties of the string at a given point; for instance, to the left of $x = 0$ we may have a light string, to the right of $x = 0$ a heavy string. A wave striking the discontinuity from the left will be partly transmitted to the string at the right, partly reflected, and the reflected wave will again have less energy and less amplitude than the incident wave, since part of the energy will appear in the transmitted wave.

Let us first consider reflection at a yielding support. We may visualize the support as an object held to a position of equilibrium by a force proportional to its displacement, and with a damping force proportional to its velocity. The string will then exert a sinusoidal applied force on this support, and will make it vibrate with simple harmonic motion, as in Chap. II. We shall find that the velocity v of the support will be related to the force $F_0 e^{j\omega t}$ acting on it by Eq. (3.4) of Chap. II,

$$ v = F_0 \frac{e^{j\omega t}}{Z} $$

where Z, the ratio of complex force to complex velocity, is analogous to the complex impedance in oscillating-circuit theory. The value of Z is a function of frequency, as we saw in Chap. II. Taking this description of the support, we may assume that the support imposes on the string the boundary condition that the force it exerts on the support, divided by the velocity of the support, is the predetermined Z. We may easily express this in analytical language. The force exerted by the string to the left of a given point, on the part to the right, has a vertical component, which we are considering, of $-T\, \partial u/\partial x$, as we saw in Chap. VIII, Sec. 1. The velocity has a vertical component $\partial u/\partial t = j\omega u$, for sinusoidal motion. Thus our boundary condition is

$$ Z = -T \frac{\partial u/\partial x}{\partial u/\partial t} = -T \frac{\partial u/\partial x}{j\omega u}, \qquad u = -\frac{T}{j\omega Z} \frac{\partial u}{\partial x}, \qquad (3.2) $$

where this condition is to be satisfied at the point of support. The case of a rigidly held support is $Z = \infty$, in which case no force, no matter how large, produces any displacement. With the finite pure imaginary impedance, there will be reflection with change of phase but no energy loss, whereas with a real or resistive component of the impedance there will be energy loss in the support.

Our problem is to find the amplitude and phase of the reflected wave, when an arbitrary incident wave strikes a yielding support. Let the disturbance be made up of arbitrary incident and reflected waves:

$$u = Ae^{j\omega(t-x/v)} + Be^{j\omega(t+x/v)}. \tag{3.3}$$

Then, substituting in (3.2), we have

$$-T\frac{\partial u/\partial x}{j\omega u} = \frac{T}{v}\frac{Ae^{-j\omega x/v} - Be^{j\omega x/v}}{Ae^{-j\omega x/v} + Be^{j\omega x/v}}. \tag{3.4}$$

We note first that, if there is no reflected wave, so that $B = 0$, the ratio is

$$Z_0 = \frac{T}{v} = \sqrt{\mu T}, \tag{3.5}$$

a constant value, called the "wave impedance"; in the derivation of (3.5) we have used the value of velocity from Eq. (1.5), Chap. VIII. Thus, if a string is terminated by a support whose resisting force is proportional to its velocity, with a constant of proportionality given by (3.5), there will be no reflected wave, and all the energy of the incident wave will flow into the support. In the general case, however, we must equate the value (3.4) to Z, the impedance of the support, putting in for x the position where the support is located. Equating these quantities, and solving, we find easily that

$$\frac{Be^{j\omega x/v}}{Ae^{-j\omega x/v}} = \frac{Z_0 - Z}{Z_0 + Z}. \tag{3.6}$$

If the support is located at $x = 0$, (3.6) gives directly the ratio B/A of reflected to incident complex amplitudes. As we pointed out earlier, we see that, if $Z = \infty$, $B = -A$, and that, if $Z = Z_0$, $B = 0$. Furthermore, we have the means of computing the value of B in any case. The quantity on the left of (3.6) is generally called the "complex reflection coefficient," and its magnitude, which as we shall show at once is related to the ratio of reflected to incident energies, is the "reflection coefficient."

The relation between reflection coefficient and energy comes at once from the fact that there is an energy flow in a wave, proportional to the square of the amplitude. The energy flow into the support is clearly the product of the force $-T\,\partial u/\partial x$ exerted on the support, and the velocity $\partial u/\partial t$ of the support. In computing this product, we must be careful to use the actual values of the force and velocity, not the complex quantities of which we are to use the real parts. To write the result explicitly, we write A and B in terms of their real and imaginary parts, in the form

$$A = A_r + jA_i, \qquad B = B_r + jB_i.$$

Furthermore, for simplicity, we compute the energy flow at the point $x = 0$. Then we have, taking the real part of (3.3),

$$u = A_r \cos \omega \left(t - \frac{x}{v} \right) - A_i \sin \omega \left(t - \frac{x}{v} \right) + B_r \cos \omega \left(t + \frac{x}{v} \right)$$
$$- B_i \sin \omega \left(t + \frac{x}{v} \right).$$

Taking x and t derivatives, and then setting $x = 0$, we have

$$-T \frac{\partial u}{\partial x} = Z_0 \omega \left[(-A_r + B_r) \sin \omega t - (A_i - B_i) \cos \omega t \right]$$
$$\frac{\partial u}{\partial t} = \omega[(-A_r - B_r) \sin \omega t - (A_i + B_i) \cos \omega t].$$

Multiplying, we have terms in $\sin^2 \omega t$, $\cos^2 \omega t$, and $\sin \omega t \cos \omega t$. Taking a time average over a cycle, the first two functions average to $\frac{1}{2}$, the last to zero. Averaging, then, the power flow P to the right across the point $x = 0$ is

$$P = \tfrac{1}{2} Z_0 \omega^2 (A_r^2 + A_i^2 - B_r^2 - B_i^2) = \tfrac{1}{2} Z_0 \omega^2 (|A|^2 - |B|^2).$$

This exhibits the flow as the difference between the flow to the right in the direct wave, and the flow to the left in the reflected wave, and shows that the energy flow in each wave is proportional to the square of the magnitude of its amplitude. Returning now to Eq. (3.6), we see that the square of the magnitude of the ratio B/A, or of

$$\frac{B}{A} e^{2j\omega x/v},$$

which of course has the same absolute magnitude, gives the ratio of reflected to incident intensity.

If a wave is reflected from a rigid support, so that we have a standing wave of the type of (3.1), with the amplitude proportional to $\sin \omega x/v$, there are nodes, at which the sine is zero, so that the amplitude is zero. In the more general case in which $|B|$ is less than $|A|$, this is no longer the case. The amplitude is proportional to

$$A e^{-j\omega x/v} + B e^{j\omega x/v}.$$

As we go along the string, the phases of the two terms vary with respect to each other. Regarding them as complex vectors in the complex plane, we see that with increasing x the first term rotates in the clockwise direction, the second in the counterclockwise direction. Twice every revolution the two vectors will be pointing in the same direction, so that their vector sum will have the magnitude $|A| + |B|$; intermediate between these values they will be pointing in the opposite directions, so that the magnitude of the sum will be $|A| - |B|$. Thus the amplitude of oscillation will go from a maximum to a minimum, and back to the maximum, but will never go through zero, or have a node. The points of maximum and minimum amplitude are called the "standing-wave maxima and minima"; we see that standing-wave minima are half a wave length apart, with the maxima in between. The ratio of amplitude at standing-wave maximum, to amplitude at standing-wave minimum, is called the "standing-wave ratio." It is clear that its value is

$$\text{Standing-wave ratio} = \frac{|A| + |B|}{|A| - |B|}.$$

For the case where $B = -A$, or a rigid support, the standing-wave ratio is infinite; for the case of no reflected wave, the standing wave ratio is unity. We can readily show that, for any case of a nonabsorbing termination (Z pure imaginary), the standing-wave ratio is infinite. It is clear with a little thought that, from measurement of the standing-wave ratio, and the position of standing-wave maximum or minimum, we can find the value of the terminal impedance Z which must terminate the line at a given x; the way of doing this is taken up in the problems. This suggests that measurement of standing waves may give a useful way of investigating the properties of the terminal impedance.

We have not yet considered the problem of a change in properties of a string. Let us suppose that for $x < 0$ we have a string with mass μ_1 per unit length, and for $x > 0$ a string with mass μ_2 per unit length. The corresponding velocities and wave impedances will be denoted v_1, v_2, and Z_1, Z_2. We now assume a direct wave in the first medium, approaching the point of separation from the left. We may assume that there will be a transmitted wave traveling to the right in the second medium, and a reflected wave traveling to the left in the first medium. Our problem is to find the reflection coefficient. This is easily done on the basis of the problem we have already solved. In the string to the right, there will be no reflected wave, so that we can apply (3.5), and find that the ratio of force to velocity is equal to Z_2, independent of position. Thus the right-hand string acts, as far as the left-hand string is concerned, like a support of impedance Z_2. We may then use (3.6) to find the ratio of reflected to incident ampli- tude in the left-hand string. Since the separation between the two comes at $x = 0$, we have

$$\frac{B}{A} = \frac{Z_1 - Z_2}{Z_1 + Z_2} = \frac{v_2 - v_1}{v_2 + v_1}.$$

It is not hard to find the amplitude of the wave in the second string, and to verify that that part of the incident energy which is not accounted for in the reflected wave all appears in the transmitted wave.

4. The General Case of the Terminated String.—We have seen in the preceding section that a wave approaching a termination or dis- continuity in a string will be partly reflected, partly transmitted. The transmission is possible only if there is some place for the energy to go: either frictional loss in the termination, or another string, which can carry the energy of the transmitted wave off to infinite distance. If there is no such place for the energy to be lost, all the energy will be reflected, but with a possible change of phase. Such a reflection can occur for a wave of any frequency. The situation is entirely changed if the string is held at two ends, or if it has two discontinuities, at each of which there is high reflection. If a string is rigidly held at two points, then we have the situation of the preceding chapter, in which it can vibrate only in certain normal modes, of definite fre- quency. For we have an additional condition to satisfy, the boundary condition at the second point where it is held, and we cannot satisfy our boundary conditions at both ends except for certain particular frequencies.

The more general case is that in which there are two discontinuities, rather than rigid supports, at two points in a string. For instance, suppose that for $x < 0$ there is a very heavy string of mass μ_1 per unit length; for $0 < x < L$ there is a much lighter string of mass μ_2 per unit length; and for $x > L$ we again have the heavy string of mass μ_1. If μ_1 were great enough, the heavy strings would act like rigid supports, and we should have the previous case, in which the light string could oscillate in certain normal modes, not communicating any energy to the supports. With a finite μ_1, however, if we set up an oscillation of the light parts of the string only, we should find that there was a reflection coefficient less than unity at the boundaries between the light and heavy string, so that there would be transmitted waves in each part of the heavy string, and the energy would gradually dissipate, traveling to infinite distances in the heavy string. Thus we should not have any normal modes, in the sense of oscillations that could persist forever. Normal modes can exist only in the presence of perfectly reflecting boundaries, which keep the energy in. In our case, we should have instead something much like a wave of amplitude decreasing exponentially with time, in the light segment of string, and we could compute a Q representing the rate of damping, which would become greater as the reflection coefficient at the discontinuities became closer to unity.

Quite a different type of solution of the same problem is obtained if a direct wave approaches the light string through the heavy string. Suppose, for instance, that a direct wave approaches the point $x = 0$ from the left, traveling to the right. There will be a reflected wave in the heavy string, for $x < 0$. Similarly, in the light string, there will be both a direct and a reflected wave. Finally in the heavy string at $x > L$ there will be only a direct wave. We can find the amplitude of these various waves, by the use of the impedance methods described in Sec. 3, or merely by the straightforward method of demanding that the displacement and slope of the curve be continuous at each of the discontinuities of density. We then find that the light string shows many properties of resonance, acting much like a resonant system with damping (coming from the energy loss in the two waves traveling out of the light string into the heavy strings at each end of it) and an external force (the direct or incident wave). The input impedance at $x = 0$, which the incident wave sees when it enters the light string, can be shown to be a sum of resonance terms, one for each of the normal modes which the light string would have if it were rigidly held, but each with appropriate Q's coming from the losses in the waves in the heavy string.

These properties of the solution are somewhat involved, but important, because of their application not only to the string, but also to other problems in physics. The same sort of thing is encountered in electrical transmission lines, in microwave transmission lines, and in reflection of electromagnetic and acoustic waves in two and three dimensions, which show very close resemblance to the waves on a string. We find analogies even in wave mechanics, where the motion of electrons and nuclear particles is governed by Schrödinger's equation. This equation shows similar properties of resonance. For instance, a nuclear particle can sometimes exist within the nucleus in what is called a "metastable state." Its wave equation corresponds to a wave within the nucleus which has a reflection coefficient very nearly, but not quite, equal to unity at the boundary of the nucleus. Thus the wave will gradually leak out, corresponding to a gradually increasing probability that the particle will be found outside the nucleus, and yielding a suggestive theory of radioactive decay. The real situation of nuclear disintegration is much more complicated than this simple picture would indicate, but this is enough to show that this type of theory can be applied to problems far more general than the vibrating string.

All the terminations of the string that we have so far mentioned absorb energy from the string, rather than delivering energy to it. It is clear that we can hold an end of a string by a device that makes it vibrate sinusoidally, setting it into oscillation. In such a case, energy will flow out of the device into the string. It is in this way that the direct wave, which we have been discussing in our problems of reflection, must be set up. At a junction between a power source and a string, acting as a load, we must have a match of impedance, just as we have had in Sec. 3 between a length of string and a load impedance. A power source can generally deliver power at any arbitrary impedance, within limits; but generally the impedance is a function of the amplitude of oscillation, and often the frequency, of the source. The load impedance then determines the amplitude and frequency of operation of the power source. The interplay of power source and vibrating string gets particularly complicated if the frequency is near a resonance frequency of the string, in which case the amplitude of oscillation becomes large, and the reaction on the power source considerable. These interactions are similar to those found in other branches of physics, as for instance in vacuum-tube oscillators operating into resonant circuits, in which a change in the circuit parameters can react back on the operation of the vacuum-tube oscillator.

Problems

1. A string of length L is pulled aside at a point a distance D from the end, and then released, as in Prob. 3, Chap. VIII. Find its subsequent motion by the methods of the present chapter.

2. A string initially at rest is struck at a distance D from the end, at $t = 0$, as in Prob. 5, Chap. VIII. Find its subsequent motion by the methods of the present chapter.

3. Find the group velocity of a disturbance on a weighted string, for which the phase velocity is given by (2.1).

4. Electromagnetic radiation can be propagated down the interior of cylindrical conducting pipes, called "wave guides." If λ_0 is the wave length of a wave in free space, given by the relation $\lambda_0 = cT$, where c is the velocity of light in free space, T the period of oscillation, and if λ_g is the wave length of the disturbance as measured along the guide (called the "guide wave length"), then it can be shown that $1/\lambda_g^2 = 1/\lambda_0^2 - 1/\lambda_c^2$, where λ_c is a constant called the "cutoff wave length." Find the phase velocity of the wave corresponding to a given angular frequency ω. Show that, if the frequency is less than a certain cutoff frequency, the phase velocity becomes imaginary, corresponding to a damped disturbance rather than a propagated wave, and find the relation of this cutoff frequency to λ_c.

5. For the wave guide of Prob. 4, find the group velocity. Show that, though the phase velocity found in Prob. 4 is greater than c, the group velocity is less than c, so that a signal cannot be transmitted down the guide with a velocity greater than c. This is an example of the general principle, from the theory of relativity, that no signal can be propagated with velocity greater than c.

6. An artificial electric line can be constructed according to Fig. 29, consisting of N identical resistanceless circuits, each containing inductance L, capacitance C, and coupled to each of its neighbors with mutual inductance M. Set up the differential equations for the currents i in the various circuits, showing that they reduce to the same form as with the weighted string.

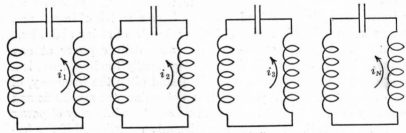

Fig. 29.—Artificial electric line.

7. Neglecting boundary conditions at the two ends of the line in Prob. 6, show that a disturbance can be propagated along the line with a definite phase velocity. Find also the group velocity. Investigate to see whether there are certain ranges of frequency for which the line attenuates a disturbance exponentially, instead of propagating it.

8. A mass M is suspended by a weightless string of length L, forming a pendulum. Vertically below the mass, and attached to it, is a stretched string of tension T, mass μ per unit length. A wave of angular frequency ω is propagated up the lower string, and is reflected from the mass M, regarded as the termination of the string. Find the amplitude of oscillation of M, as a function of frequency.

9. Solve the same problem as in Prob. 8, but with the addition of a resisting force acting on the mass M, proportional to its velocity. Find the standing-wave ratio, and the fraction of incident power absorbed in the pendulum, as a function of frequency.

10. In an infinite string of mass μ per unit length there is inserted a section of length L, which has a mass μ_1 per unit length different from μ. An incident wave from the left approaches the inserted section, being partly reflected, partly transmitted. Similarly in the inserted section there are transmitted and reflected disturbances, and in the string to the right of the insert there is only a direct wave. By assuming all these waves, and satisfying conditions of continuity at the boundaries, find the intensities of reflected and transmitted waves, showing that there are maxima of transmission when the wave length of the disturbance in the insert bears certain definite relationships to L. This problem is a close analogue to the transmission of light through a thin film, or the transmission of microwaves through a resonant cavity.

11. Consider a string fixed at both ends, $x = 0$ and $x = L$, under tension T. The string is composed of two parts, one of mass μ_1 per unit length, extending from $x = 0$ to $x = L/3$, and the other of mass μ_2 per unit length, extending from $x = L/3$ to $x = L$. Find the resonant frequencies of the motion. You will not be able to get an explicit solution.

12. Show how, by measuring the standing-wave ratio and position of the standing-wave minima in a string, the terminal impedance can be found.

CHAPTER X

THE STRING WITH VARIABLE TENSION AND DENSITY

In the last two chapters, we have considered the problem of the vibration of a string of constant density and uniform tension. These results may now be extended to the more general case of variable tension and density. We shall not be able to carry through the results in complete detail, for as we shall see, we are led to a more complicated differential equation, which we cannot solve in general. But we shall find that the theory of expansion in orthogonal functions, and all the general relations, go through just as with the uniform string, so that we can derive a good deal of information. We shall also develop perturbation methods, which can be used when the tension and density have only small deviations from constancy.

The importance of the problems considered in this chapter arises more from what they suggest than from the specific problems considered. Strings of variable density are of small practical importance. But the string is the simplest case of a vibrating continuum. Waves in three dimensions resemble waves on a string. A string of variable density resembles an optical medium of variable index of refraction, and we can use methods similar to those of this chapter in such cases as the theory of the mirage, and of the bending of radio waves in the charged layers of the upper atmosphere. Many three-dimensional problems can actually be reduced to one-dimensional cases, and they are all likely then to take on just the character of our problem of the string of variable density. In wave mechanics, for instance, most of our problems reduce to a mathematical form that is identical with that of the present chapter. The perturbation theory we develop in this chapter is one set up originally for use with variable strings, yet it has had most important effects in the development of the quantum theory.

1. Differential Equation for the Variable String.—We set up the differential equation of motion essentially as we have done in Chap. VIII. We assume, however, that the tension T and the mass per unit length μ vary from point to point along the string. Clearly, if the tension varied with x, there would be a longitudinal force,

180

along x, acting on elements of the string, unless there were compensating body forces. We shall assume such body forces, so that we still need consider only the displacement at right angles to the string. A simple example of this is a heavy string hanging vertically under the action of gravity. The tension will be partly supplied by the weight of the string itself, and since the upper part of the string must support the bottom part, it is clear that the tension will increase with the height, and yet that the string will be in equilibrium as far as longitudinal motion is concerned.

We may now retrace the arguments of Chap. VIII, Sec. 1, and see in what way the situation is different if T and μ are functions of x. The only difference comes in the derivation of Eq. (1.1) of that chapter, in which we have

$$T \frac{\partial u}{\partial x}\bigg|_{x+dx} - T \frac{\partial u}{\partial x}\bigg|_{x} = \frac{\partial}{\partial x}\left(T \frac{\partial u}{\partial x}\right) dx.$$

The equation of motion then becomes

$$\frac{\partial}{\partial x}\left(T \frac{\partial u}{\partial x}\right) = \mu \frac{\partial^2 u}{\partial t^2}.$$

If we assume a solution sinusoidal in time, u varying as $e^{i\omega t}$ times a function of x, we then have

$$\frac{d}{dx}\left(T \frac{du}{dx}\right) + \omega^2 \mu u = 0, \tag{1.1}$$

where this u is a function of x, as are T and μ.

This equation is a linear second order differential equation with variable coefficients, on account of the functions T and μ, which depend on x. There is no general method of solution of such an equation. In many practical cases the power series method can be used, as described in Appendix II. For this purpose T and μ must be expressed as power series in x. There are a number of well-known examples of (1.1), whose solutions, obtained by the power-series method, are well-known functions, and some of these form the solutions to problems of practical importance. For instance, Bessel's equation is

$$\frac{1}{x}\frac{d}{dx}\left(x \frac{du}{dx}\right) + \left(1 - \frac{m^2}{x^2}\right) u = 0, \qquad \frac{d}{dx}\left(x \frac{du}{dx}\right) + \left(x - \frac{m^2}{x}\right) u = 0,$$

whose solution is $u = J_m(x)$, and by comparison with (1.1), it represents the disturbance of a string whose tension is proportional to x, and whose density is proportional to $x - $ constant$/x$. Other problems

reducible to Bessel's equation, the equation of the Legendre polynomials, and other simple equations, are discussed in the problems.

One problem that can be solved immediately by very simple methods is that of the exponential string, in which both the tension and
density increase with x according to the exponential functions

$$T = T_0\, e^{\alpha x}, \qquad \mu = \mu_0\, e^{\alpha x}.$$

Although this problem is not of great practical importance, it is useful
to be able to get an exact solution for such a problem of variable
tension and density, so as to be able to understand the general nature
of the solution. We find easily that in such a case we can solve (1.1)
by assuming that u has an exponential form,

$$u = e^{\gamma x}. \tag{1.2}$$

Substituting (1.2) in (1.1), we find that the exponentials cancel, leaving
the equation

$$T_0\, \gamma(\alpha + \gamma) + \omega^2 \mu_0 = 0.$$

This is a quadratic for γ, whose solutions are

$$\gamma = -\frac{\alpha}{2} \pm \sqrt{-\omega^2\, \frac{\mu_0}{T_0} + \left(\frac{\alpha}{2}\right)^2}. \tag{1.3}$$

We note that when α is zero, this reduces properly to the solution

$$u = e^{\pm j\omega \sqrt{\mu_0/T_0}\, x}$$

which we found for the uniform string in Eq. (1.4), Chap. VIII.
When α is different from zero, but small, two changes are observed
in comparison to the uniform string. First, the amplitude decreases
with increasing x, according to the exponential $e^{-(\alpha/2)x}$, the amplitude
being less in the region where the tension and density are large.
Secondly, there is a second order change in the effective velocity and
wave length, which are now given by

$$v = \frac{v_0}{\sqrt{1 - (\alpha v_0/2\omega)^2}}, \qquad \lambda = \frac{\lambda_0}{\sqrt{1 - (\alpha v_0/2\omega)^2}}, \tag{1.4}$$

where

$$v_0 = \sqrt{\frac{T_0}{\mu_0}}, \qquad \lambda_0 = \frac{2\pi}{\omega}\, v_0,$$

in which the radical containing the term in α is missing for the uniform
string. We can find the order of magnitude of this second order
term by noting that $\alpha = (1/T)\, dT/dx$, or the relative rate of change

of tension with distance, and by assuming that the second order term is small enough so that approximately we can write the wave length from the first term of the second equation of (1.4). Then we have approximately

$$\frac{\alpha v_0}{2\omega} = \frac{1}{4\pi} \frac{\lambda}{T} \frac{dT}{dx},$$ (1.5)

which means that this quantity equals approximately the proportional change of tension in $(1/4\pi)$ wave lengths. If this is small enough so that its square can be neglected, the velocity and wave length are unaffected by the variations of tension and density with position, and we can determine the velocity by the equation

$$v = \sqrt{\frac{T}{\mu}} = \sqrt{\frac{T_0}{\mu_0}},$$

the velocity being found from the tension and density at a particular point of the string, which we note is independent of position. With more rapid variation of properties with position, however, we must use the quadratic terms in (1.4), and finally with a sufficiently rapid variation the radical in (1.3) and (1.4) can vanish and then become imaginary, resulting in an exponential decay of the disturbance along the string, with no real propagation at all. We note that, for any fixed value of α, this will happen for a sufficiently low frequency, so that the exponential string propagates only above a certain cutoff frequency, and forms in effect a high pass filter. The lower the value of α, however, the lower is the cutoff frequency.

2. Approximate Solution for Slowly Changing Density and Tension. In the example of the exponential string, which we just took up, we found that the solution approaches a simple limiting case if the tension and density vary slowly with position, or in particular if the quantities $(1/4\pi)(\lambda/T)(dT/dx)$ and $(1/4\pi)(\lambda/\mu)(d\mu/dx)$ are small compared with unity. We shall now show that quite generally, if these conditions are satisfied, we can get an approximate solution of the equation (1.1), correct to the first order of these small quantities. This solution has been found by many workers in different fields of mathematical physics, as for instance in the propagation of seismic waves in the earth, where the elasticity and density of the earth vary with depth; the propagation of electromagnetic waves in the upper atmosphere, where the index of refraction varies with height on account of the ionization in the Kennelly-Heaviside layer; and in wave mechanics, where we often encounter the problem of Schrödinger's equation in cases where the velocity of the electron wave varies slowly with position. In wave mechanics, it is often known as the W-K-B method, after the initials of Wentzel, Kramers, and Brillouin, who independently have made use of it. From this wide list of cases in which it applies, it is clear that it is a method of great power.

The effect of variable tension and density comes into the solution in two ways: the wave length, and the amplitude, depend on x. In our exponential string of the preceding section we had the special case where only the amplitude depended on x, the wave length being independent of x, but that was a special case. Thus, instead of $A e^{\pm j\omega \sqrt{\mu/T} \, x}$, which we have for the uniform string, the actual solution for the function of x can at least approximately be written in the form $u = A(x)e^{\pm jB(x)}$. We can easily see the form that B must have for the nonuniform string. For plainly $[B(x_2) - B(x_1)]/2\pi$ must measure the number of wave lengths between x_1 and x_2, because of the way in which B appears in the exponential function. But if λ is the wave length, regarded as a function of x, dx/λ is just the number of wave lengths in distance dx, so that the total number between x_1 and x_2 is $\int_{x_1}^{x_2} dx/\lambda$, from which evidently $B(x) = 2\pi \int dx/\lambda$. Since the wave length can presumably be written $2\pi/\lambda = \omega \sqrt{\mu/T}$, this is equivalent to

$$B(x) = \omega \int \sqrt{\frac{\mu}{T}} \, dx.$$

We shall now show that, if we set $A = \text{constant}/\sqrt[4]{\mu T}$, the resulting expression

$$A(x)e^{\pm jB(x)} = \frac{\text{constant}}{\sqrt[4]{\mu T}} \, e^{\pm j\omega \int \sqrt{\mu/T} \, dx} \qquad (2.1)$$

forms an approximate solution of the differential equation. Comparison with the solution of the exponential string in Sec. 1 shows that the amplitude factor $1/\sqrt[4]{\mu T}$ of (2.1) agrees with the factor $e^{-(\alpha/2)x}$ which we found there, whereas the phase factor of (2.1) is the approximation to the value of Sec. 1 which we find when we neglect the second order correction, or the square of the quantity (1.5).

To prove the correctness of Eq. (2.1), and to investigate the order of magnitude of its errors, we may substitute the function on the right side of (2.1) in the differential equation (1.1), and collect terms. All terms in the first order of the small quantities $(\lambda/T)(dT/dx)$ and $(\lambda/\mu)(d\mu/dx)$, or $\lambda \, d \ln T/dx$ and $\lambda \, d \ln \mu/dx$, as well as terms not involving these quantities, cancel, leaving only terms in squares and products of these small quantities, and terms in $\lambda^2\, d^2 \ln T/dx^2$ and $\lambda^2\, d^2 \ln \mu/dx^2$. These, being rates of change of small quantities, may be assumed to be small of the second order, like the squares and products. Thus we verify our statement that (2.1) is a solution correct to the first order.

If we are not satisfied with this treatment, which assumes the form of the solution and verifies it, we may proceed straightforwardly to find the functions A and B of (2.1). We substitute the function on the left side of (2.1) into the differential equation, separate real and imaginary parts (remembering that A and B are real), and find that we can separate the result into equations for A and B. These are differential equations of a complicated, nonlinear type, but when we examine the order of magnitude of the terms, and reject those which are small of the second order, the remaining differential equations can be solved, and prove to give the function on the right side of (2.1). This treatment, though straightforward, is somewhat involved. It is easy to carry part of it through. Thus if we assume that $B(x) = \omega \int \sqrt{\mu/T}\, dx$, as in (2.1), but regard the function $A(x)$ as one to be determined, and substitute the function $A(x)e^{\pm j\omega \int \sqrt{\mu/T}\, dx}$ in the differential equation, we obtain a differential equation for A, which may be written, after a little manipulation,

$$\lambda^2\left(\frac{1}{A}\frac{d^2A}{dx^2} + \frac{1}{T}\frac{dT}{dx}\frac{1}{A}\frac{dA}{dx}\right) + 4\pi j\lambda\left[\frac{1}{A}\frac{dA}{dx}\right.$$
$$\left. + \frac{1}{4}\left(\frac{1}{T}\frac{dT}{dx} + \frac{1}{\mu}\frac{d\mu}{dx}\right)\right] = 0, \quad (2.2)$$

where $\lambda = (2\pi/\omega)\sqrt{T/\mu}$. We assume that A, like T and μ, changes by only a small fraction of itself in a wave length. Thus the terms in λ^2 are of the order that we are neglecting, and we are left with the terms in λ. These terms may be rewritten in the form

$$\frac{d\ln[A(\mu T)^{1/4}]}{dx} = 0, \qquad A(\mu T)^{1/4} = \text{constant},$$

leading to the solution (2.1) which we wished to prove.

3. The Normal Modes of the String.—The approximate solution (2.1) which we have set up for the string of variable tension and density represents a traveling wave. We may, however, build up from it easily a solution holding for a string held at two points, as $x = 0$ and $x = L$. If the string is held at $x = 0$, we must have in place of (2.1) the function

$$u = \frac{\text{constant}}{\sqrt[4]{\mu T}} \sin \omega \int_0^x \sqrt{\frac{\mu}{T}} \, dx.$$

If furthermore the string is held at $x = L$, we must have the sine function equal to zero at this point, or

$$\omega \int_0^L \sqrt{\frac{\mu}{T}} \, dx = n\pi, \qquad \omega = \frac{n\pi}{\int_0^L \sqrt{\mu/T} \, dx}$$

where n is an integer. The resulting value of ω may be denoted by ω_n. We have, in other words, a set of normal modes, as with the uniform string. This suggests that we should be able to follow the general procedure of Chap. VIII, setting up normal coordinates, and expressing the general solution of the problem of the oscillating string in terms of normal modes. We shall not carry through a complete discussion of the present case, but a study of Chap. VIII will show that the main results were a consequence of the orthogonality of the normal functions of the string. We shall show that even for the string with variable tension and density we have the same orthogonality of normal functions. As a result, it is possible to carry through for the present case a treatment completely analogous to that of Chap. VIII.

To prove the orthogonality of the normal functions, we do not have to use our approximate solution of Sec. 2 at all; we can prove the result directly from the differential equation (1.1). Let us consider two normal functions u_n and u_m, which are solutions of the differential equation, associated with angular frequencies ω_n and ω_m. We then have the identities

$$\frac{d}{dx}\left(T \frac{du_n}{dx}\right) + \omega_n^2 \mu u_n = 0,$$

$$\frac{d}{dx}\left(T \frac{du_m}{dx}\right) + \omega_m^2 \mu u_m = 0.$$

We multiply the first equation by u_m, the second by u_n, subtract one from the other, and then integrate over the string. We thus obtain

$$\int_0^L \left[u_m \frac{d}{dx}\left(T \frac{du_n}{dx}\right) - u_n \frac{d}{dx}\left(T \frac{du_m}{dx}\right) \right] dx$$

$$= (\omega_m^2 - \omega_n^2) \int_0^L \mu(x) u_n u_m \, dx. \quad (3.1)$$

The left side integrated by parts yields immediately

$$\left[T\left(u_m \frac{du_n}{dx} - u_n \frac{du_m}{dx} \right) \right]\Big|_0^L - \int_0^L T\left(\frac{du_n}{dx}\frac{du_m}{dx} - \frac{du_m}{dx}\frac{du_n}{dx} \right) dx.$$

The integral obviously vanishes, and the integrated part vanishes since both u_n and u_m are zero for $x = 0$ and $x = L$. In general the integrated part would vanish if either u or du/dx vanished at the boundaries. Thus the right side of (3.1) yields as the analogue of our former orthogonality relation

$$\int_0^L \mu(x)u_n u_m \, dx = 0 \qquad \text{if } n \neq m. \quad (3.2)$$

When $n = m$, (3.1) does not demand that the integral vanish, since the factor $\omega_m^2 - \omega_n^2$ is zero. We shall assume the functions to be normalized so that

$$\int_0^L \mu(x)u_n^2 \, dx = 1. \quad (3.3)$$

The occurrence of the mass per unit length, $\mu(x)$, in the orthogonality condition (3.2), is equivalent to the occurrence of the mass m_i in the corresponding condition (2.10) of Chap. VII, where we were considering the orthogonality of normal modes for the vibrations of mass points. We could omit this factor in our treatment of the uniform string, where we wrote the orthogonality condition (2.2) of Chap. VIII, since the quantity μ was a constant independent of x.

Having proved the orthogonality and normalization relations (3.2) and (3.3), we can use these to discuss the general vibrations of the string held at $x = 0$ and $x = L$. We may write the general solution for the oscillation of the string in the form

$$u = \sum_n (A_n \cos \omega_n t + B_n \sin \omega_n t)u_n(x).$$

If the initial shape and velocity of the string at $t = 0$ are given by functions $u_0(x)$, $\dot{u}_0(x)$, as in Chap. VIII, Sec. 2, we must have

$$u_0(x) = \sum_n A_n u_n, \qquad \dot{u}_0(x) = \sum_n \omega_n B_n u_n. \quad (3.4)$$

We then have the general problem of expanding an arbitrary function in a series of normal functions, very much like our problem of Chap. VIII of expanding an arbitrary function in Fourier series. We shall show how to find the coefficients of such an expansion; the remainder of the problem, showing that the series so built up really represents

the function and that it converges, is much more difficult, and we shall
not take it up here. To find the coefficients, let us multiply each of
Eqs. (3.4) on both sides by $\mu(x)u_m(x)$, and integrate from $x = 0$ to
$x = L$. We thus have

$$\int_0^L \mu(x)u_m(x)u_0(x)\ dx = \sum_n A_n \int_0^L \mu(x)u_nu_m\ dx = A_m,$$

$$\int_0^L \mu(x)u_m(x)\dot{u}_0(x)\ dx = \sum_n \omega_n B_n \int_0^L \mu(x)u_nu_m\ dx = \omega_m B_m.$$

It is clear that our discussion of Fourier expansion, and of the uniform
string, is a special case of the general one discussed here. The differential equation of the nonuniform string, (1.1), is of a general type
called a "Sturm-Liouville equation," which includes many of the
important differential equations of mathematical physics. All equations of this general type show orthogonality properties of the sort
we have discussed. Many other interesting properties of the solutions can be deduced directly from the differential equation, including
theorems relating to the zeros of the solutions, or the nodes of the
standing waves represented by the solutions. Fourier expansion, and
the trigonometric functions, form the simplest and most familiar
example of these general methods.

4. Perturbation Theory.—One approximate method of integrating
the differential equation of the nonuniform vibrating string has
already been indicated in Sec. 2, making use of the resemblance of the
actual functions to sines and cosines. An entirely different approximate method, the method of perturbations, is also frequently useful.
This is a method that applies if the problem is very nearly a soluble
one, the density and tension varying only slightly from their values
in the soluble case. The usual application is to an almost uniform
string. For simplicity we consider only the case where the tension T
is a constant, while the density is a function $\mu(x)$, almost equal to a
function $\mu_0(x)$ for which the problem can be solved exactly. We
assume that we know the characteristic functions u_n^0 and frequencies
ω_n^0 for the soluble case, satisfying therefore the differential equations

$$T\frac{d^2u_n^0}{dx^2} + \omega_n^{0\,2}\mu_0(x)u_n^0 = 0. \tag{4.1}$$

We now remember that the functions u_n^0 form an orthogonal set, and
that any arbitrary functions can be expanded in series of such functions. Thus in particular the nth characteristic function u_n of the

real problem can be so expanded:

$$u_n = \sum_k A_{nk} u_k^0.$$

We may regard our problem as that of determining the constants A_{nk}. Considered in function space, as discussed in Sec. 4, Chap. VIII, this problem is very simple. The functions u_k^0 form one set of orthogonal unit vectors, the u_n's another, and these equations merely express one set in terms of the other; they are the equations for a rotation of coordinates in function space, from the axes characteristic of the "unperturbed" problem with density μ_0 to the "perturbed" problem with density μ.

The easiest way of getting at the conditions for rotation is simply to substitute u_n in the differential equation that we wish it to satisfy,

$$T \frac{d^2 u_n}{dx^2} + \omega_n^2 \mu u_n = 0.$$

If we do so, and use the differential equation (4.1) which the u_n^0's satisfy, we have easily

$$\sum_k A_{nk}(\omega_k^{02}\mu_0 - \omega_n^2\mu)u_k^0 = 0.$$

Now we may multiply by an arbitrary u_m^0, and integrate from 0 to L. Remembering that the u_0's are orthogonal and normalized, the result is

$$\sum_k A_{nk}(\omega_k^{02}\mu_{mk}^0 - \omega_n^2\mu_{mk}) = 0$$

where

$$\mu_{mk}^0 = \int_0^L \mu_0(x)u_m^0 u_k^0\, dx = \delta_{mk}$$

and

$$\mu_{mk} = \int_0^L \mu(x)u_m^0 u_k^0\, dx,$$

which is a quantity differing from μ_{mk}^0 only by small quantities of the order of the deviation between μ and μ_0. We have here an infinite set of simultaneous homogeneous linear equations (m can take on any value) for the unknown constants A_{nk}. These can be written, for a given n,

$$A_{n1}(\omega_1^{02} - \omega_n^2\mu_{11}) + A_{n2}(-\omega_n^2\mu_{12}) + A_{n3}(-\omega_n^2\mu_{13}) + \cdots = 0$$
$$A_{n1}(-\omega_n^2\mu_{21}) + A_{n2}(\omega_2^{02} - \omega_n^2\mu_{22}) + \cdots\cdots\cdots\cdots = 0$$
$$A_{n1}(-\omega_n^2\mu_{31}) + \cdots\cdots\cdots\cdots\cdots\cdots\cdots = 0$$
$$\cdots\cdots\cdots\cdots\cdots\cdots\cdots\cdots\cdots\cdots\cdots$$

These equations are of the type we have already met in Eq. (3.3) of Chap. V in discussing principal axes of inertia, and in Eq. (2.2) of Chap. VII in discussing the introduction of normal coordinates, and which are discussed in Appendix V. As in all such cases, the equations in general have no solutions, unless the determinant of coefficients vanishes, which provides an equation for ω_n^2, a secular equation determining the frequencies. In the present case, this equation has an infinite number of roots, one near each unperturbed frequency.

It is hardly feasible to solve the secular equation directly, though it is not hard to make an approximation to it. It is easiest, however, to proceed directly from the linear equations. If the u^0's are nearly the same as the u's, it is plain that we shall have $A_{nk} = 1$ almost, if $n = k$, or $= 0$ almost, if $n \neq k$. The only term in the equations that is large and need be considered is then that for which $n = k$ (so that A_{nk} will be large) and simultaneously $m = k$ (so that μ_{mk}^0 and μ_{mk} will be large). This term gives

$$A_{nn}(\omega_n^{02} - \omega_n^2 \mu_{nn}) = 0, \qquad \text{or} \qquad \omega_n^2 = \frac{\omega_n^{02}}{\mu_{nn}}.$$

If now $\mu = \mu_0 + \mu_1$, where μ_1 is small compared with μ_0, we have $\mu_{nn} = 1 + \int_0^L \mu_1 u_n^{02}\, dx$, so that, using the first term of a binomial expansion,

$$\omega_n^2 = \omega_n^{02} \left(1 - \int_0^L \mu_1 u_n^{02}\, dx\right), \tag{4.2}$$

correct to the first order of small quantities, but neglecting terms to the order of the square of the integral of μ_1. It is not hard to get expressions of the same order of accuracy for the A's. From (4.2), we see that the effect of a change in mass, on the frequency of vibration, is a maximum if it comes at a maximum of amplitude of the unperturbed motion, and is zero if it comes at a node.

Problems

1. A heavy uniform flexible chain hangs freely from one end. The chain performs small lateral vibrations. Show that the normal functions are $u_n = J_0[(2\omega_n/\sqrt{g})\sqrt{x}]$, where J_0 represents Bessel's function of order zero, x is the distance from the bottom of the chain to any point, g the acceleration of gravity, and ω_n is the angular frequency of the nth mode of vibration. For a chain 8 ft long, find the periods of the first few modes of vibration. (Use Jahnke and Emde's tables to get the roots of the Bessel functions.)

2. One end of a uniform flexible chain of length L is attached to a vertical rod that rotates at a constant angular velocity Ω_0. Neglect the effect of gravity, so that the chain stands out horizontally under the tension of centrifugal force. Show that the differential equation for small vibrations transverse to the length of the chain is

$$\frac{\Omega_0^2}{2}\frac{d}{dx}\left[(L^2 - x^2)\frac{du}{dx}\right] + \omega^2 u = 0.$$

Introduce the variable $y = x/L$, and solve the resulting equation by the power series method. The boundary conditions are $u(0) = 0$ and u for $y = 1$ must remain finite. Note that the latter condition can be fulfilled only if the series breaks off to form a polynomial. Calculate the first three polynomials, and derive a relation for the frequency of the nth mode of vibration. The polynomials so found are the Legendre polynomials of odd order.

3. A string stretched with a uniform tension T, and with a density α/x^2, is held at the points $x = x_1$ and $x = x_2$. Solve the equation, using the form $u = x^n$, and show that the general solution is

$$u = Ax^{\frac{1}{2}+jk} + Bx^{\frac{1}{2}-jk},$$

where $j = \sqrt{-1}$, and where k is defined by $k^2 + \frac{1}{4} = \omega^2\alpha/T$, and ω is the angular velocity. Show from this that the general form of the normal function is

$$u_n = \sqrt{x}\sin\frac{n\pi\ln(x/x_1)}{\ln(x_2/x_1)}, \qquad n = 1, 2, 3, \cdots$$

and that

$$\omega_n^2 = \frac{T}{\alpha}\left[\frac{1}{4} + \frac{n^2\pi^2}{(\ln x_2/x_1)^2}\right].$$

4. Solve the differential equation of Prob. 3 by the approximate method described in this chapter, and show that the solution has the same form as the exact solution. Show that the two solutions coincide in the limit of large n.

5. A progressive wave travels on a uniform string which at $x = 0$ is connected to a string whose density is $\mu = \mu^0 + \alpha x$. This second string is connected to a third at $x = L$ which has the constant density $\mu = \mu_0 + \alpha L$, and the whole is stretched with a uniform tension T. Using the approximate method, find the ratio of the amplitude of the wave transmitted in the third string to the original amplitude of the incident wave in the first string.

6. Consider a string of uniform density μ, length L, but with a tension T which varies slightly from its average tension T_0. Show with the help of a perturbation calculation that the angular frequency of the nth mode is given approximately by

$$\omega_n^2 = \frac{n^2\pi^2}{L^2}\frac{T_0}{\mu}\left(1 - \frac{1}{n\pi T_0}\int_0^L \frac{dT}{dx}\cos\frac{n\pi x}{L}\sin\frac{n\pi x}{L}\,dx\right).$$

7. A uniform string of density μ_0, tension T, has a small load m placed at $x = a$. Show that the frequency of the nth mode of vibration is approximately given by

$$\omega_n^2 = \frac{n^2\pi^2}{L^2}\frac{T}{\mu_0}\left(1 - \frac{2m}{\mu_0 L}\sin^2\frac{n\pi a}{L}\right).$$

Show that the effect of the additional load vanishes if it is placed at a node, and is biggest when at an antinode.

8. Show that the differential equation of Bessel's function J_m is the same as that for a string of tension $T = x$, $\mu\omega^2 = x - m^2/x$. Using the approximate method developed for the vibration problem, show that approximately

$$J_m(x) = \frac{\text{constant}}{\sqrt[4]{x^2 - m^2}} \cos \left(\int \sqrt{1 - \frac{m^2}{x^2}}\, dx - \alpha \right)$$

where $x > m$.

9. Using the approximation of Prob. 8 for J_0 and J_1, compute the approximation functions for a number of values of x, and show by a table of values how well these agree with the correct functions. Choose the arbitrary amplitude and phase factors to make the functions agree with the values of J_0 and J_1 in the tables, for example, making the zeros agree by adjusting α, and the maxima by adjusting the amplitude, taking such values as to get the best agreement possible for large x's.

10. Derive the differential equation (2.2) for A, in the approximate solution $u = Ae^{\pm j\omega \int \sqrt{\mu/T}\, dx}$.

CHAPTER XI

THE VIBRATING MEMBRANE

A membrane, such as a drumhead, can vibrate transversely, much as a string can. In many respects the problem of these vibrations is little more difficult than that of the string. The differential equation of motion is derived in an analogous way, and is more complicated only in that it includes terms for both the x and y coordinates in the plane of the membrane, similar to the single term in x which is met in the problem of the string. The complications come in, however, when we begin to consider the geometrical features of the solutions of this equation, the wave equation. In a string, a sinusoidal disturbance can travel in only two directions, to the right and to the left along the string. Our general solution of the string problem was made up by superposing waves in these two directions, regarding one as a direct, the other as a reflected, wave. In a membrane, however, the situation is the same that we should meet in considering waves on the surface of a liquid. Waves now have wave fronts, lines in the membrane all points of which are at the same phase. The perpendicular distance from one wave front to the next is the wave length, and the direction of this perpendicular is called the "wave normal." The wave propagates along the direction of the wave normal with the phase velocity, which in the simple case of the uniform membrane is independent of the frequency.

The complication arises from the fact that propagation can occur in any direction, and the wave fronts can be curves of any type. For instance, we can have circular waves, like the circular ripples set up in water when a stone is thrown into it, or linear waves, in which the wave fronts are straight lines, or in fact an infinite variety of different forms of waves. Furthermore, if a wave strikes a boundary, a line along which the membrane is held fast, it will be reflected, but in general not along the direction of the incident wave. Instead, there will be the familiar law of reflection, the angles of incidence and reflection being equal, implying that the wave normals of incident and reflected waves are on opposite sides of the normal to the bounding line. The problem of satisfying boundary conditions along the edge of the membrane then becomes complicated, particularly when we remember that the boundary can have any arbitrary shape.

This arbitrary shape of the boundary really makes the difference in simplicity between the string and the membrane. We find, with the membrane, that we generally do not get far by trying to superpose direct and reflected waves to build up a general solution. We shall show that we can do this for the rectangular membrane, but that is almost the only case in which it is practicable. For other shapes of membrane, held along the edge, we must look directly for standing-wave solutions of the wave equation, which have nodes along a family of lines, of which the boundary is one. This means that we can solve only problems with relatively simple curves for their boundaries.

The simplest cases, and the only ones that we take up in this chapter, are the rectangular and circular membranes; the methods we use for them will be sufficiently representative of the more complicated shapes that can be solved. The general method that we use is to change variables in the wave equation, introducing a set of curvilinear coordinates in which the boundary forms one of the coordinate lines. For instance, with the circular membrane we introduce polar coordinates with the center at the origin, so that the boundary is a line $r = \rho$. Then the boundary condition can be stated by saying that u, the displacement, is zero, when the coordinate in question is given the suitable value; as in the case of the circular membrane, where $u = 0$ when $r = \rho$. We shall find that in many such cases we can carry out a process of separation of variables: we assume that u is a product of one function of one of the variables, another function of another, as in the circular membrane, where we assume that u is a product of a function $\Theta(\theta)$ and a function $R(r)$. Then it turns out that we can write separate ordinary differential equations for these two functions, and can satisfy the boundary condition by means of the function $R(r)$ alone.

This method of separation of variables forms the most useful method for solving the wave equation, and similar partial differential equations, in the cases where it can be used. On the other hand, in problems for which the method cannot be used, because of the complicated form of the boundary, there is no practicable means for getting a general solution. We now take up the formulation of the differential equation for the vibrating membrane, and its solutions in the cases of rectangular and circular membranes. In connection with these solutions, we find that we have properties of orthogonality of the solutions equivalent to those found earlier for the string, which make it possible to satisfy arbitrary initial conditions at $t = 0$ in a simple manner.

1. The Differential Equation of the Vibrating Membrane.—Let us take two coordinates, x and y, in the plane of the membrane, writing u for the displacement at right angles to the plane, so that we wish a relation $u = u(x,y,t)$. Consider a small element of the membrane, bounded by dx and dy. Let the mass per unit area be μ, so that the mass of the element is $\mu \, dx \, dy$. Then its mass, times the acceleration normal to the membrane, is $\mu \, dx \, dy \, \partial^2 u/\partial t^2$. This is equal to the force arising from the tension. Let the tension be T. That is, if we cut the membrane along any line, the material on one side of the cut exerts a force on the material on the other, normal to the cut and equal to T for each unit of length of the cut. We assume that T is constant over the membrane. If the membrane were plane, the tension of its opposite edges would cancel, and we should have no resultant force. If it is curved, however, we may proceed as follows: Along the edge at $x + dx$, the tension is at right angles to the y axis, almost along the x axis, but with a small component along the u direction, equal approximately to $T(\partial u/\partial x)_{x+dx}$ per unit of length, or this times dy for the actual length dy. Similarly along the edge at x the component is $-T(\partial u/\partial x)_x \, dy$, so that the sum is approximately $T \, \partial^2 u/\partial x^2 \, dx \, dy$. The forces acting along the edges at y and $y + dy$ similarly add to $T \, \partial^2 u/\partial y^2 \, dx \, dy$, and the total force, the sum of these, is $T(\partial^2 u/\partial x^2 + \partial^2 u/\partial y^2) \, dx \, dy$. Thus the differential equation, dividing by $dx \, dy$, is

$$\mu \frac{\partial^2 u}{\partial t^2} = T\left(\frac{\partial^2 u}{\partial x^2} + \frac{\partial^2 u}{\partial y^2}\right) \tag{1.1}$$

or

$$\nabla^2 u = \frac{\mu}{T}\frac{\partial^2 u}{\partial t^2} \tag{1.2}$$

where

$$\nabla^2 u = \frac{\partial^2 u}{\partial x^2} + \frac{\partial^2 u}{\partial y^2}.$$

This is the two-dimensional form of the Laplacian, which is discussed in Appendix IV.

The simplest solution of (1.2) is

$$u = f(x - vt), \qquad v = \sqrt{\frac{T}{\mu}},$$

as in Eq. (1.2), Chap. IX. This represents a wave whose wave fronts are parallel straight lines $x = $ constant, propagated along the x axis with velocity v. Of course, a similar wave could be set up propagated in any direction, with an equation

$$u = f(lx + my - vt), \qquad l^2 + m^2 = 1, \tag{1.3}$$

where l, m are the cosines of the angles between the wave normal and the x and y axes, so that the wave fronts are the straight lines

$$lx + my = \text{constant}.$$

It can be shown at once that (1.3) is a solution of (1.2) by direct substitution. As a result of the way in which the velocity enters the problem, we may replace (1.2) by

$$\nabla^2 u - \frac{1}{v^2} \frac{\partial^2 u}{\partial t^2} = 0.$$

This is a standard form for the wave equation.

As in Chap. VIII, Sec. 1, we often wish to write u as a function of x and y, multiplied by a function of t, performing a first step toward a separation of variables. If

$$u = T(t)w(x,y),$$

then we find at once that

$$\frac{1}{w} \nabla^2 w = \frac{1}{v^2} \frac{1}{T} \frac{d^2 T}{dt^2} = -k^2$$

where the variables are separated, and where k^2 is a constant. The equation for T is then

$$\frac{d^2 T}{dt^2} + \omega^2 T = 0, \qquad T = e^{\pm i\omega t}, \quad \text{where } k^2 = \frac{\omega^2}{v^2}, \quad (1.4)$$

and the equation for w is

$$\nabla^2 w + k^2 w = 0. \tag{1.5}$$

Equation (1.5) is the wave equation with the time eliminated. Unlike the case of the string, where the corresponding equation has a trivial solution, (1.5) is an equation with a great variety of solutions, which we can handle only in special cases, as we have already indicated in our introductory remarks. The rest of this chapter will be devoted to some of these special cases.

2. The Rectangular Membrane.—Let us assume that the membrane is rectangular, u being zero, or the membrane held fast, at $x = 0$, $x = a$, $y = 0$, $y = b$. We now look for a solution of (1.5) by separation of variables, as a product of a function $X(x)$ and a function $Y(y)$. Substituting, this gives us

$$\frac{1}{X} \frac{d^2 X}{dx^2} = -k_x^2, \qquad \frac{1}{Y} \frac{d^2 Y}{dy^2} = -k_y^2, \qquad k_x^2 + k_y^2 = k^2, \tag{2.1}$$

with solutions

$$X = e^{\pm jk_x x}, \text{ or } \frac{\sin}{\cos} k_x x, \qquad Y = e^{\pm jk_y y}, \text{ or } \frac{\sin}{\cos} k_y y. \qquad (2.2)$$

If we use the exponential form, and combine with (1.4), we have

$$u = e^{j(\pm k_x x \pm k_y y \pm \omega t)}$$

in which we can take any one of the eight combinations of signs. These solutions are of the form (1.3), corresponding to sinusoidal waves propagated in the four directions given by $l = \pm k_x v/\omega$, $m = \pm k_y v/\omega$. These four directions are the four wave normals that would result from a wave in any one of the directions, after successive reflections by boundaries $x = $ constant or $y = $ constant. The sine form of (2.2) represents standing waves rather than traveling waves. Thus we can take

$$u = \sin k_x x \sin k_y y \; e^{j\omega t}, \qquad (2.3)$$

which is a standing wave for which u is always zero for $x = 0$, $y = 0$. Such a solution can be set up as a superposition of traveling waves, just as a standing wave in a string can be set up as a superposition of traveling waves. Thus we have

$$\sin k_x x \sin k_y y \; e^{j\omega t}$$
$$= -\tfrac{1}{4}[e^{j(k_x x + k_y y + \omega t)} - e^{j(-k_x x + k_y y + \omega t)} - e^{j(k_x x - k_y y + \omega t)} + e^{j(-k_x x - k_y y + \omega t)}].$$

This, in other words, is a case in which we can build up our standing-wave solution by superposing traveling waves, but the rectangular membrane is almost the only case in which this is convenient.

Using the standing-wave solution (2.3), we can satisfy our boundary conditions that $u = 0$ when $x = 0$, $x = a$, $y = 0$, $y = b$, by assuming that

$$k_x a = p\pi, \qquad k_x = p\frac{\pi}{a}, \qquad k_y b = q\pi, \qquad k_y = q\frac{\pi}{b}, \qquad (2.4)$$

where p, q are integers. These conditions fix the values of k_x and k_y, and hence of the frequency; for, combining (2.4) with (1.4) and (2.1), we find that the angular frequency is given by

$$\frac{\omega_{pq}}{v} = \pi \sqrt{\left(\frac{p}{a}\right)^2 + \left(\frac{q}{b}\right)^2}, \qquad (2.5)$$

so that, instead of having overtones whose frequencies are integral multiples of a fundamental, the frequencies are given by a much more complicated relation.

There is one interesting result of this. Pleasing musical notes depend on having the frequencies of the overtones related in simple ways to the fundamental, so that they sound well together, as with a vibrating string. In a membrane or drum, in which these relations do not hold, the sound is far less musical than with a string. This suggests other cases, which do not exactly fall within the category of the present chapter. For example, a vibrating bell acts as a two-dimensional vibrating system, a little like a membrane, and has complicated overtones which in general are not harmonics. But it has been found by trial that, if bells are made in their conventional shape, overtones are so adjusted that the loud ones are actually in tune with each other, though a slight change of shape would destroy the quality.

We note, in connection with the various possible modes of the vibrating membrane, given by different values of the integers p and q, that, if the membrane is vibrating with one overtone, the amplitude will be zero along certain lines, which will stay at rest. These nodal lines form a rectangular network, coming when $px/a = 1, 2, \cdots p - 1$, and for $qy/b = 1, 2, \cdots q - 1$. At any instant, if the membrane is displaced upward in one rectangle, it will be displaced downward in all adjacent rectangles. Such a nodal arrangement is characteristic of all sorts of standing-wave problems.

The general solution of the problem of the rectangular membrane will be a superposition of all the normal modes, with appropriate amplitudes and phases, as we found in Chap. VIII for the string. That is, we have

$$u = \sum_{p=1}^{\infty} \sum_{q=1}^{\infty} (A_{pq} \cos \omega_{pq} t + B_{pq} \sin \omega_{pq} t) \sin \frac{p\pi x}{a} \sin \frac{q\pi y}{b},$$

where ω_{pq} is given in (2.5), and where the A's and B's are arbitrary constants to be determined from the initial conditions at $t = 0$. Suppose that the displacement is given by $u_0(x,y)$ at $t = 0$, and the velocity by $\dot{u}_0(x,y)$. We must then satisfy the conditions

$$u_0(x,y) = \sum_{p=1}^{\infty} \sum_{q=1}^{\infty} A_{pq} \sin \frac{p\pi x}{a} \sin \frac{q\pi y}{b}$$

$$\dot{u}_0(x,y) = \sum_{p=1}^{\infty} \sum_{q=1}^{\infty} \omega_{pq} B_{pq} \sin \frac{p\pi x}{a} \sin \frac{q\pi y}{b}. \tag{2.6}$$

That is, we must be able to expand two arbitrary functions of x and y in terms of double series of products of sines, a sort of two-dimensional Fourier expansion. We find the coefficients as in Sec. 2, Chap. VIII. We multiply both sides of the first equation of (2.6) by

$$\left(\frac{4}{ab}\right) \sin \frac{r\pi x}{a} \sin \frac{s\pi y}{b},$$

and integrate over the surface of the membrane. We can prove at once, by elementary means, the orthogonality and normalization relations

$$\int_0^a \int_0^b \frac{4}{ab} \sin \frac{p\pi x}{a} \sin \frac{q\pi y}{b} \sin \frac{r\pi x}{a} \sin \frac{s\pi y}{b} \, dx \, dy = \delta_{pr}\delta_{qs}.$$

Thus we have

$$A_{pq} = \frac{4}{ab} \int_0^a \int_0^b u_0(x,y) \sin \frac{p\pi x}{a} \sin \frac{q\pi y}{b} \, dx \, dy$$

with a similar equation for the B's. This solves formally the problem of finding the amplitudes and phases of the normal modes, though if u_0 and $\dot{u}_0$ are complicated functions of x and y, it can of course be a very difficult problem actually to evaluate these integrals.

3. The Circular Membrane.—The differential equation for the circular membrane is the same as for the rectangular membrane, but the boundary condition is different: the displacement u is always zero on a circle of radius ρ about the origin. To solve the problem, the simplest method is to introduce polar coordinates r, θ. We must then write the wave equation (1.5) in polar coordinates. To do this we need the Laplacian in polar coordinates. In Appendix VII we discuss the vector operations in curvilinear coordinates, and in polar coordinates in particular. The problem of finding the forms of the vector operators in curvilinear coordinates is a straightforward one of changing variables in partial differentiation. We find in Appendix VII that

$$\nabla^2 u = \frac{1}{r}\frac{\partial}{\partial r}\left(r \frac{\partial u}{\partial r}\right) + \frac{1}{r^2}\frac{\partial^2 u}{\partial \theta^2}$$

in two-dimensional polar coordinates. Thus our wave equation is

$$\frac{1}{r}\frac{\partial}{\partial r}\left(r \frac{\partial u}{\partial r}\right) + \frac{1}{r^2}\frac{\partial^2 u}{\partial \theta^2} + k^2 u = 0. \qquad (3.1)$$

We shall now show that we can solve by separation of variables, letting $u = R(r)\Theta(\theta)$. Substituting in (3.1), we find

$$\frac{1}{R}\frac{1}{r}\frac{d}{dr}\left(r\frac{dR}{dr}\right) + \frac{1}{r^2}\frac{1}{\Theta}\frac{d^2\Theta}{d\theta^2} + k^2 = 0.$$

We multiply by r^2, and transfer the first and third terms to the right, obtaining

$$\frac{1}{\Theta}\frac{d^2\Theta}{d\theta^2} = -r^2\left(\frac{1}{R}\frac{1}{r}\frac{d}{dr}\left(r\frac{dR}{dr}\right) + k^2\right).$$

Since the left side is a function of θ, the right side a function of r, each must be a constant, which we may write as $-m^2$. Then

$$\frac{d^2\Theta}{d\theta^2} + m^2\Theta = 0, \qquad \Theta = A\cos m\theta + B\sin m\theta,$$

and the equation for r can be immediately changed to

$$\frac{1}{r}\frac{d}{dr}\left(r\frac{dR}{dr}\right) + \left(k^2 - \frac{m^2}{r^2}\right)R = 0. \tag{3.2}$$

By the change of variables $x = kr$ this can be changed into the form

$$\frac{1}{x}\frac{d}{dx}\left(x\frac{dR}{dx}\right) + \left(1 - \frac{m^2}{x^2}\right)R = 0. \tag{3.3}$$

This is Bessel's equation, which is discussed in Appendix VIII, and it has a solution $R = J_m(x) = J_m(kr)$, a Bessel's function of the mth order, whose properties are discussed in Appendix VIII.

Now that we have found the form of our solution, let us consider the boundary conditions. First we consider the solution for θ. At a given point of the membrane, the value of θ is determined, but not in a single-valued way. Thus, if the point corresponds to $\theta = 47°$, it would equally well correspond to $47° + 360°$, or $47° + 720°$, etc. Now Θ must surely have a definite value at each point of the membrane. Thus it must have the same value for θ, $\theta + 2\pi$, $\theta + 4\pi$, etc. In other words, Θ is periodic in θ with period 2π. But this is true if, and only if, m is an integer. Hence our first condition, necessary to make the function single-valued, is that m be an integer.

Next consider the solution for r: $R = J_m(kr)$, where now m is an integer. In Appendix VIII we find that there are two independent solutions of Eq. (3.3), one being $J_m(kr)$, which starts out for small r as r^m, and the other being $N_m(kr)$, which starts out for small r as r^{-m} (unless $m = 0$, in which case N_0 is logarithmic for $r = 0$). Since the displacement of the membrane must be finite at $r = 0$, we see that we cannot use the function $N_m(kr)$, the Neumann function, in building up our solution, and must use only the Bessel function $J_m(kr)$. Now we consider the boundary condition $u = 0$ when $r = \rho$, or at the edge of the membrane. That is, we must have $J_m(k\rho) = 0$. From the properties of Bessel's functions, we see that $J_m(x)$ is zero for certain definite values of x, say x_{mn}, $n = 1, 2, \cdots$. We may, in fact, find approximately what these values are from the asymptotic formula

$$\lim_{x \to \infty} J_m(x) = \sqrt{\frac{2}{\pi x}} \cos\left[x - \left(\frac{2m + 1}{4}\right)\pi \right]$$

which holds for large values of x. Although this formula does not hold for small x, still it is not very inaccurate for values of x considerably greater numerically than m. It shows that the Bessel function oscillates sinusoidally, the amplitude at the same time decreasing with increasing x. The values of x_{mn} are then given approximately by the condition that $x - \left(\dfrac{2m + 1}{4}\right)\pi = \left(n - \dfrac{1}{2}\right)\pi$, where $n = 1, 2,$ $\cdots$. That is, we have approximately

$$x_{mn} \sim \pi\left(\frac{m}{2} - \frac{1}{4} + n \right) \tag{3.4}$$

where $n = 1, 2, \cdots$. We see then that to satisfy our boundary conditions we must have $k\rho = x_{mn}$, where n is an integer. The only adjustable constant is k, which equals ω/v by (1.4), so that this condition determines the frequency. We should properly label the value of k, or of the angular frequency ω, by the indices m and n, since it depends on both of them. We then have

$$\omega_{mn}\frac{\rho}{v} = x_{mn}. \tag{3.5}$$

From (3.4) and (3.5) we can easily show that, to the approximation to which (3.4) is correct, we have $(m/2 - \frac{1}{4} + n)$ half wave lengths in the radius of the circle. This, however, is only a crude approximation, and the frequencies of the various modes are not exactly harmonics, or integral multiples of a fundamental frequency.

The general solution of our problem of the vibrating membrane can now be written in the form

$$u = \sum_m \sum_n (A_{mn} \cos \omega_{mn}t + B_{mn} \sin \omega_{mn}t) \cos (m\theta - \alpha_{mn})J_m(k_{mn}r), \tag{3.6}$$

where the A's, B's, and the phases α_{mn}, are arbitrary constants. A

single term of (3.6) corresponds to a single standing wave. Its
nodes are concentric circles, values of r for which $J_m(k_{mn}r)$ is zero,
of which of course the boundary is one; and radii, determined by
$\cos(m\theta - \alpha_{mn}) = 0$. Some nodes in various normal modes are shown
in Fig. 30. It is readily seen that there are m radial nodes, n circular
nodes provided we count the boundary. The arbitrary constant
α_{mn} determines the angles at which the radial nodes come; changing
it simply rotates the whole nodal pattern. The constants A and B
determine the amplitude and phase of the disturbance as a function

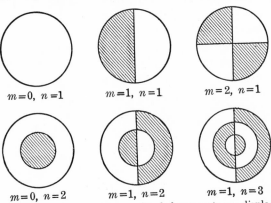

$m=0,\ n=1$ $m=1,\ n=1$ $m=2,\ n=1$

$m=0,\ n=2$ $m=1,\ n=2$ $m=1,\ n=3$

Fig. 30.—Nodes of a circular membrane. Shaded segments are displaced in opposite
phase to unshaded.

of the time. We may, if we choose, consider that there are two
separate waves possible for each frequency, $\cos m\theta J_m$ and $\sin m\theta J_m$.
Such a case, of two separate modes of the same frequency, is called
"degeneracy"; and we shall see in a problem that the same thing is
true of the square membrane. In a degenerate case, with two or more
possible vibrations of the same frequency, it is plain that any linear
combination of these vibrations gives a possible vibration of the same
frequency.

4. Initial Conditions with the Circular Membrane.—Suppose we
know that at $t = 0$, the displacement of the membrane is given by
$F(r,\theta)$, and the velocity by $G(r,\theta)$. We can write the whole solution, in
a slightly more general way than before,

$$u = \sum_{m,n} [(A_{mn}\cos\omega_{mn}t + B_{mn}\sin\omega_{mn}t)\cos m\theta$$
$$+ (C_{mn}\cos\omega_{mn}t + D_{mn}\sin\omega_{mn}t)\sin m\theta]J_m(k_{mn}r).$$

Thus, writing displacement and velocity at $t = 0$, we have

$$F(r,\theta) = \sum_{mn} (A_{mn} \cos m\theta + C_{mn} \sin m\theta) J_m(k_{mn}r)$$

$$G(r,\theta) = \sum_{mn} \omega_{mn}(B_{mn} \cos m\theta + D_{mn} \sin m\theta) J_m(k_{mn}r).$$

The A's, B's, C's, D's must be chosen to fit these conditions. Both conditions are of the same sort. They require us to find the coefficients of an expansion of a function of r and θ in series of products of sines or cosines and Bessel's functions. Now it proves to be true that both the sines or cosines and the Bessel's functions are orthogonal, and as a result of this we can make the expansions we desire in the usual way, as with Fourier series. Let us take the first equation, multiply by $\cos p\theta J_p(k_{pq}r)$, and integrate over the area of the membrane. That is, we integrate with respect to r from 0 to ρ, and with respect to θ from 0 to 2π, the element of area being $r\,dr\,d\theta$. Then we have

$$\int_0^\rho \int_0^{2\pi} F(r,\theta) \cos p\theta J_p(k_{pq}r) r\,dr\,d\theta$$

$$= \sum_{mn} \int_0^{2\pi} (A_{mn} \cos m\theta + C_{mn} \sin m\theta)$$

$$\cos p\theta\,d\theta \int_0^\rho r J_m(k_{mn}r) J_p(k_{pq}r)\,dr.$$

By the orthogonal property of the sine and cosine, the right side is zero unless $m = p$, giving

$$\sum_n \pi A_{pn} \int_0^\rho r J_p(k_{pn}r) J_p(k_{pq}r)\,dr.$$

But we shall prove in the next paragraph that the J's are orthogonal in the sense that

$$\int_0^\rho r J_p(k_{pn}r) J_p(k_{pq}r)\,dr = 0 \qquad \text{if } n \neq q. \quad (4.1)$$

Using this fact, our sum reduces to a single term,

$$\pi A_{pq} \int_0^\rho r J_p^2(k_{pq}r)\,dr.$$

If the last integral, which could be easily computed if we knew the properties of Bessel's functions better, and whose value is given in Appendix VIII, were denoted by c_{pq}, then we should have

$$A_{pq} = \frac{1}{\pi c_{pq}} \int_0^\rho \int_0^{2\pi} F(r,\theta) \cos p\theta J_p(k_{pq}r) r\,dr\,d\theta,$$

determining the coefficients A in terms of a double integral. Similarly we could get formulas for the B's, C's, D's. Of course, in an actual case, these integrals might be very difficult to compute, but nevertheless we have a general solution of our problem.

In the preceding paragraph we have used the orthogonal property of Bessel's functions. We can prove this property directly from the differential equation, as was done in the preceding chapter for the nonuniform vibrating string. From (3.2) we have

$$\frac{1}{r}\frac{d}{dr}\left(r\frac{dJ_p(k_{pn}r)}{dr}\right) + \left(k_{pn}^2 - \frac{p^2}{r^2}\right)J_p(k_{pn}r) = 0$$

$$\frac{1}{r}\frac{d}{dr}\left(r\frac{dJ_p(k_{pq}r)}{dr}\right) + \left(k_{pq}^2 - \frac{p^2}{r^2}\right)J_p(k_{pq}r) = 0.$$

Multiply the first by $rJ_p(k_{pq}r)$, the second by $rJ_p(k_{pn}r)$, subtract, and integrate from 0 to ρ. The result is

$$\int_0^\rho \left\{J_p(k_{pq}r)\frac{d}{dr}\left[r\frac{dJ_p(k_{pn}r)}{dr}\right] - J_p(k_{pn}r)\frac{d}{dr}\left[r\frac{dJ_p(k_{pq}r)}{dr}\right]\right\} dr$$

$$= (k_{pq}^2 - k_{pn}^2)\int_0^\rho rJ_p(k_{pq}r)J_p(k_{pn}r)\,dr. \quad (4.2)$$

As in the discussion of Eq. (3.1) of Chap. X, the left side of (4.2) can be shown to be zero by integration by parts. Then the right side must be zero, and either $k_{pn}^2 - k_{pq}^2$ is zero, which is not true unless n and q refer to the same overtone (unless the mode is degenerate), or the integral is zero, which we wished to prove in order to verify Eq. (4.1). The orthogonality is not quite of the form discussed in Chap. X, for the differential equation is of slightly different form, the quantity $(k^2 - p^2/r^2)r$ appearing in place of $\omega^2\mu$, so that the final result is not just like integrating μ times the product of the functions to get zero.

Problems

1. A rectangular drum is 20 by 40 cm, its whole mass is 100 g, and the total pull on the faces is 50 and 100 kg, respectively. Find the frequencies, in cycles per second, of the five lowest modes of vibration, and sketch the nodes for each.

2. The special case of degeneracy arises when a rectangular membrane is square. Then the two modes of vibration $e^{i\omega t}\sin(n\pi x/X)\sin(m\pi y/X)$ and $e^{i\omega t}\sin(m\pi x/X)\sin(n\pi y/X)$ have the same frequency (where we let $X = Y$). Thus any linear combination of these is a solution, again with this frequency. Consider the combinations

$$e^{i\omega t}\left(A\sin\frac{n\pi x}{X}\sin\frac{m\pi y}{X} + B\sin\frac{m\pi x}{X}\sin\frac{n\pi y}{X}\right).$$

Work out the nodes in the case $n = 1$, $m = 2$, for (1) $B = A$; (2) $B = -A$; (3) $B = 2A$.

3. A rectangular membrane is struck at its center, starting from rest, in such a way that at $t = 0$ a small rectangular region about the center may be considered to have a velocity v, and the rest has no velocity. Find the amplitudes of the various overtones.

4. Imagine n and m plotted as two rectangular coordinates. Show that a curve of constant ω, plotted in these coordinates, is an ellipse. Each integral value of n and m corresponds to an overtone, so that, if we draw the point corresponding to each overtone, the number of points within such an ellipse gives the number of overtones with angular velocity less than ω. Note that the number of such points per unit area of the plane is just one, and so find an approximate formula, using the area of the ellipse, for the number of overtones of frequency less than ω, and also for the number between ω and $\omega + d\omega$. Check up this approximation by the exact values of Prob. 1.

5. In the circular membrane, suppose that $m = 0$, and that k is very large, so that there are many circular nodes. Consider a small region near the edge of the membrane. The few nodes in this neighborhood will be almost straight lines, as if we were near the edge of a rectangular membrane. Find the asymptotic wave length, using the fact that $J_m(x)$ approaches $\cos(x - \alpha)$ at large x, and show that the wave length is connected with the velocity and frequency in the usual manner.

6. Derive Eq. (3.1) by a direct application of Newton's law of motion, using an element of area of the circular membrane bounded by the lines r, $r + dr$, θ, $\theta + d\theta$. What form does this equation take if the tension and density vary with position?

7. Set up the wave equation in three-dimensional spherical coordinates, in which $x = r \sin \theta \cos \varphi$, $y = r \sin \theta \sin \varphi$, $z = r \cos \theta$. Show that it is

$$\frac{1}{r^2} \frac{\partial}{\partial r} \left(r^2 \frac{\partial u}{\partial r} \right) + \frac{1}{r^2 \sin \theta} \frac{\partial}{\partial \theta} \left(\sin \theta \frac{\partial u}{\partial \theta} \right) + \frac{1}{r^2 \sin^2 \theta} \frac{\partial^2 u}{\partial \varphi^2} = \frac{1}{v^2} \frac{\partial^2 u}{\partial t^2}.$$

Separate variables in this equation. Show that the function of φ is $\sin m\varphi$ or $\cos m\varphi$, where m is an integer. Show that the equations for r and θ are, respectively,

$$\frac{1}{r^2} \frac{d}{dr} \left(r^2 \frac{dR}{dr} \right) + \left(\frac{\omega^2}{v^2} - \frac{C}{r^2} \right) R = 0,$$

where ω, C are constants; and

$$\frac{1}{\sin \theta} \frac{d}{d\theta} \left(\sin \theta \frac{d\Theta}{d\theta} \right) + \left(C - \frac{m^2}{\sin^2 \theta} \right) \Theta = 0.$$

8. The equation for θ in Prob. 7 is called "Legendre's equation." Let $\Theta = \sin^m \theta \, F(\cos \theta)$. Find the differential equation for F, solving in power series in $\cos \theta$, and show that the series breaks off if $C = l(l + 1)$, where l is an integer. The resulting functions are called $P_l^m(\cos \theta)$, and are known as "associated Legendre functions." Compute the first few Legendre functions.

9. In the equation for r in Prob. 7, prove that $R = [J_{l+\frac{1}{2}}(x)]/\sqrt{x}$, where $x = \omega r/v$.

10. Prove that two functions u_n and u_m, satisfying differential equations of the form

$$\frac{d}{dx} \left[T(x) \frac{du_n}{dx} \right] + [\mu(x)\omega_n^2 - f(x)]u_n = 0,$$

with different ω_n's, but chosen so that both u_n and u_m are zero at $x = 0$ and $x = L$, satisfy the orthogonality condition $\int_0^L \mu(x)u_n(x)u_m(x) \, dx = 0$.

CHAPTER XII

STRESSES, STRAINS, AND VIBRATIONS
OF AN ELASTIC SOLID

In the preceding chapters, we have been treating the vibrations of elastic strings and membranes, one- and two-dimensional bodies, and now we pass to the three-dimensional case, or the elastic solid. Of course, the strings and membranes were really elastic solids, of particular shapes, but there are several ways in which we must generalize our previous treatment. First, in the strings and membranes, the rigidity of the material itself was not great enough to affect the vibration, whereas, in the problems we now take up, this rigidity, or the elastic properties of the material in general, will be important. Thus we may imagine all gradations of the problem of a stretched wire, from the limiting case of a very thin long wire under large tension, when our previous theory is applicable, down to a short thick bar under small tension or even no tension at all, when the restoring force on a particle, far from coming from the tension on the ends, comes from the distortion of the bar itself. Secondly, with the strings and membranes, we considered only transverse vibrations, whereas here we discuss longitudinal vibrations as well. Of course, strings can vibrate longitudinally, but we have so far neglected this phase of their motion. Thirdly, a very important aspect of the problems of strings and membranes has arisen from the fact that they were limited in space, the membranes being very thin pieces of material, the strings thin in two dimensions. But, although some of the problems of the present chapter have this property, we shall also consider vibrations and waves in extended media going, in the limiting case, to infinity in all dimensions, as sound waves in an infinite gas or solid. It is these sound waves which show the best analogy to our one- and two-dimensional wave equations.

1. Stresses, Body and Surface Forces.—The first step in discussing the behavior of an elastic solid is to find the force acting on an infinitesimal volume element, and to set this equal to mass times acceleration for a dynamic case, or to set the force equal to zero for a problem in static elasticity. The forces may be divided into two classes: (1)

volume or body forces, such as gravity, which act on each volume element of the body; and (2) surface forces, with which neighboring parts of the medium act on each other, and which are transmitted across surfaces, or the forces transmitted across the bounding surface of the whole body. The tensions we have met with string and membrane are examples of surface forces, as are gas pressures, or shearing forces in a twisted rod. To specify such a force, we imagine a surface element da to be drawn somewhere in the body, with a normal n. The material on either side of da exerts a force on the material on the other side; thus this force is a push normal to the surface if there is a pressure in the body, it is a tension if that is the form of stress, or it may be a shearing force, tangential to the surface. The force exerted by the material on one side, on the material on the second side, and the other force exerted by the material on the second side back on the first side, are action and reaction, and are equal and opposite, so that one always has an ambiguity of sign in dealing with these forces, or as we call them "stresses." We adopt the following convention: We imagine da to be part of the surface bounding a volume, and n to be the outer normal. Then the force we deal with is the force exerted by the outside on the material inside the volume, over da. This force will be a vector, and proportional to da. We call its x, y, and z components $T_1\,da$, $T_2\,da$, $T_3\,da$, respectively; in the present chapter we shall refer to the x, y, and z axes as the x_1, x_2, and x_3 axes, which makes it possible to write certain formulas in an abbreviated way.

The components T_1, T_2, T_3 will of course depend on the direction of the normal n to the surface element da. It proves to be possible to specify the properties of a stress completely if we choose three unit areas at a point, one normal to each of the three coordinate axes, and give the components of the force acting across each. Thus let the three components of force per unit area acting across unit area normal to the x_1 axis be T_{11}, T_{21}, T_{31}; the three components of force acting across unit area normal to the x_2 axis T_{12}, T_{22}, T_{32}; and so on. Thus for the surfaces normal to the x_1, x_2, and x_3 axes, we have the three force vectors, or nine quantities,

$$
\begin{array}{ccc}
T_{11} & T_{21} & T_{31} \\
T_{12} & T_{22} & T_{32} \\
T_{13} & T_{23} & T_{33}
\end{array}
$$

which we may symbolize by T_{ij}, where i, $j = 1$, 2, 3. These nine quantities form the stress tensor, and they show properties like those of other tensors as discussed in Appendix V. The significance of the three components T_{11}, T_{21}, T_{31} is illustrated in Fig. 31. The diagonal terms of the array, T_{11}, T_{22}, T_{33} are called the "normal stresses" or pressures, since the force components are normal to the surface, and the remaining terms are called "shearing" or "tangential" stresses.

It is easily shown, and is taken up in a problem, that the force per unit area across an arbitrary surface that has direction cosines

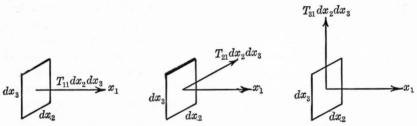

FIG. 31.—Components of force acting across dx_2dx_3.

α_1, α_2, α_3, has an x_1 component equal to $\alpha_1 T_{11} + \alpha_2 T_{12} + \alpha_3 T_{13}$. That is, we may write the x_i component of the force per unit area across this surface as

$$F_i = \sum_j T_{ij}\alpha_j. \qquad (1.1)$$

As with the other tensors we have already met, it is always possible by making a proper rotation of axes, to reduce any stress tensor to a diagonal form, in which no shearing stresses are present. Thus let us set up new axes x_1', x_2', x_3', rotated with respect to the x_1, x_2, x_3 axes. We let the direction cosines of the x_1' axes, with respect to the x_1, x_2, x_3 axes, be α_{11}, α_{21}, α_{31}; these then are the components, along x_1, x_2, x_3, of a unit vector along x_1'. Similarly for unit vector along x_2' the components are α_{12}, α_{22}, α_{32}, and for unit vector along x_3' they are α_{13}, α_{23}, α_{33}. The nine quantities α_{ij} form a tensor, and its components satisfy certain conditions, discussed in Appendix IV. They satisfy first the normalization and orthogonality conditions

$$\sum_r \alpha_{ri}\alpha_{rj} = \delta_{ij}.$$

The summation represents simply the scalar product of unit vectors along the x_i' and x_j' axes. Since these axes are assumed to be orthogonal, the scalar product is zero if i and j are different, while if i and j are the same, the result is the square of the magnitude of unit vector, which of course is unity. Similarly they satisfy the other form of normalization and orthogonality conditions

$$\sum_r \alpha_{ir}\alpha_{jr} = \delta_{ij} \tag{1.2}$$

which follows by similar arguments, when we note that α_{11}, α_{12}, and α_{13} represent the components of unit vector along x_1, with respect to the axes x_1', x_2', x_3', and so on. Various other conditions satisfied by the α's are taken up in Appendix IV.

We may now show how to rotate axes so as to reduce a stress tensor to a diagonal form. We wish to express the statement that the force acting across a unit area normal to the x_i' axis has only an x_i' component, or equals a constant T_i' times unit vector along x_i'. By (1.1), the x_j component of force across unit plane normal to x_i' is $\sum_k T_{jk}\alpha_{ki}$. We wish this to be equal to T_i', multiplied by α_{ji}, the component along x_j of a unit vector along x_i'. Thus our condition is

$$\sum_k T_{jk}\alpha_{ki} = T_i'\alpha_{ji}, \qquad \sum_k (T_{jk} - T_i'\delta_{jk})\alpha_{ki} = 0. \tag{1.3}$$

Here we have the same sort of set of simultaneous homogeneous linear equations which we have met every time we have tried to reduce a tensor to diagonal form, and as usual the equations have no solution unless the determinant of coefficients vanishes. This provides a secular equation for T_i', which, being a cubic equation, has three roots. These are called the "principal stresses," and the new axes that are determined by the values of α_{ki} that we find from (1.3) are called the "principal axes of stress."

The situation regarding principal axes becomes clearer if we consider several simple examples of stress systems. The simplest stress is probably the hydrostatic pressure. There the force acting across a unit area is always at right angles to the area, and its magnitude is by definition the pressure P. The force acts into the body, and hence is of negative sign. Thus we have $T_{11} = T_{22} = T_{33} = -P$, all other components being equal to zero. This tensor is already diagonal, so that the x_1, x_2, x_3 axes are principal axes. Since these are any rectangular axes, we see that any axes are principal axes for a hydrostatic pressure (just as, in considering moments of inertia for a rigid body, any rectangular axes would be principal axes for a spherical body). A second simple stress is a tension, say in the x_1 direction. Then the unit area perpendicular to x_1 has a force T across it, normal to the area, but there is no force exerted across faces perpendicular to x_2 or x_3. In other words, $T_{11} = T$, all other components of the stress being zero, so that again we have principal axes. In this case, unlike hydrostatic pressure, the principal axes are determined by the stress: it is clear that one of the principal axes must be along the direction of the tension, the other two being any two axes at right angles to the tension, and at right angles to each other.

A more interesting and complicated example of a stress is a shear. In Fig. 32a we have a cube of material, with equal and opposite

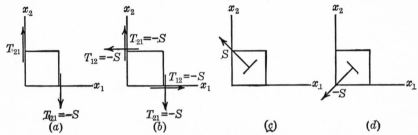

FIG. 32.—Diagram of shearing stress. (a) Shear over the faces perpendicular to the x_1 axis. (b) Additional shear over faces perpendicular to the x_2 axis necessary to balance the turning moment of the shear indicated in (a). (c) and (d) Stress system of (b) referred to principal axes, tension in (c), pressure in (d).

tangential forces exerted across the faces normal to x_1, the forces acting in the x_2 direction. Over the right face, the force exerted on the material is in the $-x_2$ direction, so that for this face we have $T_{21} = -S$, a constant, and $T_{11} = T_{31} = 0$. Over the opposite face, both force and direction of normal are reversed, so that the stress components are unchanged. But now we notice an important feature of shearing stress: the two forces we have mentioned exert a torque or couple on the cube, and if they were the only forces acting, it could not be in equilibrium. To get equilibrium, we must at the same time have tangential forces exerted across the faces perpendicular to the x_2 axis, as in Fig. 32b. These forces are equal in magnitude to the others, so that the torques obviously balance, and we have $T_{12} = T_{21} = -S$, all other components of the stress being equal to zero. By proceeding in a similar manner, we can show that in general $T_{ij} = T_{ji}$, or the stress tensor is symmetric about its diagonal.

Since the stress tensor is not diagonal in the coordinates of Fig. 32, it is obvious that these are not principal axes of stress for a shear. We can find the principal axes by inspection, in this simple case: they are obviously the axes rotated 45° with respect to the x_1 and x_2 axes. Let us check this fact by using our general method. The general form of (1.3) is

$$(T_{11} - T'_i)\alpha_{1i} + T_{12}\alpha_{2i} + T_{13}\alpha_{3i} = 0$$
$$T_{21}\alpha_{1i} + (T_{22} - T'_i)\alpha_{2i} + T_{23}\alpha_{3i} = 0$$
$$T_{31}\alpha_{1i} + T_{32}\alpha_{2i} + (T_{33} - T'_i)\alpha_{3i} = 0.$$

In our special case these reduce to

$$-T'_i\alpha_{1i} - S\alpha_{2i} = 0$$
$$-S\alpha_{1i} - T'_i\alpha_{2i} = 0$$
$$-T'_i\alpha_{3i} = 0. \tag{1.4}$$

The secular equation is

$$T'_i(T'^2_i - S^2) = 0$$

of which the solutions are

$$T'_i = \pm S, 0.$$

We take the cases $-S$, S, 0, as referring to the x'_1, x'_2, x'_3 axes, respectively. Substituting the values in (1.4), and solving for the α's, we find

$$\alpha_{11} = \alpha_{21} = \frac{1}{\sqrt{2}}, \qquad \alpha_{31} = 0$$
$$\alpha_{12} = -\alpha_{22} = -\frac{1}{\sqrt{2}}, \qquad \alpha_{32} = 0$$
$$\alpha_{13} = \alpha_{23} = 0, \qquad \alpha_{33} = 1. \tag{1.5}$$

In finding these values, (1.4) determines only the ratios of the α's, not their absolute values. These are found by using in addition the normalization condition (1.2), from which we find everything but the sign; this is determined to make a right-handed set of coordinates. The axes determined by (1.5) are, as we have stated, rotated through 45° with respect to the original axes, as shown in Fig. 32c and 32d. The force across a plane normal to the x'_1 axis is a pressure, or negative tension, of magnitude $-S$, and across a plane normal to the x'_2 axis it is a positive tension of magnitude S. We see thus that a shearing stress, by proper rotation of axes, is reduced to tensions along two principal axes, and this forms a simple illustration of our statement that any stress can be reduced to a diagonal form by proper rotation of coordinates.

2. Strains and Hooke's Law.—In the preceding section we have found the nature of the stress, the force exerted by one part of a body on another across the bounding surface. Next we must consider Hooke's law, which states that a stress within a body is always associated with a strain or deformation of the body, and more specifically that the stress is proportional to the strain, provided that stress and strain are sufficiently small.   To investigate the mathematical formulation of Hooke's law, we must first ask how we describe a strain mathematically.

To begin with, we imagine the body unstrained.   Then, in the process of deformation, we imagine that the particle originally at x_1, x_2, x_3 has been displaced to a point $x_1 + \xi_1$, $x_2 + \xi_2$, $x_3 + \xi_3$.   The three quantities ξ_1, ξ_2, ξ_3 are functions of x_1, x_2, x_3, and are the three components of a vector, the displacement, which is a function of position.   Such a vector field reminds us of a force field, as a gravitational or electric force field, where the force vector on unit mass or charge, respectively, is a function of position.   The displacement is by no means the same thing as the strain: the body might be displaced bodily, without involving any stress or strain at all.   It is only when the displacement of one side of a small element of volume is different from the other, so that the element is distorted in size or shape, that we have a strain.   In other words, the essential quantities in determining the strain are the derivatives of ξ_1, ξ_2, ξ_3, with respect to x_1, x_2, x_3.   Of the nine partial derivatives $\partial \xi_i / \partial x_j$, we readily find that only six quantities, $\partial \xi_i / \partial x_i$, where $i = 1, 2, 3$, and

$$\frac{\partial \xi_i}{\partial x_j} + \frac{\partial \xi_j}{\partial x_i},$$

act like strain components, whereas the three remaining components $(\partial \xi_i / \partial x_j - \partial \xi_j / \partial x_i)$ are related to rigid rotation of the body without involving a strain.   To show this, we set these six quantities equal to zero, and find what type of displacement we have when only the three remaining quantities differ from zero.   Expanding the components of displacement by Taylor's series about a point x_0, and using our special assumptions, we have

$$\xi_1 = \frac{1}{2}\left(\frac{\partial \xi_1}{\partial x_3} - \frac{\partial \xi_3}{\partial x_1}\right)(x_3 - x_{30}) - \frac{1}{2}\left(\frac{\partial \xi_2}{\partial x_1} - \frac{\partial \xi_1}{\partial x_2}\right)(x_2 - x_{20})$$

$$\xi_2 = \frac{1}{2}\left(\frac{\partial \xi_2}{\partial x_1} - \frac{\partial \xi_1}{\partial x_2}\right)(x_1 - x_{10}) - \frac{1}{2}\left(\frac{\partial \xi_3}{\partial x_2} - \frac{\partial \xi_2}{\partial x_3}\right)(x_3 - x_{30})$$

$$\xi_3 = \frac{1}{2}\left(\frac{\partial \xi_3}{\partial x_2} - \frac{\partial \xi_2}{\partial x_3}\right)(x_2 - x_{20}) - \frac{1}{2}\left(\frac{\partial \xi_1}{\partial x_3} - \frac{\partial \xi_3}{\partial x_1}\right)(x_1 - x_{10}).$$

Expressing this in vector language, it is

$$\xi = \tfrac{1}{2}[\text{curl } \xi \times (x - x_0)]. \tag{2.1}$$

Comparing with the vector description of rotational motion in Chap. V, we see that (2.1) means that the displacement ξ under these conditions represents a rotation of magnitude $\frac{1}{2}|\text{curl } \xi|$ about the direction of the vector curl ξ. Since a rotation is a rigid motion, not involving any distortion of a body, we see why it is that such a displacement does not correspond to a strain of the body.

We have, then, six components of strain, $\partial \xi_i / \partial x_i$, and

$$\frac{\partial \xi_i}{\partial x_j} + \frac{\partial \xi_j}{\partial x_i},$$

and six components of stress, T_{ii}, and $T_{ij} = T_{ji}$. Hooke's law states that the strain components are linear functions of the stress components, or vice versa. This would mean six linear equations, with 36 coefficients, which would act as elastic constants. In the most general type of substance, a completely anisotropic crystal, 21 of these really are independent, giving a tremendous number of elastic constants. The reason 21 coefficients are independent is derived from the existence of an elastic potential energy, quadratic in the strain components, and containing therefore 6 terms in squares of strain components, and 15 cross terms, each with an independent coefficient. The stresses are derivatives of the potential energy with respect to the strains, leading to the linear relations between stress and strain, with the 21 independent constants. With isotropic substances showing no crystalline structure, however, most of these constants are either zero or can be written in terms of each other, and there are only two independent elastic constants, called λ and μ. Using these constants, the relations between stress and strain can be shown to have the following form:

$$T_{ij} = \lambda \delta_{ij} \sum_k \frac{\partial \xi_k}{\partial x_k} + \mu \left(\frac{\partial \xi_i}{\partial x_j} + \frac{\partial \xi_j}{\partial x_i} \right). \tag{2.2}$$

Though we shall not give a real proof of this formula, we shall now discuss its interpretation, and show that it is plausible.

In the first place, (2.2) shows one property that must be shown by a relation between stress and strain in an isotropic body: it retains the same form if we rotate the coordinates. The proof of this is indicated in the problems. To show it, we must first find how to get the components of a tensor with respect to rotated axes; this is easily done by a slight extension of the methods of Sec. 1. We can then show that the quantity $\sum_k \partial \xi_k / \partial x_k$, which really is simply div ξ, is invariant, or that it equals $\sum_k \partial \xi_k'/\partial x_k'$. Thus it follows that the first term of (2.2) has the same form in rotated coordinates. To carry out this proof for the second term, we find the components of the tensor $\partial \xi_i/\partial x_j + \partial \xi_j/\partial x_i$ with respect to rotated coordinates, and find that they are $\partial \xi_i'/\partial x_j' + \partial \xi_j'/\partial x_i'$, so that the second term of (2.2) likewise retains its same form in rotated coordinates. It can be shown, in fact, that the combination (2.2) is the most general combination of first partial derivatives that possesses this property, and it is in this way that it is proved that (2.2) is the most general form of Hooke's law for an isotropic body. For a nonisotropic body, of course, the body itself has preferred axes, and it is by no means necessary that the elastic equations should have the same form in any set of rotated axes.

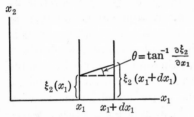

FIG. 33.—Angle of deformation in a shearing strain.

Next we consider the meaning of the terms of (2.2). First we consider a pure shearing strain. For instance, we let $\partial \xi_2/\partial x_1 = \tan \theta$, all other components being zero, as in Fig. 33. Then (2.2) tells us that $T_{12} = T_{21} = \mu \tan \theta$. By our previous discussion, T_{12} and T_{21} equal the shearing stress S, so that μ is the ordinary shear modulus, the ratio of shearing stress to the tangent of the angle of shear. It is not hard to see that the term in μ is set up in such a way that, even if we consider a shear in terms of its principal axes, in which both stress and strain form diagonal tensors, it still expresses correctly the relation between stress and strain. We now consider the first term of (2.2). The quantity div $\boldsymbol{\xi}$ which appears in it is easily seen to be the increase in volume of unit volume, when the body is deformed. The stress resulting from this term is seen at once to be of the nature of a hydrostatic pressure, since it has only diagonal terms, and they are the same in all three directions. Thus the first term of (2.2) is of the nature of a compressibility term, stating that the pressure is proportional to the change of volume. For a liquid, for which there is no shearing stress and μ is zero, the first term of (2.2) is the only one present, and λ is directly related to the compressibility. For a solid, however, the situation is not so simple. Let us assume that the strain is a pure dilatation, $\partial \xi_1/\partial x_1 = \partial \xi_2/\partial x_2 = \partial \xi_3/\partial x_3$, all other components equal to zero. Then we have

$$\frac{\partial \xi_1}{\partial x_1} + \frac{\partial \xi_2}{\partial x_2} + \frac{\partial \xi_3}{\partial x_3} = \text{div } \xi = \frac{\Delta V}{V}$$

where ΔV is the increase in the volume V on account of the displacement. From (2.2) we now have

$$T_{11} = T_{22} = T_{33} = -P = \left(\lambda + \frac{2}{3}\mu\right)\frac{\Delta V}{V}. \tag{2.3}$$

The compressibility κ is defined as the fractional decrease of volume produced by unit pressure; that is,

$$\kappa = -\frac{1}{P}\frac{\Delta V}{V} = \frac{1}{\lambda + \frac{2}{3}\mu}. \tag{2.4}$$

Thus we see that for a liquid λ is the reciprocal of the compressibility, but that for a solid it does not have such a simple physical significance. It is perhaps best to describe it from Eq. (2.4), remembering that the compressibility κ and the shear modulus μ have elementary physical meanings.

3. Static Elasticity.—Problems in static elasticity may be handled by use of Hooke's law (2.2), combined with the fundamental law of statics, that the total force on a body must be zero for it to be at rest, with no acceleration. The total force in this case is the sum of all the surface forces, found by integrating the component of force across each element of area, as computed from the stresses by (1.1), plus any body forces that may be present. The problem is to find the deformed shape of a body under the action of certain external forces; that is, to find the displacement vector ξ_i as a function of the coordinates x_i. As an illustration of the methods that may be used to solve problems in static elasticity, we shall discuss the stretching of a wire. Let the wire be stretched along the x_1 axis, and let the stress be a pure tension T, so that $T_{11} = T$, and all other stress components are zero. Then each volume element of the wire will be in equilibrium, for opposite faces perpendicular to the x_1 axis will have equal and opposite forces, equal to the tension times the area, and faces perpendicular to the x_2 and x_3 axes will have no forces exerted over them. Boundary conditions can then be satisfied over the surface of the wire: over the ends, the wire is to be pulled with a tension T, and over the cylindrical surfaces there is assumed to be no applied stress.

The x_1, x_2, x_3 axes are principal axes for the stress we have assumed, and by symmetry they are also principal axes for the strain, so that we meet only the diagonal components of (2.2), which are

$$T = (\lambda + 2\mu)\frac{\partial \xi_1}{\partial x_1} + \lambda\frac{\partial \xi_2}{\partial x_2} + \lambda\frac{\partial \xi_3}{\partial x_3}$$

$$0 = \lambda\frac{\partial \xi_1}{\partial x_1} + (\lambda + 2\mu)\frac{\partial \xi_2}{\partial x_2} + \lambda\frac{\partial \xi_3}{\partial x_3}$$

$$0 = \lambda\frac{\partial \xi_1}{\partial x_1} + \lambda\frac{\partial \xi_2}{\partial x_2} + (\lambda + 2\mu)\frac{\partial \xi_3}{\partial x_3}. \qquad (3.1)$$

Subtracting the third from the second, we have $\partial \xi_2/\partial x_2 = \partial \xi_3/\partial x_3$. Using this relation, either the second or third gives

$$\frac{\partial \xi_2}{\partial x_2} = -\sigma\frac{\partial \xi_1}{\partial x_1}, \quad \text{where } \sigma = \frac{\lambda}{2(\lambda + \mu)}$$

and where σ is called "Poisson's ratio." Since λ and μ are always positive, it is obvious that Poisson's ratio is never greater than $\frac{1}{2}$. We have found, then, that as the wire is stretched (positive $\partial \xi_1/\partial x_1$), it contracts sideways (negative $\partial \xi_2/\partial x_2$ and $\partial \xi_3/\partial x_3$) and the ratio of sideways contraction per unit width, to lengthwise stretch per unit length, is given by Poisson's ratio. Actual materials have Poisson's ratio of the order of magnitude of $\frac{1}{3}$. Now we put this expression back in the first equation of (3.1), obtaining

$$T = E\frac{\partial \xi_1}{\partial x_1}, \text{ where } E = (\lambda + 2\mu - 2\lambda\sigma). \qquad (3.2)$$

The elastic modulus E, giving the tension, or force per unit area, divided by the elongation per unit length, is Young's modulus, and we have found one way of writing Young's modulus in terms of other elastic constants. In the problems are other ways of writing relations between the various elastic constants.

To contrast with this case of the stretched wire, which is allowed to shrink sideways as it stretches, we may consider the case of the stretching or squeezing of a body that is not allowed to deform in the direction at right angles to the stretching or squeezing. For instance, suppose we had a cylinder and tightly fitting piston, filled the cylinder with a piece of rubber of the same size as the cylinder, and then pushed in the piston, so that the cylinder would not allow the rubber to expand at right angles to the motion of the piston. Then, if the piston moves along the x_1 direction, it is clear that ξ_1 is different from zero, and proportional to x_1, but that ξ_2 and ξ_3 must be zero, since the body cannot expand sideways. The x_1, x_2, x_3 axes are still principal axes, but we may no longer assume that the stresses T_{22} and T_{33} are zero. In fact, they cannot be, for it is obvious physically that the rubber will press outward on the wall of the cylinder, so that the wall in turn must exert a normal stress on the rubber.   Thus (2.2) becomes

$$T_{11} = (\lambda + 2\mu) \frac{\partial \xi_1}{\partial x_1}$$

$$T_{22} = \lambda \frac{\partial \xi_1}{\partial x_1} = T_{33}. \tag{3.3}$$

The first of these equations shows that the force along the x_1 direction is proportional to the elongation in that direction, as in (3.2), but now the elastic modulus concerned is $\lambda + 2\mu$, which is larger than Young's modulus, as we see by comparison with (3.2).   If the body is actually squeezed in the x_1 direction instead of elongated, $\partial \xi_1/\partial x_1$ is of course negative, so that T_{11} is negative, representing a pressure instead of a tension.   Furthermore we see from the last equations of (3.3) that there is also a pressure at right angles to the direction in which the body is squeezed, even though the body is not deformed in that direction at all.

It is instructive to notice the three different relations between T_{11} and $\partial \xi_1/\partial x_1$, the normal stress and strain along one of the principal axes, in the three cases we have considered: the case of hydrostatic compression, in which (2.3) may be rewritten $T_{11} = (3\lambda + 2\mu) \partial \xi_1/\partial x_1$, and in which the pressures along x_2 and x_3 are equal to that along x_1, and great enough to cause equal compressions along the three axes; the case of Eq. (3.3), in which the pressures along x_2 and x_3 are merely enough to keep the body from expanding transversely, and where $T_{11} = (\lambda + 2\mu) \partial \xi_1/\partial x_1$; and finally the case of (3.2), in which we may rewrite the relation in the form $T_{11} = [\lambda + 2\mu - \lambda^2/(\lambda + \mu)] \partial \xi_1/\partial x_1$, in which there are no pressures at all along x_2 and x_3, so that the body expands in these directions if it is compressed along the x_1 direction. For equal strains along the x_1 axis, we see that the stress becomes less along the x_1 axis, as there is less and less stress along the x_2 and x_3 axes, as we should expect physically.

4. Equations of Motion of an Elastic Body.—In the examples of the preceding section, and in the problems at the end of the chapter, we see some of the ways of solving problems in static elasticity.   We now consider the more general problem of the dynamics of elastic bodies, the motions resulting when the forces are not balanced.   The underlying principle which of course we must use is Newton's equation of motion: we must set up the total force acting on an element of volume, and set this equal to the mass times the acceleration, just as we have done in discussing the vibrating string and membrane. Let us find the force on a small element of volume, having sides dx_1, dx_2, dx_3. Over the face at $x_1 + dx_1$, there will be a force $T_{11}(x_1 + dx_1)$, $T_{21}(x_1 + dx_1)$, $T_{31}(x_1 + dx_1)$ per unit area. Similarly exerted over the face at x_1 there will be a force $-T_{11}(x_1)$, $-T_{21}(x_1)$, $-T_{31}(x_1)$. The x_1 component of the resulting force is

$$T_{11}(x_1 + dx_1) - T_{11}(x_1) = \partial T_{11}/\partial x_1 \, dx_1$$

per unit area, or $\partial T_{11}/\partial x_1 \, dx_1 \, dx_2 \, dx_3$ for the area $dx_2 \, dx_3$. The x_2 and x_3 components are $\partial T_{21}/\partial x_1 \, dx_1 \, dx_2 \, dx_3$ and $\partial T_{31}/\partial x_1 \, dx_1 \, dx_2 \, dx_3$, respectively. In the same way we can find the three components of force exerted over each of the two other pairs of faces. Adding, we have for the total x_1 component of force

$$(\partial T_{11}/\partial x_1 + \partial T_{12}/\partial x_2 + \partial T_{13}/\partial x_3) \, dx_1 \, dx_2 \, dx_3.$$

Thus we may write the ith component of force on the element $dx_1 \, dx_2 \, dx_3$ as

$$dF_i = \sum_j \frac{\partial T_{ij}}{\partial x_j} \, dx_1 \, dx_2 \, dx_3.$$

The summation, which is a vector, is defined as the divergence of the tensor T_{ij}, and we see that the divergence of a stress tensor equals the force per unit volume.

To set up the equation of motion, we write the force dF_i acting on a small element of volume equal to the mass times the acceleration. If ρ is the density, the mass of the element $dx_1 \, dx_2 \, dx_3$ is $\rho dx_1 \, dx_2 \, dx_3$, and its acceleration has components $\partial^2 \xi_i/\partial t^2$. Thus we have the equations

$$\sum_j \frac{\partial T_{ij}}{\partial x_j} = \rho \frac{\partial^2 \xi_i}{\partial t^2}, \qquad i = 1, \, 2, \, 3. \tag{4.1}$$

To convert this into an equation of motion for the displacement, we must use Hooke's law, substituting for the stresses in terms of the strains by (2.2). We then find

$$\rho \frac{\partial^2 \xi_i}{\partial t^2} = \sum_j \left[(\lambda + \mu) \frac{\partial^2 \xi_j}{\partial x_i \, \partial x_j} + \mu \frac{\partial^2 \xi_i}{\partial x_j^2} \right], \qquad i = 1, \, 2, \, 3. \tag{4.2}$$

This very general partial differential equation is hard to work with, and indicates the fact that elastic waves in solids are very complicated things. We can set up a simple case, however, by considering a plane wave: a wave in which the displacement is a function of distance in one direction only, as for instance a function of x_1 only, as well as of time.

Assuming then that any derivative with respect to x_2 or x_3 is zero, the three components of (4.2) reduce to

$$\rho \frac{\partial^2 \xi_1}{\partial t^2} = (\lambda + 2\mu) \frac{\partial^2 \xi_1}{\partial x_1^2}$$

$$\rho \frac{\partial^2 \xi_2}{\partial t^2} = \mu \frac{\partial^2 \xi_2}{\partial x_1^2}$$

$$\rho \frac{\partial^2 \xi_3}{\partial t^2} = \mu \frac{\partial^2 \xi_3}{\partial x_1^2}. \tag{4.3}$$

These equations have the form of the wave equation, which we have already met in connection with the stretched string in Eq. (1.1), Chap. VIII, and for the vibrating membrane in Eq. (1.1), Chap. XI.

We see from (4.3) that plane waves of two types can exist. The first equation deals with a displacement in the direction of propagation of the wave. This is a longitudinal wave, and comparison with our previous solutions for the string and the membrane shows that sinusoidal waves, or in fact other types of waves, can be propagated with a velocity $\sqrt{(\lambda + 2\mu)/\rho}$. The second and third equations deal with displacements at right angles with the direction of propagation, or with transverse waves, and their velocity is similarly $\sqrt{\mu/\rho}$. From this we see that the velocity of longitudinal waves is always greater than that of transverse waves. Furthermore, we see that in a liquid, in which shearing stresses are not present, and in which $\mu = 0$, transverse waves cannot exist. These simple solutions, plane longitudinal and transverse waves, can be propagated quite independently in an infinite

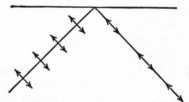

Fig. 34.—Incident transverse wave, with longitudinal reflected wave.

solid, but the problem becomes very complicated when we consider boundary conditions at the surface of a finite solid. In general, when a wave of one type is reflected from a surface, then unless the reflection is at normal incidence, longitudinal motion will generally be partly converted into transverse, and vice versa. In Fig. 34 we show diagrammatically how this could be, the transverse motion in the incident wave evidently being in such a direction as to be partly transformed into longitudinal motion in the reflected wave. For this reason, the complete treatment of the vibrations of an elastic solid is a very complicated problem. An example is found in geophysical problems, where one is interested in the propagation of earthquake waves through the earth. This case is made even more difficult by the fact that the elastic properties of the earth change as a function of depth, so that one must use solutions of the form we have discussed in Chap. X, in connection with strings whose properties depend on position.

One application of the theory of the waves in an elastic solid has at least historical interest. When it was discovered that light was a transverse wave motion, an attempt was made to identify these waves with the transverse vibrations of an elastic solid, called the "ether." The general properties, and even some of the details, such as the quantitative laws giving the fraction of light reflected and transmitted at a boundary, were correctly worked out, the reflection being treated by analogy with our discussion of reflection of waves in strings at a point of discontinuity of density, in Chap. IX. But the difficulty, which could not be overcome, was that of eliminating the longitudinal waves, which certainly do not occur in optics, but which were inherent in the elastic solid theory. This difficulty does not occur in the present electromagnetic theory, where only transverse waves are allowed by the fundamental differential equations. This lack of longitudinal waves makes the problem of optical wave motion on the whole simpler than that of elastic waves.

The simplest case of elastic waves is that found in a fluid, where transverse waves are impossible. Our general equation (4.2) is complicated largely because it is a vector equation, dealing with the three components of displacement, and because it combines longitudinal and transverse waves in a single equation. We can describe a longitudinal wave in terms of the displacement along the direction of motion, but we can equally well describe it in terms of the change of density, a scalar (or in terms of the pressure, which is related to the change of density through the compressibility). We have seen that the change of density is given by $\sum_i (\partial \xi_i / \partial x_i)$, a scalar quantity. We may find the equation satisfied by this quantity by differentiating (4.2) with respect to x_i, and summing over i. When we do this, we find that we have the equation

$$\rho \frac{\partial^2}{\partial t^2} \left(\sum_i \frac{\partial \xi_i}{\partial x_i} \right) = (\lambda + 2\mu) \nabla^2 \left(\sum_i \frac{\partial \xi_i}{\partial x_i} \right). \tag{4.4}$$

This is a three-dimensional wave equation for the quantity $\sum_i (\partial \xi_i / \partial x_i)$,

and describes wave propagation with a velocity that is the same that we found earlier for a longitudinal wave. We note that the elastic constant concerned in longitudinal wave propagation in an extended medium is that found in (3.3), resulting statically from a deformation in which a body is squeezed, while enough sideways stress is applied to keep it from expanding or contracting in the direction at right angles to the deformation. For the particular case of a fluid, in which μ is zero, and λ reduces to the reciprocal of the compressibility, we see that the velocity is given by $1/\sqrt{\kappa\rho}$. This well-known formula is familiar for sound waves in a gas, such as we are concerned with in the theory of propagation of sound in the atmosphere.

The three-dimensional wave equation, of the form given in (4.4), possesses a great variety of solutions, which we shall not discuss, though we take some of them up in the problems. We can have not only plane waves, but for instance spherical waves, in which the wave diverges from a point source, traveling outward along radii. This is the type of disturbance propagated out from a source of sound. We can have various plane or spherical waves superposed, and in this way can find phenomena of interference and diffraction. The problem of wave motion in three dimensions is a very broad one, which is met not only in elastic waves, such as we see here, but in electromagnetic waves and optics as well, as we have already mentioned.

Furthermore, as we have also mentioned, the simplest case of three-dimensional waves is that of sound waves in a fluid, where only longitudinal waves are possible, and where the problem can be treated by a scalar wave equation, as (4.4). The next more complicated case is that of electromagnetic or optical waves, in which only transverse waves occur, so that we need a vector wave equation, with a single velocity of propagation, and in which we have two directions of polarization, the vector representing the disturbance (which in that case is the electric or magnetic field vector) being at right angles to the direction of propagation, in either of two directions. The most complicated case is that of elastic waves in a solid, in which longitudinal and transverse waves both occur, with different velocities, as we have considered in the present section.

All these cases are greatly simplified, however, by the fact that we are dealing with isotropic media, in which there are no preferred directions. In a crystal, there are generally axes determined by the crystal structure, fixed in the crystal, and the velocity of propagation is different in different directions. Whether we are dealing with elastic or with electromagnetic waves, the problem of crystals is very difficult, and we shall not attempt even to suggest the sort of situation arising when we try to give a general discussion of wave propagation, beyond saying that a wave starting out from a point source spreads out, not with spherical wave fronts, but in ellipsoidal wave fronts, and that three separate ellipsoids, corresponding to the three possible directions of displacement, independently spread out from a single vibrating point within a solid.

Problems

1. In Fig. 35, let the normal to the inclined face of the prism have direction cosines l, m, n. Compute the total forces exerted by an arbitrary stress on the prism, and prove that the net force is zero, and the prism is in equilibrium, only if the force per unit area over the face perpendicular to n has x component $lT_{11} + mT_{12} + nT_{13}$, and so on.

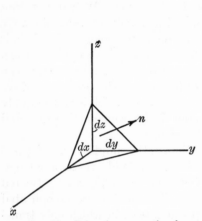

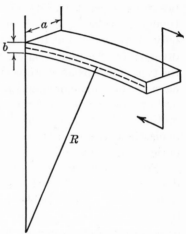

Fig. 35.—Prism for computing force exerted by stresses across a face with arbitrary normal n.

Fig. 36.—Bent beam.

2. Prove that in terms of Young's modulus and Poisson's ratio we have

$$\lambda = \frac{E\sigma}{(1 + \sigma)(1 - 2\sigma)}, \qquad 2\mu = \frac{E}{1 + \sigma}.$$

3. Assume a body is under pure hydrostatic pressure P. Show that the distortion is a decrease of all dimensions by a fixed fraction. Show that the fractional change in volume is $\partial \xi_1/\partial x + \partial \xi_2/\partial y + \partial \xi_3/\partial z$. Using this, show that the compressibility κ of a solid under hydrostatic pressure, which by definition is the fractional decrease of volume divided by the pressure, equals $3(1 - 2\sigma)/E$.

4. A rectangular beam held at one end is bent into an arc of a circle, the radius of curvature of its central section being R. Find the stress distribution throughout the beam, showing that the beam will be kept in equilibrium by a torque or couple of the sort indicated in Fig. 36. Show that for a given torque the curvature of the beam is inversely proportional to ab^3E, where E is Young's modulus.

5. A circular cylinder of height h rests in equilibrium under the action of gravity. Take a coordinate system with the xy plane in the top base of the cylinder and the positive z axis pointing downward. Show that the only component of stress different from zero is $T_{33} = -\rho g z$, if ρ is the density of the cylinder. Using Hooke's law show that the strains are $\partial \xi_1/\partial x = \partial \xi_2/\partial y = (\sigma/E)\rho g z$, and $\partial \xi_3/\partial z = -(1/E)\rho g z$, and find the other partial derivatives. Integrate these expressions to find the components of the displacement of any point of the medium, remembering that the strains are partial derivatives. Show that a horizontal plane section of the cylinder becomes a paraboloid of rotation due to the deformation. Show that the radius of the cylinder increases from top to bottom when it is thus deformed.

6. A spherical shell of inner radius R_1, outer radius R_2, contains a fluid of pressure P_1, and is immersed in a second fluid of lower pressure P_2. It can be shown that the displacements of points on account of the pressure are given by $\xi_1 = x(A + B/r^3)$, $\xi_2 = y(A + B/r^3)$, $\xi_3 = z(A + B/r^3)$. Verify these values by computing the stresses at any point, substituting in the equations of motion, and showing that they result in equilibrium. Show further that the force across an area normal to the radius is itself normal to the surface, so that the stress within the sphere can be balanced by hydrostatic pressures within and without.

7. In the shell of Prob. 6, determine A and B so that the pressure will have the proper values at R_1 and R_2. Discuss the stress within the shell, showing that the principal axes at any point are along the radius and two arbitrary directions at right angles, and find the tension or pressure along the directions at right angles, discussing the final result physically, with special reference to possible breaking of the shell under excessive pressure inside.

8. Consider a beam of rectangular cross section under compression. Find expressions for the components of normal and shearing stresses on a slant section of the beam, the normal to the section making an angle θ with the long axis of the beam. For what value of θ is the shearing stress a maximum?

9. Show, following the argument outlined in the text, that Eq. (2.2) is invariant under an arbitrary rotation of coordinates.

10. Derive the wave equation for torsional waves traveling along the axis of a solid right circular cylindrical rod. What is the velocity of propagation of these waves?

11. Using the discussion of the wave equation in spherical coordinates, given in Probs. 7 to 9, Chap. XI, consider the propagation of sound in a fluid, as given by Eq. (4.4). Show that a simple spherical wave is given by $(1/r)\{f[t - (r/v)] + g[t + (r/v)]\}$, where r is the distance from the source, v is the velocity of propagation, and f, g are two arbitrary functions. Discuss the physical nature of this solution.

CHAPTER XIII

FLOW OF FLUIDS

The distinction between a liquid and a solid is that a liquid flows under a shearing stress, and a solid does not. At first sight the distinction is clear; on closer examination it is not so obvious. Many solids show the phenomenon of creep; that is, under a continued stress, they flow, rather than behaving like the perfect solids of the preceding chapter, and undergoing a displacement proportional to the stress, which does not increase as time goes on. The creep is very slow, however, and the motion is opposed by a force like viscous resistance. All liquids show viscosity to some extent. That is to say, they can support a shearing stress, but it is proportional to the velocity, rather than to the displacement as with a solid, and the shearing stress per unit velocity gradient is the coefficient of viscosity. If the viscous resistance is moderately small, the material behaves like an ordinary liquid, and there is no question about its nature; but if it is very large, it may be so great that it takes a very long time for the material to flow, and it approaches a solid with the phenomenon of creep. Materials exist that act like a solid when subjected to sudden stresses, but flow like a liquid under the action of long-continued stresses, no matter how small. Examples like these prepare us for finding a similarity between the flow of fluids and the theory of elasticity, and in fact we can set up a combined theory that comprises both types of substances. At the beginning, however, we shall consider a so-called "perfect fluid," for which there is no viscosity, and for which the shear modulus is zero. Later we shall inquire regarding the changes in the theory resulting from viscosity.

The practical matter in which the theory of fluid flow differs from that of elasticity is that the displacement of the particles can become very large, whereas in elasticity it is always treated as small. If we follow a particle of fluid during its motion, it traces out a line, which we may call a "line of flow." The instantaneous velocity, or time rate of change of the displacement vector ξ, is always in the direction of the lines of flow. This velocity, as a function of position, forms a vector field, or a vector defined at each point of space. We have already met such vector fields, not only in the displacement vector of the preceding chapter, but in our discussion of forces and potentials in Chap. III, for the force is defined at every point of space and forms a vector field. Much of the theory of hydrodynamics, or the flow of fluids, applies to other problems in flow, or in vector fields, such as the flow of heat, the flow of electric current, and the behavior of electric and magnetic fields. All these problems, though so different physically, are mathematically similar and can be treated by the same analytical methods, and for that reason a study of the flow of fluids is particularly important and fundamental in theoretical physics.

1. Velocity, Flux Density, and Lines of Flow.— Before we can consider the dynamics of fluid flow, we must consider carefully the kinematics of flow, the lines of flow that we just mentioned. At every point of a flowing medium, we can define the velocity, a vector (the time rate of change of the displacement ξ, which we used in the preceding chapter).

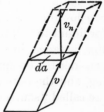

Fig. 37.—Flux through an area da.

We denote this velocity by **v**, and note that it has components v_1, v_2, v_3, equal to ξ_1, ξ_2, ξ_3, respectively. Also we can give the density ρ, and both ρ and **v** are in general functions of position (x_1, x_2, x_3) and of time. We may now ask, how much material will flow across any area per second? This total flow across a surface is called a "flux." In Fig. 37, we consider an infinitesimal surface element da. With da as a base we erect a prism, the slant height being the velocity **v**, which in general is not normal to da. Evidently the material in the prism will just be that which crosses da in 1 sec, since in this time it will move a distance **v**, and fill the dotted prism. But this is ρ (the density) times the volume of the prism (the base da times the altitude v_n, where n is the normal to the surface), or $\rho v_n \, da$. The quantity $\rho \mathbf{v}$ is called the "flux density," and we may denote it by **f**. Then, for a finite area, the total flux will be the sum of the contributions from all the surface elements, or a surface integral

$$\iint f_n \, da = \iint \rho v_n \, da.$$

In some kinds of flow, such as heat flow, there is an analogue to the flux, but not to the density and velocity separately, so that one regards the flux density as being the more fundamental vector field.

We can draw lines through the medium, the lines of flow, tangent at every point to the velocity vector. Similarly we can set up tubes of flow, the elements of their surfaces being lines of flow. We can consider the substance to flow through these tubes, as water flows through

a pipe, never passing outside, since the velocity is always tangential
to the surface of the tube. In hydrodynamics these lines of flow are
called "streamlines," and the sort of flow in which they are independent
of time is called "streamline flow." We may now prove an important
theorem called the "equation of continuity," which states that, as a
fluid flows along, its total amount is conserved, since matter cannot be
created or destroyed.

Consider a fixed volume in a flowing fluid. The amount of fluid in
the volume is $\iiint \rho \, dv$, and this can change in two ways. First, liquid
can flow into the volume over the surface. Secondly, it may be possible
for liquid to be produced within the volume without having flowed in.
For instance, in a swimming pool, for all practical purposes we may
consider the opening of the inlet pipe as a region where fluid is appearing, and the outlet as a place where it is disappearing. Such regions
are called "sources" and "sinks," respectively. Then we have

$$\iiint \frac{\partial \rho}{\partial t} \, dv = \text{rate of inflow over the surface}$$
$$+ \text{ rate of production inside.}$$

We have just seen that the rate of flow over any surface, or flux, is
$\iint f_n \, da$. This represents outflow if n is the outer normal to a closed
surface, so that we must change sign to get the inflow. If in addition
we assume that the rate of production of material per unit volume is P,
we have

$$\iiint \frac{\partial \rho}{\partial t} \, dv = -\iint f_n \, da + \iiint P \, dv, \tag{1.1}$$

the volume integrals being over the whole region we are considering,
the surface integral over the surface enclosing this volume.

We may now transform (1.1) by the divergence theorem of vector
analysis, which is proved in Appendix IV, and which states that

$$\iint f_n \, da = \iiint \text{div } \mathbf{f} \, dv,$$

in which $\mathbf{f}$ is any vector function of position, the surface integral is the
surface integral of its normal flux outward over a closed surface, and the
volume integral of the divergence is taken over the volume enclosed
by the surface. Substituting in (1.1), we have an equation between
volume integrals. This equation must hold no matter what the volume
over which the integrals are extended; and this is impossible unless the
integrands themselves satisfy the same equation, since we may take
the volume as small as we please, and so small as to include only an

infinitesimal volume surrounding a given point, over which the integrands will be constant.   Thus we have

$$\frac{\partial \rho}{\partial t} = - \operatorname{div} \mathbf{f} + P. \tag{1.2}$$

This is the equation of continuity.   We may note several special cases. If there is no production of fluid in the volume considered, it becomes

$$\frac{\partial \rho}{\partial t} + \operatorname{div} \mathbf{f} = 0,$$

or, using $\mathbf{f} = \rho \mathbf{v}$,

$$\frac{\partial \rho}{\partial t} + \operatorname{div} (\rho \mathbf{v}) = 0.$$

For an incompressible fluid, for which ρ is constant, (1.2) becomes

$$\operatorname{div} \mathbf{f} = P.$$

This holds also for a steady state, for which the density at a given point of space is independent of time, even for a compressible fluid. This equation shows the physical meaning of the divergence of a flux vector: it measures the rate of production of the flowing substance, per unit volume.   Finally, if no substance is being produced at the point in question, and the density is independent of time, $\operatorname{div} \mathbf{f} = 0$, and we have a divergenceless flow.

   The equation of continuity allows us to use a convention that is convenient not only in hydrodynamics but also in electrostatics and magnetostatics: to give a certain physical meaning to the number of lines of flow per unit area, letting the number of lines crossing unit area perpendicular to the flow be numerically equal to the magnitude of the flux density.   We could surely do this, but we might have the necessity of sometimes letting lines start or stop, to keep the right number.   We can prove, however, that with a divergenceless flow this would not be necessary.   The lines start or stop only at places where the divergence is different from zero; that is, they start at sources, stop at sinks.   For an elementary proof, let us take a short section of a tube of flow, bounded by two surfaces normal to the flow.   Let one of them have an area A_1, the other A_2, and let the magnitude of the flux over one face be f_1, over the other f_2.   Then the total current in over one face is $f_1 A_1$, and out over the other is $f_2 A_2$.   If the flow is divergenceless, these are equal.   But the number of lines per unit area on the first is f_1, so that the number cutting one end of the tube is $f_1 A_1$, and the number emerging at the other end is $f_2 A_2$.   Since these are equal, no lines are lost or start within. In other words, in a divergenceless flow, lines never start of stop except at sources or sinks. For a more general proof, we note that the number of lines crossing a surface element da, by definition, is $f_n\, da$. Then the number emerging from a closed surface, and which therefore have started within the surface, is $\iint f_n\, da$. But by the divergence theorem this is $\iiint \operatorname{div} \mathbf{f}\, dv$, and is zero if the flow is divergenceless.

2. Irrotational Flow and the Velocity Potential.—In Chap. III we studied vector fields like our flux vector; we were interested then in forces. We saw that, under certain conditions, a force could be written as a gradient of a potential function. The condition was that the work done in taking a particle around any closed path should be zero, or that the field should be conservative: $\int \mathbf{F} \cdot \mathbf{ds} = 0$ around any contour. We had another way of stating the condition: it was $\operatorname{curl} \mathbf{F} = 0$ everywhere. In a similar way, if the curl of our velocity vector is zero, we can introduce a potential function here. It is now to be regarded as a purely mathematical device, used simply by analogy with our previous cases, and having nothing to do with potential energy.

A flow whose curl is everywhere zero is called an "irrotational flow." It is easy to prove that in a whirlpool the curl is different from zero, a nonvanishing curl indicating in fact exactly a whirlpool. Now physically we are acquainted with two sorts of fluid flow: streamline flow and turbulent flow. In the latter, eddies or whirlpools form, and the curl of the velocity is not zero. But in the former, there are no eddies, the curl of the velocity is zero, and the flow is irrotational. We shall show in a later section that this follows from the equations of motion of the fluid. We shall show that, as a small amount of fluid moves along its path, the curl of its velocity does not change. Thus, if it starts from a region where the velocity has no curl, this condition will persist throughout its motion, and the motion will be irrotational. On the other hand, a typical case in which the motion is not irrotational is that of a fluid flowing rapidly through a pipe, if we consider the effect of viscosity. A real fluid clings to the wall of a pipe, and the fluid close to the wall is moving slowly. If that farther from the wall is moving rapidly, the velocity will have a curl in the region near the wall, since the magnitude of the velocity vector changes in a direction transverse to the direction of the vector. Since the curl remains constant as the fluid travels along, there can be a formation of vortices, or whirlpools, which can in some cases detach themselves from the wall of the tube, and result in a complicated whirlpool motion within the body of the liquid. This is a simple picture of the origin of turbulence, the condition in which the curl of the velocity is not zero, and which is the case contrasting with that of irrotational or streamline flow.

Returning to the case of streamline flow, we can introduce a potential function, called the velocity potential φ, defined by $\mathbf{v} = -\operatorname{grad}\varphi$. The velocity potential, of course, is not a potential energy; its analogy with potential energies is mathematical rather than physical. Nevertheless, we can draw surfaces of constant velocity potential, or equipotentials, and the lines of flow will cut the equipotentials at right angles. Using the equation of continuity, and assuming that ρ is constant, as for an incompressible fluid, we have as the general equation for the velocity potential

$$\operatorname{div}(\rho\mathbf{v}) =$$
$$-\rho \operatorname{div}\operatorname{grad}\varphi = -\rho\nabla^2\varphi = P, \quad (2.1)$$

reducing to Laplace's equation $\nabla^2\varphi = 0$ for a steady state where there are no sources or sinks.

The introduction of a velocity potential satisfying Laplace's equation makes it possible in many cases to solve hydrodynamic problems by analogy with similar problems in other branches of physics, as electrostatics. The electrostatic potential satisfies Laplace's equation, the lines of force being normal to the equipotentials, so that any set of electrostatic equipotentials can be used for a suitable

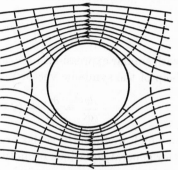

Fig. 38.—Lines of flow and equipotentials for flow about a cylinder. Full lines indicate lines of flow, dotted lines equipotentials. In a corresponding electrical problem with charges distributed within the cylinder, and placed in a uniform external electric field, the dotted lines would be lines of force, full lines equipotentials.

hydrodynamic problem. For instance, in Fig. 38 we show the lines of flow and equipotentials for streamline flow of a liquid about a cylinder. The same lines, however, represent lines of force resulting from a certain distribution of charges on the axis of the cylinder, superposed on a uniform electric field.

3. Euler's Equations of Motion for Ideal Fluids.—The equation of continuity, supplemented by the condition that the curl of the velocity is zero for streamline flow, serves to determine the velocity of flow in a liquid, but does not determine the pressure, or make any connection with forces. The equation of continuity by itself is only a kinematical, rather than a dynamical, law. It is one of two fundamental equations governing fluid motion. The other is essentially the Newtonian law, force equals mass times acceleration. For a continuous medium, we have already seen how this is to be formulated in the preceding chapter, where we wrote the force on an element of volume in terms of the stresses. As we have already mentioned, an ideal fluid is characterized by the fact that it supports no shear and hence $\mu = 0$. For this case the six stress components reduce to one, namely,

$$T_{11} = T_{22} = T_{33} = -p,$$

and $T_{12} = T_{23} = T_{31} = 0$, if p denotes the pressure in the fluid. Furthermore, if there is flow of the fluid, one must consider the velocity of each particle as a function of x_1, x_2, x_3, and t, and hence

$$\frac{dv_1}{dt} = \frac{\partial v_1}{\partial t} + v_1 \frac{\partial v_1}{\partial x_1} + v_2 \frac{\partial v_1}{\partial x_2} + v_3 \frac{\partial v_1}{\partial x_3}, \tag{3.1}$$

with similar expressions for v_2 and v_3. Written in vector form with the help of the symbolic vector ∇, this is

$$\frac{dv_1}{dt} = \frac{\partial v_1}{\partial t} + (\mathbf{v} \cdot \nabla)v_1 = \frac{\partial v_1}{\partial t} + (\mathbf{v} \cdot \text{grad})v_1$$

in which we form the scalar product of $\mathbf{v}$ and ∇ and then operate on v_1. Our general equations of motion become in this case

$$\rho X_i - \frac{\partial p}{\partial x_i} = \rho \left[\frac{\partial v_i}{\partial t} + (\mathbf{v} \cdot \text{grad})v_i \right], \tag{3.2}$$

where i can be 1, 2, 3, and where X_i represents the body force (as gravitation) per unit mass, which we disregarded in the preceding chapter. Dividing by the density, (3.2) becomes

$$X_i - \frac{1}{\rho} \frac{\partial p}{\partial x_i} = \frac{\partial v_i}{\partial t} + (\mathbf{v} \cdot \text{grad})v_i. \tag{3.3}$$

These are the Euler equations of hydrodynamics. In them ρ (the density) is considered a known function of the pressure as given by the equation of state of the substance. We then have p, v_i, as functions of x_i and t. The three equations (3.3) and the equation of continuity provide the necessary four equations to give a unique solution. For the case of hydrostatic equilibrium, these equations reduce to the form

$$X_i = \left(\frac{1}{\rho}\right) \frac{\partial p}{\partial x_i},$$

from which such familiar things as Archimedes' principle immediately follow.

Using Euler's equations (3.3), we can prove a theorem due to Lagrange, relating to the curl of the velocity, from which we arrive at the understanding of irrotational flow. We shall try to find the time rate of change, following along with the flow, of the curl of the velocity. That is, we shall find d/dt (curl $\mathbf{v}$). The x_1 component of this quantity is $d/dt(\partial v_3/\partial x_2 - \partial v_2/\partial x_3)$. Remembering that

$$\frac{d}{dt} = \frac{\partial}{\partial t} + v_1 \frac{\partial}{\partial x_1} + v_2 \frac{\partial}{\partial x_2} + v_3 \frac{\partial}{\partial x_3},$$

as we see from (3.1), we find easily that

$$\frac{d}{dt}\left(\frac{\partial v_3}{\partial x_2} - \frac{\partial v_2}{\partial x_3}\right) = \left(\frac{\partial}{\partial x_2}\frac{dv_3}{dt} - \frac{\partial}{\partial x_3}\frac{dv_2}{dt}\right) - \frac{\partial v_1}{\partial x_2}\frac{\partial v_3}{\partial x_1} - \frac{\partial v_2}{\partial x_2}\frac{\partial v_3}{\partial x_2}$$
$$- \frac{\partial v_3}{\partial x_2}\frac{\partial v_3}{\partial x_3} + \frac{\partial v_1}{\partial x_3}\frac{\partial v_2}{\partial x_1} + \frac{\partial v_2}{\partial x_3}\frac{\partial v_2}{\partial x_2} + \frac{\partial v_3}{\partial x_3}\frac{\partial v_2}{\partial x_3}. \quad (3.4)$$

We shall now transform the terms on the right side of (3.4). We note that (3.3) can be rewritten $dv_i/dt = X_i - (1/\rho)(\partial p/\partial x_i)$. It is convenient to introduce a quantity Π, defined by the equation

$$\Pi = \int_0^p \frac{dp}{\rho(p)} \quad (3.5)$$

whose gradient is

$$\operatorname{grad} \Pi = \frac{d\Pi}{dp} \operatorname{grad} p = \frac{1}{\rho} \operatorname{grad} p.$$

Then (3.3) takes the form

$$\frac{dv_i}{dt} = X_i - \operatorname{grad}_i \Pi. \quad (3.6)$$

The first two terms of the right side of (3.4),

$$\left(\frac{\partial}{\partial x_2}\frac{dv_3}{dt} - \frac{\partial}{\partial x_3}\frac{dv_2}{dt}\right),$$

are the x_1 component of the curl of the quantity (3.6). We assume that the body forces X_i are derivable from a potential; then their curl vanishes. Furthermore the curl of any gradient vanishes. Hence the first two terms of the right side of (3.4) vanish. For the remaining terms, we assume that the fluid is incompressible, so that the divergence of its velocity is zero, or

$$\frac{\partial v_1}{\partial x_1} + \frac{\partial v_2}{\partial x_2} + \frac{\partial v_3}{\partial x_3} = 0. \quad (3.7)$$

Combining (3.7) with (3.4), we find

$$\frac{d}{dt}\operatorname{curl}_1 \mathbf{v} = \frac{\partial v_1}{\partial x_1}\operatorname{curl}_1 \mathbf{v} + \frac{\partial v_2}{\partial x_1}\operatorname{curl}_2 \mathbf{v} + \frac{\partial v_3}{\partial x_1}\operatorname{curl}_3 \mathbf{v}. \qquad (3.8)$$

This equation is the one from which we may draw conclusions about the behavior of curl $\mathbf{v}$. If at any time curl $\mathbf{v}$ is zero, the right-hand side of (3.8) vanishes. The equation then tells us that the time rate of change of curl $\mathbf{v}$ also vanishes. Hence after an infinitesimal increment of time curl $\mathbf{v}$ is still zero, the argument can be repeated, and we conclude that curl $\mathbf{v}$ must remain permanently zero. Thus we conclude that if the fluid starts out its motion with a velocity that has no curl (as, for instance, if it starts from rest) its curl will not subsequently differ from zero, and the motion will be irrotational.

4. Irrotational Flow and Bernoulli's Equation.—For irrotational flow in an incompressible fluid, we have found in (2.1) that the velocity potential satisfies Laplace's equation, so that we can find the lines of flow by solution of that equation. This does not tell us, however, how rapidly the fluid moves along the tubes of flow, but merely defines these tubes geometrically. To find the details of the motion, we must go back to Euler's equations, which take a particularly simple form in this case. If $\mathbf{v} = -\operatorname{grad}\varphi$, we then have

$$(\mathbf{v}\cdot\operatorname{grad})v_1 = -\left(\mathbf{v}\cdot\operatorname{grad}\frac{\partial\varphi}{\partial x_1}\right)$$

$$= \frac{\partial\varphi}{\partial x_1}\frac{\partial^2\varphi}{\partial x_1^2} + \frac{\partial\varphi}{\partial x_2}\frac{\partial^2\varphi}{\partial x_1\,\partial x_2} + \frac{\partial\varphi}{\partial x_3}\frac{\partial^2\varphi}{\partial x_1\,\partial x_3}$$

$$= \frac{1}{2}\frac{\partial}{\partial x_1}\left[\left(\frac{\partial\varphi}{\partial x_1}\right)^2 + \left(\frac{\partial\varphi}{\partial x_2}\right)^2 + \left(\frac{\partial\varphi}{\partial x_3}\right)^2\right]$$

so that

$$(\mathbf{v}\cdot\operatorname{grad})\mathbf{v} = \operatorname{grad}\left(\frac{v^2}{2}\right).$$

Introducing our quantity Π from (3.5), Euler's equation for the steady state, where $\mathbf{v}$ is independent of time, then becomes

$$\mathbf{X} = \operatorname{grad}\left(\Pi + \frac{v^2}{2}\right).$$

As a result of this equation, we see that, for irrotational flow to occur, $\mathbf{X}$ must be the gradient of a certain quantity, or $\mathbf{X}$ must be a conservative force, derivable from a potential; this is reasonable, since we have already used the assumption that $\mathbf{X}$ is a conservative force in evaluating (3.4), from which the irrotational flow is derived. We may then set $\mathbf{X} = -$ grad V, and Euler's equation becomes

$$\text{grad}\left(V + \Pi + \frac{v^2}{2}\right) = 0,$$

or integrated,

$$V + \Pi + \frac{v^2}{2} = \text{constant.}$$

This is Bernoulli's equation. For the special case of an incompressible fluid, ρ is independent of p, so that Π is equal to p/ρ. In that case the equation may be written

$$\rho V + p + \tfrac{1}{2}\rho v^2 = \text{constant.}$$

Bernoulli's equation is essentially an energy integral, the term ρV representing the potential energy per unit volume, p the contribution to the energy resulting from the pressure, and $\tfrac{1}{2}\rho v^2$ the kinetic energy per unit volume. As we have stated, Bernoulli's equation, supplemented for a compressible fluid by the relation giving density as a function of pressure, determines the pressure at each point of space, when the velocity and external potential are known. For instance, if there is no external force field ($V = 0$), we see that the pressure decreases at points where the velocity is high, which means at points where the tubes of flow narrow down. Bernoulli's equation, combined with the equation of continuity, forms the well-known method for handling elementary problems of the flow of fluids in pipes when viscosity is neglected.

5. Viscous Fluids and Poiseuille's Law.—We have already mentioned that ideal nonviscous fluids support no shearing stresses, but that this is not true of viscous fluids. Consider a viscous liquid flowing horizontally, the lower layers dragging along the bottom, and the velocity increasing with height, so that $v_1 = v_1(x_2)$, other components of v are zero, if the $x_1 x_3$ plane is horizontal, x_2 is vertical. Then if we imagine a horizontal element of area in the liquid at a given height, the material above the element of area will pull tangentially on the material below it on account of viscosity, thus exerting a shearing stress. Experimentally, this stress, which is T_{12}, is proportional to the rate of increase of horizontal component of velocity with height: if k is the coefficient of viscosity, $T_{12} = k \, \partial v_1/\partial x_2$. This is a special case of the general laws governing stresses in a viscous medium, connecting the stresses with the rates of change of the velocity components with position.

In the preceding chapter we gave the general form of Hooke's law, the law giving stresses in an elastic medium in terms of the strains. By analogy we can set up the relations for a viscous fluid, but now the stresses are proportional, not to the strain components themselves, but to their time derivatives. By comparison with Eq. (2.2), Chap. XII, we see that k takes the place of the shear modulus, and that the component of strain $\partial \xi_i/\partial x_j + \partial \xi_j/\partial x_i$ must be replaced by its time derivative, $\partial v_i/\partial x_j + \partial v_j/\partial x_i$. Thus we have the following relations between the stress and strain components for liquids:

$$
\begin{aligned}
T_{ij} &= \lambda \delta_{ij} \sum_k \frac{\partial \xi_k}{\partial x_k} + k \left(\frac{\partial v_i}{\partial x_j} + \frac{\partial v_j}{\partial x_i} \right) \\
&= -p\delta_{ij} + k \left(\frac{\partial v_i}{\partial x_j} + \frac{\partial v_j}{\partial x_i} \right)
\end{aligned}
\tag{5.1}
$$

where we have included the ordinary pressure of the liquid in addition to the viscous stresses. We see that the example we used above, in which v_1 was a function of x_2, and the other components of v were zero, is consistent with (5.1). We may now insert the stress components (5.1) in the equation of motion, Eq. (4.1) of Chap. XII. We assume an incompressible fluid, for which div $\mathbf{v} = 0$, by the equation of continuity, and we consider body forces as well as stresses. Then we find for the equation of motion

$$
\rho X_i - \frac{\partial p}{\partial x_i} + k\nabla^2 v_i = \rho \frac{dv_i}{dt},
\tag{5.2}
$$

differing from (3.3) by the term $k\nabla^2 v_i$.

As a simple and important special case of (5.2), we consider Poiseuille's law, governing the streamline flow of a viscous fluid through a tube. Consider an incompressible liquid flowing in a steady state in a horizontal cylinder of radius R parallel to the long axis of the cylinder (x_1 axis). We have $v_2 = v_3 = 0$, and since there are no body forces $X_i = 0$. The equation of continuity becomes $\partial v_1/\partial x_1 = 0$, so that v_1 is a function of x_2 and x_3 alone. Then

$$
\frac{dv_1}{dt} = v_1 \frac{\partial v_1}{\partial x_1} + v_2 \frac{\partial v_1}{\partial x_2} + v_3 \frac{\partial v_1}{\partial x_3} = 0.
$$

Furthermore, if we take the divergence of the fundamental equations of motion, we have

$$
\rho \text{ div } \mathbf{X} - \text{div grad } p + k\nabla^2 (\text{div } \mathbf{v}) = \rho \frac{d}{dt} (\text{div } \mathbf{v}).
$$

Now by the equation of continuity div $\mathbf{v} = 0$, and in our case of no external forces this reduces to

$$\text{div grad } p = \nabla^2 p = 0.$$

In our problem $\partial p/\partial x_2 = \partial p/\partial x_3 = 0$, so that $d^2 p/dx_1^2 = 0$. The pressure is thus a linear function of x_1, so that we have a constant pressure gradient in the tube. Of the three components of (5.2), only the x_1 component is left:

$$\frac{dp}{dx_1} = k\left(\frac{\partial^2 v_1}{\partial x_2^2} + \frac{\partial^2 v_1}{\partial x_3^2}\right),$$

and since dp/dx_1 is constant, equal to a, say, and we have cylindrical symmetry, this reduces to

$$\frac{1}{r}\frac{d}{dr}\left(r\frac{dv_1}{dr}\right) = \frac{a}{k},$$

where r is the distance from the axis of the cylinder. Integrated, this yields $v_1 = \frac{ar^2}{4k} + b \ln r + c$, and, since v_1 is finite for $r = 0$, $b = 0$. If the liquid clings to the walls of the cylinder, $v_1 = 0$ when $r = R$, so that we find

$$v_1 = \frac{a}{4k}(r^2 - R^2).$$

Thus the liquid flows in cylindrical tubes of constant velocity. This type of motion is called "laminar motion." The velocity varies parabolically across a diameter of the cylinder.

The amount of liquid flowing per second through a cylindrical ring of thickness dr, radius r, is

$$dQ = 2\pi r v_1 \, dr,$$

so that the total discharge rate of such a cylinder is

$$Q = 2\pi \int_0^R r v_1 \, dr = -\frac{\pi a R^4}{8k} = \frac{\pi R^4}{8kL}(p_2 - p_1)$$

where we have placed the constant pressure gradient $a = -(p_2 - p_1)/L$. This law, known as Poiseuille's law, furnishes a convenient experimental method of determining the coefficient of viscosity of liquids.

Problems

1. Liquid is confined between two parallel plates, so that it flows in two dimensions. At a certain point, a pipe discharges liquid at a constant rate into the region. Find the velocity potential, and velocity, as a function of position.

Show by direct calculation that the flow outward over any circle about the source
is the same.

2. A shallow tray containing fluid has a source at one point, an equal sink at
another, so that liquid flows in two dimensions from source to sink. Find the
equation of the equipotentials and the lines of flow, prove that they are circles,
and plot them. (*Suggestion:* Since the equations are linear, the potential or flux
due to two sources is the sum of the solutions for the separate sources.)

3. Prove that $(\partial/\partial x)(1/r)$ is a solution of Laplace's equation. Investigate
the lines of flow connected with this as a potential. Draw the lines, in the xy plane.
What sort of physical situation would be described by this case?

4. Consider an ideal fluid at rest. It is subjected to an impulsive pressure
$(p) = \int_0^\tau p\, dt$, where τ indicates the interval of time during which the pressure is
applied. If no body forces act on the fluid, prove by integrating Euler's equations
that the impulsive pressure divided by the density of the fluid equals the velocity
potential of the ensuing motion. This is the physical significance of a velocity
potential.

5. Show for a liquid in equilibrium under the action of gravity that the pressure varies linearly with the depth below the surface. Calculate the total force
exerted on the surface of a submerged body by the liquid, and show that the
resultant force is directed upward and is given in magnitude by Archimedes'
principle. [*Hint:* If a vector has only one component different from zero, for
example, A_x, then the divergence theorem becomes $\int \dfrac{\partial A_x}{\partial x}\, dv = \int A_x \cos(n,x)\, da$.]

6. The free surface of a liquid is one of constant pressure. If an incompressible fluid is placed in a cylindrical vessel and the whole rotated with constant
angular velocity ω, show that the free surface becomes a paraboloid of revolution.
(*Hint:* Introduce a fictitious potential energy to take care of centrifugal force, and
use the hydrostatic equations.)

7. A gas maintained at constant pressure p, flows steadily out of a small hole
into the atmosphere, pressure p_0. Assume the density constant. Find the
expressions for the velocity of efflux and for the force exerted on the gas container
due to the efflux. If the gas is oxygen at a pressure of 4 atm in the tank, calculate
the efflux velocity (1) with the density constant, and (2) taking into account the
variation of density with pressure, assuming an adiabatic expansion.

8. Calculate the rate of discharge of a cylindrical pipe standing vertically, the
liquid flowing in laminar flow under the action of gravity alone.

9. The velocity potential for streamline flow around a long cylinder whose
axis is normal to the flow is

$$V\left(r + \frac{a^2}{r}\right)\cos\theta,$$

where r, θ, z are cylindrical coordinates and a is the cylinder radius. Compute
the force per unit length exerted by the fluid on the front half of the cylinder.

10. Consider the laminar flow of a fluid in a cylindrical tube under the action
of a constant pressure gradient (Poiseuille's law). Find the angular velocity of
fluid rotation as a function of position in the tube. Show that the axes of rotation
(vortex lines) are concentric circles about the axis of the tube. Compute the
maximum angular velocity for the case of water in a capillary of diameter 2.0 mm

under a pressure gradient of 0.004 atm/cm.   At what points of the fluid does this maximum occur?

11. A perfect gas at constant temperature is in equilibrium under the action of gravity. Find the relation between the pressure of the gas and the height above the surface of the earth.

12. Carry through the derivation of the laws of motion of viscous fluids using the modified form of Hooke's law and the general equations of motion of an elastic medium.

APPENDIX I

NUMERICAL INTEGRATION OF DIFFERENTIAL EQUATIONS

The principle underlying the numerical integration of differential equations is outlined in the text: we replace derivatives by differences, and construct a table of values, using each entry in the table to help us in constructing the next entry. We illustrate by a simple example in which we know the solution by elementary methods, the equation $d^2x/dt^2 + x = 0$, whose solution of course is the sine or cosine. From Eq. (1.10), Chap. I, we have

$$x(t_1 + \delta t) - 2x(t_1) + x(t_1 - \delta t) = -(\delta t)^2 x(t_1)$$

or

$$x(t_1 + \delta t) = [2 - (\delta t)^2]x(t_1) - x(t_1 - \delta t). \qquad (1)$$

From Eq. (1), knowing two successive entries in a table of $x(t)$ as a function of t, we can clearly find the next entry. The procedure will be more accurate the smaller the interval δt is taken, for then the difference approaches the derivative more closely. To start the process we must know two successive entries in the table; this is equivalent to knowing the value of the function and its first derivative, which are required to define a solution of a second order differential equation. Let us assume that $x(0) = 0$, which means that we are looking for the sine rather than the cosine, and that $x(\delta t) = \delta t$ (so that we shall get the sine, instead of a constant times the sine). In Table 1 we compute for the case $\delta t = 0.1$ radian. We give the computed values from Eq. (1), and for comparison we give the exact values. It is clear that the agreement is good to a unit in the third place, so that in this case we do not have to take smaller intervals to get a satisfactory three-figure accuracy.

This simple illustration shows how easy it is to find numerical solutions of a differential equation of really very satisfactory accuracy. Of course, no one would solve the equation for the sine or cosine this way, but the method is equally simple for more complicated equations, for which no other simple solution is available. For instance, consider the equation $d^2x/dt^2 + f(x,t) = 0$, which, in the general case of arbitrary function f, cannot be solved by elementary means. Written

239

in the form analogous to (1), this becomes

$$x(t_1 + \delta t) = 2x(t_1) - (\delta t)^2 f[x(t_1),t_1] - x(t_1 - \delta t).$$

Except for the algebraic job of computing the function $f[x(t_1),t_1]$ for each entry in succession, this is no harder than the case we have already considered.

TABLE 1

t	$x(t)$ exact = $\sin t$	$x(t) = \sin t$ calculated by numerical integration
0.0	0.000	0.000 (assumed)
0.1	0.100	0.100 (assumed)
0.2	0.199	$(1.99)(0.100) - 0.000 = 0.199$
0.3	0.296	$(1.99)(0.199) - 0.100 = 0.296$
0.4	0.389	$(1.99)(0.296) - 0.199 = 0.390$
0.5	0.479	$(1.99)(0.390) - 0.296 = 0.480$
0.6	0.565	$(1.99)(0.480) - 0.390 = 0.565$
0.7	0.644	$(1.99)(0.565) - 0.480 = 0.644$
0.8	0.717	$(1.99)(0.644) - 0.565 = 0.717$
0.9	0.783	$(1.99)(0.717) - 0.644 = 0.783$
1.0	0.841	$(1.99)(0.783) - 0.717 = 0.841$
1.1	0.891	$(1.99)(0.841) - 0.783 = 0.891$
1.2	0.932	$(1.99)(0.891) - 0.841 = 0.932$
1.3	0.964	$(1.99)(0.932) - 0.891 = 0.964$
1.4	0.985	$(1.99)(0.964) - 0.932 = 0.986$
1.5	0.997	$(1.99)(0.986) - 0.964 = 0.998$

For an equation containing a first as well as a second derivative, the method indicated in Eq. (1.9), Chap. I, is not so good as another procedure that we can easily set up. That equation suggested that dx/dt could be approximated by $[x(t_1) - x(t_1 - \delta t)]/\delta t$. It could equally well be represented, however, by $[x(t_1 + \delta t) - x(t_1)]/\delta t$. One of these will generally be too large, one too small, and we can do even better by taking our interval centered on t_1 for which we wish the derivative, using

$$\frac{dx}{dt} \sim \frac{x(t_1 + \delta t/2) - x(t_1 - \delta t/2)}{\delta t}.$$

Using this procedure necessitates keeping twice as many entries in the table, or using half the interval. It also requires that we know more values in the table before we can start our numerical integration.

Let us illustrate these points by solving Bessel's equation for the function $J_1(x)$.   This equation is

$$\frac{d^2y}{dx^2} + \frac{1}{x}\frac{dy}{dx} + \left(1 - \frac{1}{x^2}\right)y = 0. \tag{2}$$

Replacing the derivatives by differences, the equation takes the form

$$y(x + \delta x) = -\frac{\delta x}{x}\, y\left(x + \frac{\delta x}{2}\right) + \left[2 - (\delta x)^2\left(1 - \frac{1}{x^2}\right)\right]y(x)$$
$$+ \frac{\delta x}{x}\, y\left(x - \frac{\delta x}{2}\right) - y(x - \delta x).$$

Thus each entry in the table depends on the values of the four preceding entries.   To get started with the integration, we must then have some independent way of estimating the function, and this is often done by using a power-series solution, described in Appendix II.   In Table 2 we show the first few entries, again for $\delta x = 0.1$ (that is, for $\delta x/2 = 0.05$). The first four entries are taken from the known correct values of $J_1(x)$, which can be easily found from the series.   Here again the calculation

TABLE 2

x	$J_1(x)$ exact	$J_1(x)$ calculated by numerical integration
0.0	0.0000	0.0000 (assumed)
0.05	0.0250	0.0250 (assumed)
0.10	0.0499	0.0499 (assumed)
0.15	0.0748	0.0748 (assumed)
0.20	0.0995	$-(0.1/0.1)(0.0748) + [2 - 0.01(1 - 100)](0.0499)$ $+ (0.1/0.1)(0.0250) - 0.0000 = 0.0994$
0.25	0.1240	$-(0.1/0.15)(0.0994) + [2 - 0.01(1 - 44.4)](0.0748)$ $+ (0.1/0.15)(0.0499) - 0.0250 = 0.1240$
0.30	0.1483	$-(0.1/0.2)(0.1240) + [2 - 0.01(1 - 25)](0.0994)$ $+ (0.1/0.2)(0.0748) - 0.0499 = 0.1482$
0.35	0.1723	$-(0.1/0.25)(0.1482) + [2 - 0.01(1 - 16)](0.1240)$ $+ (0.1/0.25)(0.0994) - 0.0748 = 0.1719$
0.40	0.1960	$-(0.1/0.3)(0.1719) + [2 - 0.01(1 - 11.1)](0.1482)$ $+ (0.1/0.3)(0.1240) - 0.0994 = 0.1960$
0.45	0.2194	$-(0.1/0.35)(0.1960) + [2 - 0.01(1 - 8.20)](0.1719)$ $+ (0.1/0.35)(0.1482) - 0.1240 = 0.2185$
0.50	0.2423	$-(0.1/0.4)(0.2185) + [2 - 0.01(1 - 6.25)](0.1960)$ $+ (0.1/0.4)(0.1719) - 0.1482 = 0.2426$

is good to three places, though not to four; for four-figure accuracy, we should need to take our intervals closer together, or to use more complicated formulas, expressing the derivatives in terms of higher differences.

From these two simple examples, of which the second is typical of the sort of differential equation whose solution must often be found by numerical integration, we see that the actual labor of integrating a differential equation numerically is not great. If we need a table of values, it is often no harder to obtain it this way than by evaluation of a fairly complicated analytical expression, if we have been able to integrate the equation analytically. One of the first lessons of mathematical physics is that, if a problem can be reduced to the solution of an ordinary differential equation, it is to all intents and purposes solved, since, if no simpler methods present themselves, we can always construct a solution of the differential equation by numerical integration.

APPENDIX II

POWER-SERIES METHOD FOR DIFFERENTIAL EQUATIONS

A differential equation defines a function, or more generally a family of functions. Most of these functions are not the elementary ones, such as algebraic, trigonometric, or exponential functions, or Bessel's functions, elliptic functions, and others whose properties have been carefully investigated. The familiar functions are familiar largely because tables of values have been computed for them, and because simple analytical relationships are known concerning them. When we are faced with an unfamiliar function, defined by a new differential equation, we may ask how to investigate it. First, we may find that it can be written analytically in terms of familiar functions; in that case, our problem is solved. If that is not the case, however, we may name the function, if we please, but that does not carry us very far. To understand it better, we must construct a table of values, and find its analytic properties. The table of values can be found by numerical integration, as in Appendix I, but this is sometimes not convenient, and it is of no use for investigating analytic properties. The question presents itself, can we not get some general method of describing functions analytically, applicable equally to familiar and to unfamiliar functions?

The most useful such general method is that of expansion in power series. We are familiar in the first place with Taylor's expansion, by which a power series can be found to represent a known function. If we know a function $f(x)$, and if we know its analytical properties, Taylor's theorem tells us that we can write the function in the form

$$f(x) = A_0 + A_1 x + A_2 x^2 + A_3 x^3 + \cdots$$
$$A_n = \frac{1}{n!} \frac{d^n f(x)}{dx^n} \bigg|_{x=0}. \tag{1}$$

By a slight extension, we may expand, not about $x = 0$, but about any point $x = a$:

$$f(x) = A_0 + A_1(x - a) + A_2(x - a)^2 + A_3(x - a)^3 + \cdots$$
$$A_n = \frac{1}{n!} \frac{d^n f(x)}{dx^n} \bigg|_{x=a}. \tag{2}$$

243

This expansion is often useful, in at least two ways: sometimes it allows us to prove analytic relations between functions, showing that these relations hold for the power-series expansion; and the series gives us a practical way to compute the function. This is the case if the terms of the series decrease rapidly enough so that a good approximation to the sum of the series is found by taking a finite, and not unreasonably large, number of terms, and either neglecting the further terms, or computing some sort of approximate sum of the remaining terms of the series. We are led thus to consider the convergence of power series. This is a broad subject, and we shall give only a sketch of some of its simplest and most useful features.

A series is said to converge if the sum of the first n terms approaches a limit as n becomes infinite; this limit is defined as the sum of the series. If the sum of n terms approaches a limit, this means that the sum, for a large value of n, is arbitrarily close to the sum of the series, and can be used practically as a way of approximating to the function represented by the series. As a general rule, a power series in x converges for small values of x, and diverges for large x, in which case the sum of the first n terms approaches no limit, either because it grows larger without limit as n increases, or because it oscillates.

There is a simple rule by which we can tell in many cases whether a series converges or diverges, though it does not invariably give us the answer. Surely a series cannot converge unless its successive terms get smaller and smaller. We can investigate this by the ratio test, taking the ratio of the nth term to the one before, and seeing how this ratio changes as we go out in the series. If the limiting ratio is less than 1, the series converges; if it is greater than 1, it diverges. If the ratio is just 1, the test gives no information. Thus, for example, with the series $x + x^2/2 + x^3/3 + \cdots$, the ratio of the term in x^n to that in x^{n-1} is $\dfrac{x^n}{n} \dfrac{n-1}{x^{n-1}} = \dfrac{(n-1)}{n} x$. As n approaches infinity, $n-1$ and n become approximately equal, so that the ratio approaches x. Thus we see that, if x is less numerically than unity, this series converges; if x is greater than unity, it diverges; if $x = 1$, we cannot say. From other information, we know that the series when $x = 1$, which is

$$1 + \tfrac{1}{2} + \tfrac{1}{3} + \tfrac{1}{4} + \cdots,$$

diverges. But with the similar series $x + x^2/2^2 + x^3/3^2 + \cdots$ where the ratio of terms also approaches x as we go out in the series, and the series again diverges for x greater numerically than unity, and converges for x less than unity, we have just the other situation at $x = 1$: the series $1 + \frac{1}{2}^2 + \frac{1}{3}^2 + \cdots$ converges.

Further insight into the convergence properties of power series is furnished by investigating the singularities of the function which the series represents. By Taylor's series (1) or (2), it is clear that, for a power series to converge, and for the coefficients to decrease as we go out in the series, all the derivatives of the function must be finite at the point $x = a$ about which the expansion is made, since otherwise some coefficients of the expansion will be infinite. Thus, for example, we cannot expand $1/x$ in power series in x: we have $f(0) = \frac{1}{0} = $ infinite, and all the derivatives are also infinite. Such a point is called a "singularity" of the function. But by expanding about another point we can avoid this difficulty. Thus we can expand $1/x$ about a, if $a \neq 0$. Determining the coefficients by (2), we find

$$\frac{1}{x} = \frac{1}{a} - \frac{(x - a)}{a^2} + \frac{(x - a)^2}{a^3} - \frac{(x - a)^3}{a^4} + \cdots. \tag{3}$$

From this we can understand that a function can be expanded in power series about a point that is not a singular point.

There is then a general rule regarding the convergence of the resulting series. This rule must be stated for complex values of x, described in the complex plane. In this complex plane, there will be certain points at which the function has a singularity (as in the case of the function $1/x$, which has a singularity at the origin). The expansion (2), in power series in powers of $x - a$, which is called an expansion about the point a, then will converge for all points in the complex plane lying inside a circle, with center at a, whose boundary passes through the singularity that lies closest to a. It will diverge at all points outside this circle, which is called the "circle of convergence." It will converge less and less rapidly as the boundary of the circle of convergence is approached, so that for practical computation a series is not useful near the edge of its circle of convergence.

There is no general rule governing convergence on the boundary of the circle. In the series (3), for instance, suppose for illustration that a is a positive real number. Then the circle of convergence will have its center on the real axis, and will have a radius a, extending along the real axis from $x = 0$ to $x = 2a$. Applying the ratio test to (3), we see that the ratio of the nth term to the $(n - 1)$st is $-(x - a)/a$, which approaches 1 as x approaches zero, and approaches -1 as x approaches 2, leading in each case to a lack of convergence. This example is instructive, in that it shows that a series can fail to converge at a point like $x = 2$ in this case, at which the function is perfectly well behaved, simply because the boundary of the circle of convergence passes through this point.   It is clear from this example that, to get a rapidly convergent series, we should expand about a point a which is far from all the singularities of the function.   By judicious choice of the point about which the power-series expansion is carried out, then, we can often obtain rapidly converging series, convenient for numerical calculation.

At some singular points, the function behaves like $1/x^n$, an inverse power of x.   Such a singularity is called a "pole."   If $f(x)$ has a pole of order n at the origin, then by definition $x^n f(x)$ has no singularity at the origin, and can be expanded in power series $A_0 + A_1 x + \cdots$. Thus we have for $f(x)$ the expression

$$f(x) = \frac{A_0}{x^n} + \frac{A_1}{x^{n-1}} + \cdots \tag{4}$$

an infinite series starting with inverse powers, but turning into an ordinary series of positive powers after its nth term.   A similar theorem holds for expansion about a pole at $x = a$.   A singularity that is not a pole is called an "essential singularity."   An example of an essential singularity is that possessed by the function $e^{-1/x}$ at $x = 0$. This function approaches 0 as x approaches 0 through positive values, but becomes infinite as x approaches 0 through negative values, and no inverse power $1/x^n$ has such a behavior.

In some classes of functions, an expansion about a singularity is possible.   In such cases, the series does not converge, for any range of $x - a$, no matter how small, and yet the series may be useful for numerical calculation.   These series are called "asymptotic," or "semiconvergent" series.   They have the property that their terms decrease for some time with increasing n, so that the sum of the first n terms appears to be approaching a limit; but then the terms, after going through a minimum value, start to increase again, ultimately increasing without limit.   It can then be shown that, by summing just up to the smallest term of the series, the sum so found differs from the true function by less than the last term of the sum, so that, if this last term is small in comparison with the sum, it forms a valid approximation.   This approximation is completely lost if we make the mistake of keeping more terms of the series, beyond this smallest term.

In practical calculation by means of series, certain devices are often convenient in estimating the contribution of the remaining terms beyond the nth, so that we can sum the first n, and then estimate the remainder. Thus a series can often be approximately summed by comparison with an integral. For example,

$$1 + \frac{1}{2^n} + \frac{1}{3^n} + \cdots = \sum_{z=1}^{\infty} \frac{1}{z^n} = \int^{\infty} \frac{dz}{z^n} \qquad \text{approximately.} \quad (5)$$

The approximation is rather poor for the small values of z, but becomes better for large z values, on which the convergence depends. It would be a good approximation, for instance, to write $\dfrac{1}{10^n} = \displaystyle\int_{9\frac{1}{2}}^{10\frac{1}{2}} \dfrac{dz}{z^n}$, and on this basis we could write approximately

$$\frac{1}{10^n} + \frac{1}{11^n} + \frac{1}{12^n} + \cdots = \int_{9\frac{1}{2}}^{\infty} \frac{dz}{z^n} = \frac{1}{(n-1)(9\frac{1}{2})^{n-1}},$$

if n is greater than unity. Thus we could find the sum

$$1 + \frac{1}{2}^2 + \frac{1}{3}^2 + \cdots$$

as the sum from 1 to $\frac{1}{9}^2$, plus the integrated terms. We should find in this way

$$1 + \frac{1}{2}^2 + \frac{1}{3}^2 + \cdots$$
$$= (1.0000 + 0.2500 + 0.1111 + 0.0625 + 0.0400 + 0.0277 + 0.0204$$
$$+ 0.0156 + 0.0123) + \frac{1}{9\frac{1}{2}} = 1.5396 + 0.1053 = 1.6449.$$

Now it can be shown that this sum is equal to $\pi^2/6$ (one way to do this is to use the Fourier expansion for the function x^2, which is

$$x^2 = \frac{1}{3} - \frac{4}{\pi^2}\left(\cos \pi x - \frac{1}{2^2} \cos 2\pi x + \frac{1}{3^2} \cos 3\pi x \cdots \right),$$

and set $x = 1$). But $\pi^2/6$ is equal to 1.6449, so that our simple process has given a correct value of the sum to five significant figures, and correspondingly has given us a simple way of accurately computing π. We note that the remaining terms, starting with $1/10^2$, which we approximate by an integral, amount to 0.1053, or a very large correction, so that if we had not used our method of replacing a sum by an integral it would have been quite out of the question to get an accurate value of the sum by adding a practicable number of terms. In practice, then, this integral method often makes it convenient to sum a series, when otherwise it would be out of the question.

The integral method we have just used is convenient for a series whose terms are all of the same sign. For an alternating series, however, the situation is different. If the positive terms by themselves converge, and if the negative terms by themselves converge (that is, if the series is what is called "absolutely convergent"), then we can replace the positive or negative terms separately by integrals, after the manner of Eq. (5), and subtract one integral from the other. There are important cases, however, of series that are not absolutely convergent, but nevertheless converge. For instance, the series

$$1 - \tfrac{1}{2} + \tfrac{1}{3} - \tfrac{1}{4} + \tfrac{1}{5} - \cdots$$

converges, though the series $1 + \tfrac{1}{2} + \tfrac{1}{3} + \tfrac{1}{4} + \cdots$ does not. We can interpret these series in terms of the expansion

$$\ln (1 + x) = x - \frac{x^2}{2} + \frac{x^3}{3} - \frac{x^4}{4} \cdots ,$$

so that the first series is the value of this when $x = 1$, and we might well expect the series to converge to $\ln 2$, whereas the second is the value for $x = -1$, which is the series representing $\ln (0)$, which of course is infinite. The divergence for $x = -1$ is at once shown also from Eq. (5), setting $n = 1$, in which case the integral diverges logarithmically; (5) furnishes a converging result only for n greater than unity. The circle of convergence of the expansion of $\ln (1 + x)$ must clearly have unit radius, since the singularity of the function closest to the origin is at $x = -1$. Thus for the case $x = 1$ we are on the boundary of the circle of convergence, and our rules do not tell us whether we have convergence or not; they just tell us that the series converges within the circle, and diverges outside, but there is no universal behavior on the circumference of the circle. Thus we are left with the series $1 - \tfrac{1}{2} + \tfrac{1}{3} - \tfrac{1}{4} + \cdots$ and inquire how we can evaluate it.

In a series $C_0 - C_1 + C_2 - C_3 + \cdots$, in which the C's decrease slowly and regularly, we note that each of the C's will be approximately the average of the preceding and following C; that is,

$$C_k \sim \tfrac{1}{2}(C_{k-1} + C_{k+1}),$$

or $\tfrac{1}{2}C_{k-1} - C_k + \tfrac{1}{2}C_{k+1}$ is approximately zero. Thus we may write the series in the form

$$C_0 - C_1 + C_2 - \cdots - C_{k-2} + \tfrac{1}{2}C_{k-1} + (\tfrac{1}{2}C_{k-1} - C_k + \tfrac{1}{2}C_{k+1}) \\ + (\tfrac{1}{2}C_{k+1} - C_{k+2} + \tfrac{1}{2}C_{k+3}) + \cdots . \quad (6)$$

Since each of the brackets is approximately zero, we can leave them out, and find that the sum of the series is approximately the sum of the terms up to a certain point, plus half the next term. In other words, all the terms beginning with a certain term, and extending to infinity, equal approximately half the first term of this sequence. To illustrate this method, we may replace the series $1 - \frac{1}{2} + \frac{1}{3} - \cdots$ by the sum of the terms through $\frac{1}{9}$, minus $\frac{1}{2}$ of $\frac{1}{10}$. This gives

$$(1.000 - 0.500 + 0.333 - 0.250 + 0.200 - 0.167$$
$$+ 0.143 - 0.125 + 0.111) - 0.050 = 0.695.$$

This is an approximation to $\ln 2 = 0.6931$. It is clear that we have not taken enough terms to get three-figure accuracy, though the error is less than 1 per cent. This is a particularly poorly convergent series, and, even using our rule, we need more than 10 terms to get a satisfactory estimate. We could do considerably better, however, by noting that the sum, as we compute it, is too large if we stop with a negative term, but too small if we stop with a positive one. Thus if we had continued, and added in the term -0.100, but had then taken

$$\tfrac{1}{2}(\tfrac{1}{11}) = 0.046$$

to represent the remainder, we should have found 0.691 for the approximation. The average of this and 0.695 should be better than either of the numbers, and in fact agrees to three figures with the correct value 0.693.

We have now given a discussion of power series, their convergence, and some practical suggestions for simplifying the process of computing numerically by means of them. The reason for being interested in power series in connection with differential equations is that in many cases it is possible to determine directly the power-series expansion of the solution of a differential equation, without previously knowing anything about the function represented by the series. Thus this provides a method for investigating new functions defined by differential equations.

The method of finding the series is to assume that the solution can be expanded in power series, substitute the series in the differential equation, with unknown coefficients, and solve for the coefficients by algebraic methods. We shall show how this is done by two simple examples, using the equations for $\sin x$ and $J_1(x)$ which we have already used as examples of numerical integration in Appendix I. Suppose we have the differential equation $d^2y/dx^2 + y = 0$, and assume that the solution can be expressed as a series

$$y = A_0 + A_1 x + A_2 x^2 + \cdots.$$

Then d^2y/dx^2, differentiating term by term, equals

$$2A_2 + (3 \cdot 2)A_3 x + (4 \cdot 3)A_4 x^2 + \cdots,$$

and the differential equation, combining terms, is

$$(A_0 + 2A_2) + [A_1 + (3 \cdot 2)A_3]x + [A_2 + (4 \cdot 3)A_4]x^2 + \cdots$$
$$+ [A_n + (n + 1)(n + 2)A_{n+2}]x^n + \cdots = 0.$$

This equation states that a certain power series in x is identically zero, for any value of x; this cannot be the case unless each of the coefficients is zero, since the Taylor expansion of zero has all its terms equal to zero. Thus we obtain the equations

$$A_0 + 2A_2 = 0, \qquad A_2 = -\frac{1}{2} A_0$$

$$A_1 + (3 \cdot 2)A_3 = 0, \qquad A_3 = -\frac{1}{3!} A_1$$

$$A_2 + (4 \cdot 3)A_4 = 0, \qquad A_4 = -\frac{1}{3 \cdot 4} A_2 = \frac{1}{4!} A_0, \qquad \text{etc.,}$$

so that

$$y = A_0 \left(1 - \frac{x^2}{2!} + \frac{x^4}{4!} - \frac{x^6}{6!} + \cdots \right) + A_1 \left(x - \frac{x^3}{3!} + \frac{x^5}{5!} - \cdots \right).$$

This solution contains two arbitrary constants, A_0 and A_1, as we must expect from a second order differential equation. The two brackets represent two particular solutions of the differential equation; the first equals unity when $x = 0$, and has zero slope at that point, and we recognize it as cos x, whereas the second equals zero when $x = 0$, and has unit slope at that point, and we recognize it as sin x. We have thus found the power series for the sine and cosine, directly from the differential equation.

These power series are useful both for numerical calculation and for proving analytical properties of the functions (at least, they would be useful in this way if the properties of the trigonometric functions were not so familiar). Thus, as an illustration of their use for numerical calculation, let us compute sin 1 from them. This should be

$$(1.0000 - 0.1667 + 0.0083 - 0.0002 + 0.0000) = 0.8414,$$

with an error of only a unit in the fourth place. This series clearly converges so rapidly that we do not need to use our special rules for estimating the remaining terms. We may easily check the convergence by the ratio test: the ratio of the term in x^n, to that in x^{n-2}, is

$$\frac{x^2}{n(n - 1)},$$

which decreases to zero as n becomes great enough, no matter how large x may be. Thus the series converges for any value of x; its circle of convergence is infinitely large.

This situation is characteristic of the trigonometric and exponential functions, which of course are closely related. The reason is that their only singularity is at infinity. The sine and cosine are nowhere infinite, for real values of the argument; but for a pure imaginary value of the argument, sin x becomes the hyperbolic sine of $x \sqrt{-1}$, which becomes infinite when x approaches infinity. Thus the function has a singularity at infinity, and it is an essential singularity, since different values are found for the function as we approach infinity along the real and along the imaginary axis. A power-series expansion about the point at infinity is thus impossible (this can be shown to be equivalent to the statement that sin x cannot be expanded in powers of $1/x$), but the expansion about any other point converges for all finite values of the argument, and in fact converges rapidly enough so that the series is convenient for computation. As an illustration of the way in which the series can be used to prove analytical properties of the functions, we may indicate merely that the relations $d \sin x/dx = \cos x$, $d \cos x/dx = - \sin x$, follow immediately from the series representation of the functions.

As a second more complicated example we take the equation for $J_1(x)$, $d^2y/dx^2 + (1/x) \, dy/dx + (1 - 1/x^2)y = 0$, as in Eq. (2), Appendix I. Inserting our power-series solution, we have the equation

$$2A_2 + (2 \cdot 3)A_3x + (3 \cdot 4)A_4x^2 + (4 \cdot 5)A_5x^3 + \cdots$$
$$+ \frac{A_1}{x} + 2A_2 + \quad 3A_3x + \quad 4A_4x^2 + \quad 5A_5x^3 + \cdots$$
$$+ A_0 + \quad A_1x + \quad A_2x^2 + \quad A_3x^3 + \cdots$$
$$- \frac{A_0}{x^2} - \frac{A_1}{x} - A_2 - \quad A_3x - \quad A_4x^2 - \quad A_5x^3 - \cdots = 0.$$

Equating the coefficient of each power of x to zero, we first find that $A_0 = A_2 = A_4 = \cdots = 0$, and that $A_3 = -A_1/(2 \cdot 4)$,

$$A_5 = - \frac{A_3}{(4 \cdot 6)} = \frac{A_1}{(2 \cdot 4 \cdot 4 \cdot 6)},$$

etc., so that the solution is

$$y = A_1 \left(x - \frac{x^3}{2 \cdot 4} + \frac{x^5}{2 \cdot 4 \cdot 4 \cdot 6} - \cdots \right). \tag{7}$$

The series in the bracket is defined as $2J_1(x)$, the function $J_1(x)$ being half the bracket. Thus we have found a series representation of the Bessel's function. As with the trigonometric function, a ratio test shows us that the series converges for any finite value of x, so that the circle of convergence is infinite. The function as a matter of fact shows a singularity at infinity similar to that shown by the trigonometric functions; $J_1(x)$ remains finite for all real values of x, oscillating as the trigonometric functions do, though with an amplitude that decreases as x increases, whereas for pure imaginary values of x it increases in a manner suggesting the exponential or hyperbolic functions. The series (7) is convenient for numerical calculation. Thus, for $x = \frac{1}{2}$, we have $J_1(0.5) = \frac{1}{2}(0.5000 - 0.0156 + 0.0001) = 0.2423$, correct to four figures.

We have found only one solution of Bessel's equation, though the equation is a second order differential equation. By general principles there must be another solution, and we may reasonably ask how we have happened to miss it. The answer should occur to us at once: we have assumed an expansion in power series about $x = 0$, and such an expansion can always be carried out unless the function has a singularity at $x = 0$. Thus we may well assume that the other solution that we desire has such a singularity. In that case, if the singularity is a pole rather than an essential singularity, it should be possible to expand the function in a series of the form (4), assuming

$$y = \left(\frac{1}{x^n}\right)(A_0 + A_1 x + A_2 x^2 + \cdots).$$

Let us see if we can get such a solution. Substituting in Bessel's equation, we find that the equation setting the coefficient of the term in x^{-n-2} equal to zero is $(n^2 - 1)A_0 = 0$. To satisfy this, we must have $n = \pm 1$. $n = -1$ corresponds to the case of $J_1(x)$, which we have already discussed. This suggests that the other solution starts with x^{-1}, as in fact it does. When we carry out the next step, however, we find a difficulty: the equations governing the coefficients A_1, A_2, etc., state that all these coefficients are infinite. This is another way of saying that an expansion of the form (4) cannot be carried out. The reason proves to be that the function we are looking for has a singularity at the origin which is not a simple pole. It has in fact not merely the singularity $1/x$, but also a logarithmic singularity, so that it can be expanded in a series of the form (4), with a logarithmic term added on. The resulting function, which we shall discuss further in Appendix VIII, is called a "Neumann's function," and is denoted by $N_1(x)$.

Problems

1. Plot $-\dfrac{1}{x} + \dfrac{1}{x^2}$ as a function of x, and show that it has a minimum at $x = 2$. Expand in Taylor's series about this point, obtaining an expansion

$y = A_0 + A_2(x - 2)^2 + A_3(x - 2)^3 + \cdots$, where necessarily the coefficient A_1 is zero. Now plot on the graph the successive approximations

$$y = A_0,$$
$$y = A_0 + A_2(x - 2)^2,$$
$$y = A_0 + A_2(x - 2)^2 + A_3(x - 2)^3,$$
$$y = A_0 + A_2(x - 2)^2 + A_3(x - 2)^3 + A_4(x - 2)^4,$$

observing how they approximate the real curve more and more accurately.

2. *a.* Derive the series for the exponential, cosine, and sine series, directly from Taylor's theorem.

b. Differentiate the series for sin x term by term, and show that the result is the series for cos x.

3. In the series for e^x, set $x = 1$, obtaining a series for e. Using this series, compute the value of e to four decimal places.

4. Why does one always have series for $\ln(1 + x)$ in powers of x, rather than for $\ln x$? From the series for $\ln(1 + x)$, compute logarithms to base e of 1.1, 1.2, 1.3, 1.4, 1.5.

5. The function $1/(x - j)$, where $j = \sqrt{-1}$, has a singularity for $x = j$, but not for any real value of x. Show that nevertheless the series expansion about $x = 0$ diverges for x greater than 1 or less than -1, obtaining the power series by Taylor's theorem, and separating real and imaginary parts of the series. This is an example of a case in which the series diverges because of singularities for complex values of x.

6. As a result of an experiment, we are given the table of values following:

x	y
1	7.0
2	11.1
3	15.2
4	19.3
5	23.2
6	27.1
7	30.8
8	34.5
9	38.2
10	41.7

Try to devise some practicable scheme for telling whether this function (in which, being a result of experiment, the values are only approximations) can be represented within the error of experiment by a linear, quadratic, cubic, etc., polynomial. Get the coefficients of the resulting series, and use them to find the value of the function and its slope at $x = 0$. Plot the points, the curve that approximates them, and the straight line tangent to the curve at $x = 0$. It is legitimate to use graphical methods if you wish.

7. Expand $\tan^{-1} x$ in a power series about $x = 0$. *Hints:*

(a) $\dfrac{d}{dx} \tan^{-1}(x) = \dfrac{1}{1 + x^2}$

(b) $\dfrac{1}{1 + x^2} = 1 - x^2 + x^4 - x^6 + \cdots$

(c) $\displaystyle\int \dfrac{d}{dx}(\tan^{-1} x)\, dx = \tan^{-1} x + c.$

What is the range of convergence of the resulting series? Calculate from this series the value of $\pi/4 = \tan^{-1} 1$ correct to 5 per cent. How many terms of the series are necessary to obtain this accuracy?

8. By a procedure analogous to that used in Prob. **7** expand $\sin^{-1} x$ in a power series about $x = 0$. Find the range of convergence for this series.

9. From the known Taylor's series for e^x, write the corresponding series for e^{-x^2}. By integrating this series obtain to 1 per cent a value for $\int_0^1 e^{-x^2}\, dx$, whose correct value is 0.748.

10. Make use of the binomial theorem to obtain an expansion of $\sqrt{1 + \sqrt{x}}$ in ascending powers of $x^{\frac{1}{2}}$. What is the range of convergence?

11. Discuss by the ratio test the convergence of the following series:

(a) $x + \dfrac{x^2}{2} + \dfrac{x^3}{3} + \dfrac{x^4}{4} + \cdots$

(b) $x + \dfrac{x^2}{2^2} + \dfrac{x^3}{3^2} + \dfrac{x^4}{4^2} + \cdots$

(c) The binomial expansion of $(1 + x)^k$, for nonintegral k.

(d) The series for e^x.

12. Show that our theorem about the sum of an alternating series holds only when the ratio of magnitudes of successive terms approaches unity as we go out in the series. Apply the theorem to the series $\frac{1}{2}^2 - \frac{1}{3}^2 + \frac{1}{4}^2 - \cdots$.

APPENDIX III

PROPERTIES OF COMPLEX NUMBERS

A complex number is usually written $A + Bi$, where A and B are real, $i = \sqrt{-1}$. The electrical engineers generally denote $\sqrt{-1}$ by j rather than i, so as to reserve the symbol i for a current, and we shall follow that convention in this volume. A complex number is often plotted in a diagram; we let abscissas represent real parts of numbers, ordinates the imaginary parts, so that A measures the abscissa, B the ordinate, of the point representing $A + Bj$. Every point in the plane corresponds to a complex number, and vice versa. All real numbers lie along the axis of abscissas, all pure imaginaries along the axis of ordinates, and the other complex numbers between. But it is also often convenient to think of a complex number as being represented, not merely by a point, but by the vector from the origin out to the point. The fundamental reason for this is that these vectors obey the parallelogram law of addition, just as force or velocity vectors do (see Fig. 39, Appendix IV). The vector treatment is suggestive in many ways. For example, we can consider the angle between two complex numbers. Thus, any real number, and any pure imaginary number, are at an angle of 90° to each other. Or, the number $1 + j$ is at an angle of 45° with either 1 or j. When a complex number is regarded as a vector, we can describe it by two quantities: the absolute magnitude of the vector, or its length, $\sqrt{A^2 + B^2}$, and the angle that it makes with the real axis, or $\tan^{-1} B/A$.

These two quantities, the absolute magnitude of a complex number and its phase angle, have very close connection with complex exponential functions. Let us investigate the function e^{jx} by series methods. We have at once

$$e^{jx} = 1 + jx - \frac{x^2}{2!} - \frac{jx^3}{3!} + \frac{x^4}{4!} \cdots$$

$$= \left(1 - \frac{x^2}{2!} + \frac{x^4}{4!} - \cdots\right) + j\left(x - \frac{x^3}{3!} + \cdots\right)$$

$$= \cos x + j \sin x.$$

Similarly we have

$$e^{-jx} = \cos x - j \sin x.$$

255

We can solve for cos x by adding these equations and dividing by 2, or for sin x by subtracting and dividing by $2j$:

$$\cos x = \frac{e^{ix} + e^{-ix}}{2}, \qquad \sin x = \frac{e^{ix} - e^{-ix}}{2j}.$$

These theorems are fundamental in the study of exponential and sinusoidal functions.

Let us now consider the complex number $e^{i\theta}$, where θ is a real quantity. As we have seen, this equals $\cos \theta + j \sin \theta$, so that the real part is $\cos \theta$, the imaginary part sin θ. The vector representing this number is then a vector of unit magnitude, for $\sqrt{\cos^2 \theta + \sin^2 \theta} = 1$. Further, it makes just the angle θ with the real axis. We can see interesting special cases. The number $e^{\pi i/2} = j$, as we can see at once from the vector diagram, or from the fact that it equals $\cos \pi/2 + j \sin \pi/2 = j$. Similarly $e^{\pi i} = -1$, $e^{2\pi i} = e^{4\pi i} = \cdots = 1$. This last result shows that the exponential function of an imaginary argument is periodic with period $2\pi j$, similar to the sine and cosine of a real argument.

Next we look at the number $re^{i\theta}$, where r, θ are both real. It differs from $e^{i\theta}$ in that both real and imaginary parts are multiplied by the same real factor r, which simply increases the length of the vector to r, without changing the angle. Thus $re^{i\theta}$ is a vector of length r, angle θ. As a result, we can easily write any complex number in complex exponential form: $A + Bj = re^{i\theta}$, where $r = \sqrt{A^2 + B^2}$, $\theta = \tan^{-1} B/A$, or $A = r \cos \theta$, $B = r \sin \theta$. We may use these results to show what happens when two complex numbers are multiplied together. Suppose we wish to form the product $(A + Bj)(C + Dj)$. Of course, multiplying directly, this equals $(AC - BD) + (AD + BC)j$, so that we can easily find real and imaginary parts of the product, but this is not very informing. It is better to write $(A + Bj) = r_1 e^{i\theta_1}$, $(C + Dj) = r_2 e^{i\theta_2}$. Then the product is $(r_1 e^{i\theta_1})(r_2 e^{i\theta_2}) = r_1 r_2 e^{i(\theta_1 + \theta_2)}$. That is, the magnitude of the product of two complex numbers is the product of the magnitudes, and the angle is the sum of their angles.

Suppose we have a complex number $re^{i\theta}$, and consider the closely related number $re^{-i\theta}$. The second is called the "conjugate" of the first. If we have a complex number in the form $A + Bj$, its conjugate is $A - Bj$. Or in general, if we change the sign of j wherever it appears in a complex number, we obtain its conjugate. Graphically, the vector representing the conjugate of a number is the mirror image of the vector representing the number itself, in the axis of real numbers. Now conjugate numbers have two important properties: the sum of a number and its conjugate is real (for the imaginary parts just cancel in taking the sum), and the product is real (for this equals $r^2e^{j(\theta-\theta)} = r^2$). The second fact is useful in finding the absolute magnitude of a complex number; if z is complex, $\bar{z}$ its conjugate (this is the usual notation), then $\sqrt{z\bar{z}}$ equals the absolute magnitude of z. From the other fact, we may find the real and imaginary parts of complex numbers: $(z + \bar{z})/2$ equals the real part of z, and, as we can easily show, $(z - \bar{z})/2j$ equals the imaginary part. We see examples in our relations between sinusoidal and exponential functions, where e^{-jx} is the conjugate of e^{jx}, so that $(e^{jx} + e^{-jx})/2$ should, and does, equal the real part of e^{jx}, or $\cos x$, and $(e^{jx} - e^{-jx})/2j$ equals the imaginary part, or $\sin x$.

Problems

1. Given a complex number represented by a vector, what is the nature of the vector representing its square root? Its cube root? Find the three cube roots of unity, the four fourth roots, the five fifth roots, plotting them in the complex plane, and giving real and imaginary components of each. With one of the cube roots, in terms of its real and imaginary parts, cube by direct multiplication and show that the result is unity.

2. Find real and imaginary parts of $\sqrt{A + Bj}$, $1/(A + Bj)$, $1/\sqrt{A + Bj}$, where A, B are real.

3. Show that $\ln(-a) = \pi j + \ln a$, or $3\pi j + \ln a$, or in general $n\pi j + \ln a$, where n is an odd integer.

4. Prove that, if we have a complex solution of the problem of a vibrating particle, the real part of this complex function is itself a solution of the problem.

APPENDIX IV

VECTORS

The study of vectors and vector operations involves two branches: vector algebra, including the addition and multiplication of vectors, and the relations between the components of vectors in different coordinate systems; and vector analysis, including the differential vector operations, corresponding integral relations, and the general theorems concerning integrals. We shall treat both subdivisions in this appendix.

Vectors and Their Components.—We shall denote a vector, a quantity having direction as well as magnitude, by bold-faced type, as **F**. Vectors are often described by giving their components along three axes at right angles, as F_x, F_y, F_z. Their mathematical relationships are conveniently stated in terms of their components. Thus their law of addition is the parallelogram law; in terms of components, this means that, if two vectors **F** and **G** have components F_x, F_y, F_z, and G_x, G_y, G_z, respectively, the components of the sum **F** + **G** are $(F_x + G_x)$, $(F_y + G_y)$, $(F_z + G_z)$, as we show graphically in Fig. 39. To multiply a vector by a constant, as C, the vector must be increased in length by the factor C, leaving its direction unchanged; this amounts to multiplying each component by the constant C, so that the components of $C\mathbf{F}$ are CF_x, CF_y, CF_z. Often a constant like C is called a "scalar," to distinguish it from a vector. A scalar is a quantity that has magnitude but not direction, a vector having both magnitude and direction.

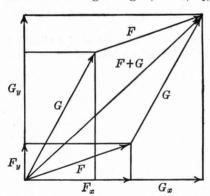

FIG. 39.—Parallelogram law for addition of vectors. The vector **F** + **G**, the diagonal of the parallelogram of sides **F**, **G**, is the vector sum of **F** and **G**. Its x component is $F_x + G_x$, its y component $F_y + G_y$.

It is often useful to write vectors in terms of three so-called "unit vectors," **i, j, k.** Here, **i** is a vector of unit length, pointing along the

258

x axis, and similarly **j** has unit length and points along the y axis, and **k** along the z axis. Now, we can build up a vector **F** out of them, by forming the quantity $\mathbf{i}F_x + \mathbf{j}F_y + \mathbf{k}F_z$. This is the sum of three vectors, one along each of the three axes, and the first, which is just the component of the whole vector along the x axis, is F_x, and the other components likewise are F_y and F_z. Thus the final vector has the components F_x, F_y, F_z, and is just the vector **F**.

By the magnitude of a vector we mean its length. By the three-dimensional analogy to the Pythagorean theorem, by which the square of the diagonal of a rectangular prism is the sum of the squares of the three sides, the magnitude of the vector **F** equals $\sqrt{F_x^2 + F_y^2 + F_z^2}$. We often speak of unit vectors, vectors whose magnitude is 1. The component of a vector in a given direction is simply the projection of the vector along a line in that direction. It evidently equals the magnitude of the vector, times the cosine of the angle between the direction of the vector and the desired direction. As a special example, the component of a vector **F** along the x axis is F_x, and this must equal the magnitude of **F**, times the cosine of the angle between **F** and x. If this angle is called (F,x), then we must have

$$\cos (F,x) = \frac{F_x}{\sqrt{F_x^2 + F_y^2 + F_z^2}}$$

with similar formulas for y and z components. The three cosines of the angles between a given direction, as the direction of the vector **F**, and the three axes, are called "direction cosines," and are often denoted by letters l, m, n, so that in this case we have $l = \cos (F,x)$, etc. It follows immediately that $l^2 + m^2 + n^2 = 1$. We can make a simple interpretation of the direction cosines of any direction: they are the components of a unit vector in the desired direction, along the three coordinate axes.

Scalar and Vector Products of Two Vectors.—Multiplication of two vectors is a somewhat arbitrary process, governed by rules that we must postulate. It has proved to be convenient to define two entirely independent products, called the "scalar product" and the "vector product." We shall first consider the scalar product. The scalar product of two vectors **F** and **G** is denoted by $\mathbf{F} \cdot \mathbf{G}$, and by definition it is a scalar, equal to either (1) the magnitude of **F** times the magnitude of **G** times the cosine of the angle between; or (2) the magnitude of **F** times the projection of **G** on **F**; or (3) the magnitude of **G** times the projection of **F** on **G**. From the preceding section we see that these definitions are equivalent. It is often useful to have the scalar product of two vectors in terms of the components along x, y, and z. We find this by writing in terms of **i**, **j**, and **k**. Thus we have

$$\begin{aligned}
\mathbf{F} \cdot \mathbf{G} &= (\mathbf{i}F_x + \mathbf{j}F_y + \mathbf{k}F_z) \cdot (\mathbf{i}G_x + \mathbf{j}G_y + \mathbf{k}G_z) \\
&= (\mathbf{i}\cdot\mathbf{i})F_xG_x + (\mathbf{i}\cdot\mathbf{j})F_xG_y + (\mathbf{i}\cdot\mathbf{k})F_xG_z \\
&\quad + (\mathbf{j}\cdot\mathbf{i})F_yG_x + (\mathbf{j}\cdot\mathbf{j})F_yG_y + (\mathbf{j}\cdot\mathbf{k})F_yG_z \\
&\quad + (\mathbf{k}\cdot\mathbf{i})F_zG_x + (\mathbf{k}\cdot\mathbf{j})F_zG_y + (\mathbf{k}\cdot\mathbf{k})F_zG_z.
\end{aligned}$$

But, by the fundamental definition,

$$\begin{aligned}
\mathbf{i}\cdot\mathbf{i} &= \mathbf{j}\cdot\mathbf{j} = \mathbf{k}\cdot\mathbf{k} = 1, \\
\mathbf{i}\cdot\mathbf{j} &= \mathbf{j}\cdot\mathbf{i} = \mathbf{j}\cdot\mathbf{k} = \mathbf{k}\cdot\mathbf{j} = \mathbf{k}\cdot\mathbf{i} = \mathbf{i}\cdot\mathbf{k} = 0. \tag{1}
\end{aligned}$$

Thus

$$\mathbf{F} \cdot \mathbf{G} = F_xG_x + F_yG_y + F_zG_z. \tag{2}$$

The scalar product has many uses, principally in cases in which we are interested in the projection of vectors. For example, the scalar product of a vector with a unit vector in a given direction equals the projection of the vector in the desired direction. The scalar product of a vector with itself equals the square of its magnitude, and is often denoted by F^2. The scalar product of two unit vectors gives the cosine of the angle between the directions of the two vectors. To prove that two vectors are at right angles, we need merely prove that their scalar product vanishes.

The vector product of two vectors **F** and **G** is denoted by $(\mathbf{F} \times \mathbf{G})$, and by definition it is a vector, at right angles to the plane of the two vectors, equal in magnitude to either (1) the magnitude of **F** times the magnitude of **G** times the sine of the angle between them; or (2) the magnitude of **F** times the projection of **G** on the plane normal to **F**; or (3) the magnitude of **G** times the projection of **F** on the plane normal to **G**. We must further specify the sense of the vector, whether it points up or down from the plane. This is shown in Fig. 40, where we see that **F, G,** and

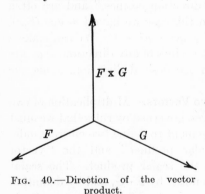

Fig. 40.—Direction of the vector product.

$\mathbf{F} \times \mathbf{G}$ have the same relations as the coordinates x, y, z in a right-handed system of coordinates. Another way to describe the rule in words is that, if one rotates **F** into **G,** the rotation is such that a right-handed screw turning in that direction would be driven along the direction of the vector product. From this rule, we note one interesting fact: if we interchange the order of the factors, we reverse the vector. Thus $(\mathbf{F} \times \mathbf{G}) = -(\mathbf{G} \times \mathbf{F})$.

We can compute the vector product in terms of the components, much as we did with the scalar product. Thus we have

$$
\begin{aligned}
\mathbf{F} \times \mathbf{G} = {} & (\mathbf{i} \times \mathbf{i})F_xG_x + (\mathbf{i} \times \mathbf{j})F_xG_y + (\mathbf{i} \times \mathbf{k})F_xG_z \\
& + (\mathbf{j} \times \mathbf{i})F_yG_x + (\mathbf{j} \times \mathbf{j})F_yG_y + (\mathbf{j} \times \mathbf{k})F_yG_z \\
& + (\mathbf{k} \times \mathbf{i})F_zG_x + (\mathbf{k} \times \mathbf{j})F_zG_y + (\mathbf{k} \times \mathbf{k})F_zG_z.
\end{aligned}
$$

But now, as we readily see from the definition,

$$
(\mathbf{i} \times \mathbf{i}) = (\mathbf{j} \times \mathbf{j}) = (\mathbf{k} \times \mathbf{k}) = 0
$$

(as, in fact, the vector product of any vector with itself is zero), and

$$
\begin{aligned}
(\mathbf{i} \times \mathbf{j}) = -(\mathbf{j} \times \mathbf{i}) = \mathbf{k}, \qquad (\mathbf{j} \times \mathbf{k}) = -(\mathbf{k} \times \mathbf{j}) = \mathbf{i}, \\
(\mathbf{k} \times \mathbf{i}) = -(\mathbf{i} \times \mathbf{k}) = \mathbf{j}.
\end{aligned} \tag{3}
$$

Hence, rearranging terms, we have

$$
\mathbf{F} \times \mathbf{G} = \mathbf{i}(F_yG_z - F_zG_y) + \mathbf{j}(F_zG_x - F_xG_z) + \mathbf{k}(F_xG_y - F_yG_x) \tag{4}
$$

Vector products are particularly useful in problems relating to moments, angular velocities, rotations, etc., such as are taken up in Chap. V. One additional simple application comes when we may wish to prove two vectors to be parallel. To do this, we need only show that their vector product vanishes.

Vector Components in Rotated Coordinates.—There is nothing special about the coordinate system in which our relations of the previous sections have been stated; obviously we must be able to rotate coordinates, and retain the same form for such things as Eqs. (2) and (4), stating the values of the scalar and vector products in terms of their components. Often it is desirable to find how the components of a vector are to be described in terms of rotated coordinates, and in this section we shall investigate the nature of a rotation of coordinates, and show that the scalar and vector products retain their forms in a rotated system.

As a first step in setting up rotated coordinates, let us set up three unit vectors $\mathbf{i'}$, $\mathbf{j'}$, $\mathbf{k'}$, pointing along the $x'y'z'$ axes of the rotated system. Since these vectors are of unit magnitude and at right angles to each other, they must naturally satisfy the equations

$$
\begin{aligned}
\mathbf{i'}^2 = \mathbf{j'}^2 = \mathbf{k'}^2 = 1, \qquad \mathbf{i'} \cdot \mathbf{j'} = \mathbf{j'} \cdot \mathbf{k'} = \mathbf{k'} \cdot \mathbf{i'} = 0, \\
\mathbf{i'} \times \mathbf{j'} = \mathbf{k'}, \qquad \mathbf{j'} \times \mathbf{k'} = \mathbf{i'}, \qquad \mathbf{k'} \times \mathbf{i'} = \mathbf{j'},
\end{aligned} \tag{5}
$$

analogous to (1) and (3). Remembering now that the component of one unit vector in the direction of another is the cosine of the angle between them, we may write the relations between $\mathbf{i}$, $\mathbf{j}$, $\mathbf{k}$ on the one hand, and $\mathbf{i}'$, $\mathbf{j}'$, $\mathbf{k}'$ on the other, in either of two alternative forms

$$\mathbf{i} = \mathbf{i}' \cos (x,x') + \mathbf{j}' \cos (x,y') + \mathbf{k}' \cos (x,z')$$
$$\mathbf{j} = \mathbf{i}' \cos (y,x') + \mathbf{j}' \cos (y,y') + \mathbf{k}' \cos (y,z')$$
$$\mathbf{k} = \mathbf{i}' \cos (z,x') + \mathbf{j}' \cos (z,y') + \mathbf{k}' \cos (z,z') \tag{6}$$

or

$$\mathbf{i}' = \mathbf{i} \cos (x,x') + \mathbf{j} \cos (y,x') + \mathbf{k} \cos (z,x')$$
$$\mathbf{j}' = \mathbf{i} \cos (x,y') + \mathbf{j} \cos (y,y') + \mathbf{k} \cos (z,y')$$
$$\mathbf{k}' = \mathbf{i} \cos (x,z') + \mathbf{j} \cos (y,z') + \mathbf{k} \cos (z,z'). \tag{7}$$

For convenience in notation, we shall rewrite these cosines in the form

$$\begin{aligned}
\cos (x,x') &= \alpha_{11}, & \cos (x,y') &= \alpha_{12}, & \cos (x,z') &= \alpha_{13} \\
\cos (y,x') &= \alpha_{21}, & \cos (y,y') &= \alpha_{22}, & \cos (y,z') &= \alpha_{23} \\
\cos (z,x') &= \alpha_{31}, & \cos (z,y') &= \alpha_{32}, & \cos (z,z') &= \alpha_{33}.
\end{aligned} \tag{8}$$

We shall now demonstrate a number of properties of the α_{ij}'s, before proceeding to use them. These properties follow from the relations (1), (3), and (5).

From Eq. (1), together with (6) and (8), we have

$$\sum_r \alpha_{pr}\alpha_{qr} = \delta_{pq}, \qquad \text{where } \delta_{pq} = 1 \text{ if } p = q, = 0 \text{ if } p \neq q. \tag{9}$$

The relations for $p \neq q$, stating that the vectors $\mathbf{i}$, $\mathbf{j}$, $\mathbf{k}$ are orthogonal to each other, are called "orthogonality relations," and those for $p = q$, stating that the magnitudes of $\mathbf{i}$, $\mathbf{j}$, and $\mathbf{k}$ are unity, are called "normalization conditions." It is from these orthogonality and normalization conditions in the rotation of vectors that the notation has arisen in such cases as the theory of normal coordinates, as discussed in Chap. VII, Sec. 2, and in the case of orthogonal functions, as discussed in Chap. X, Sec. 3, for the vibrating string, and in Chap. XI, Sec. 4, for the vibrating membrane.

Using in a similar way Eqs. (5) and (7), we can prove the analogous relations

$$\sum_r \alpha_{rp}\alpha_{rq} = \delta_{pq}. \tag{10}$$

From the vector products in Eqs. (3) and (5) we can prove relations that we shall write in terms of their components:

$$\alpha_{11} = \alpha_{22}\alpha_{33} - \alpha_{23}\alpha_{32}, \qquad \alpha_{12} = \alpha_{23}\alpha_{31} - \alpha_{33}\alpha_{21},$$
$$\alpha_{21} = \alpha_{13}\alpha_{32} - \alpha_{33}\alpha_{12}, \qquad \alpha_{22} = \alpha_{33}\alpha_{11} - \alpha_{31}\alpha_{13},$$
$$\alpha_{31} = \alpha_{12}\alpha_{23} - \alpha_{22}\alpha_{13}, \qquad \alpha_{32} = \alpha_{21}\alpha_{13} - \alpha_{11}\alpha_{23},$$
$$\alpha_{13} = \alpha_{32}\alpha_{21} - \alpha_{22}\alpha_{31}$$
$$\alpha_{23} = \alpha_{31}\alpha_{12} - \alpha_{11}\alpha_{32}$$
$$\alpha_{33} = \alpha_{11}\alpha_{22} - \alpha_{12}\alpha_{21}. \tag{11}$$

These relations may be stated in terms of the determinant of the α's,

$$\Delta = \begin{vmatrix} \alpha_{11} & \alpha_{12} & \alpha_{13} \\ \alpha_{21} & \alpha_{22} & \alpha_{23} \\ \alpha_{31} & \alpha_{32} & \alpha_{33} \end{vmatrix}. \tag{12}$$

It will be seen at once that they state that each element of the determinant equals its own cofactor. Furthermore, from the fact that $\mathbf{i} \cdot (\mathbf{j} \times \mathbf{k}) = \mathbf{i} \cdot \mathbf{i} = 1$, we can prove at once that the determinant (12) equals unity. It is easily shown that (11) can be derived in an alternative manner by solving Eqs. (6) for $\mathbf{i}'$, $\mathbf{j}'$, $\mathbf{k}'$, or solving (7) for $\mathbf{i}$, $\mathbf{j}$, $\mathbf{k}$, using the formulas for solving sets of simultaneous linear algebraic equations in terms of determinants. For we then have

$$\mathbf{i}' = \frac{\begin{vmatrix} \mathbf{i} & \alpha_{12} & \alpha_{13} \\ \mathbf{j} & \alpha_{22} & \alpha_{23} \\ \mathbf{k} & \alpha_{32} & \alpha_{33} \end{vmatrix}}{\begin{vmatrix} \alpha_{11} & \alpha_{12} & \alpha_{13} \\ \alpha_{21} & \alpha_{22} & \alpha_{23} \\ \alpha_{31} & \alpha_{32} & \alpha_{33} \end{vmatrix}} = \mathbf{i}(\alpha_{22}\alpha_{33} - \alpha_{23}\alpha_{32}) + \mathbf{j}(\alpha_{13}\alpha_{32} - \alpha_{33}\alpha_{12}) \\ + \mathbf{k}(\alpha_{12}\alpha_{23} - \alpha_{22}\alpha_{13}) \tag{13}$$

in which we have used the fact that the determinant (12) equals unity. Taking the scalar product of (13) with $\mathbf{i}$, $\mathbf{j}$, and $\mathbf{k}$, respectively, we have three of the equations (11), and the others follow in a similar manner.

Now that we have investigated the properties of a rotation of coordinates, we may at once find the components of a vector with respect to the new rotated coordinates. The component F'_x of a vector $\mathbf{F}$ along the x' axis is the scalar product of $\mathbf{F}$ with the unit vector $\mathbf{i}'$; thus, using (7), we have

$$F'_x = \alpha_{11}F_x + \alpha_{21}F_y + \alpha_{31}F_z$$
$$F'_y = \alpha_{12}F_x + \alpha_{22}F_y + \alpha_{32}F_z$$
$$F'_z = \alpha_{13}F_x + \alpha_{23}F_y + \alpha_{33}F_z. \tag{14}$$

To write these in more condensed form, we may write $F_x = F_1$, $F_y = F_2$, $F_z = F_3$, $F'_x = F'_1$, etc., so that we can indicate the subscript by an index, such as i, j, etc. Then we may rewrite (14) in the form

$$F'_i = \sum_j \alpha_{ji} F_j. \tag{15}$$

Similarly we find

$$F_i = \sum_j \alpha_{ij} F'_j. \tag{16}$$

We may now use these relations, plus the orthogonality relations, to investigate the form of the scalar product in the rotated coordinates. We have

$$\mathbf{F} \cdot \mathbf{G} = \sum_i F_i G_i = \sum_{ijk} \alpha_{ij} F'_j \alpha_{ik} G'_k$$

$$= \sum_{jk} F'_j G'_k \sum_i \alpha_{ij} \alpha_{ik} = \sum_{jk} F'_j G'_k \delta_{jk}$$

$$= \sum_j F'_j G'_j.$$

Thus, using the orthogonal property of the transformation, we have shown that the scalar product has the same form in the rotated as in the original coordinates. The corresponding proof for the vector product is left for a problem; it is easier to carry it out by writing the components out explicitly, and it requires for its proof the relations (11) between the α's.

The Differentiation of Vectors.—We have seen that there are at least three processes of multiplication involving vectors: the multiplication of a vector by a scalar, the scalar product of two vectors, and the vector product of two vectors. In a somewhat similar way there are a number of differential operations involving vectors, all with their special uses. The simplest of these is the differentiation of a vector with respect to a scalar. The most familiar example is that encountered in Chap. III, where we have a displacement vector $\mathbf{r}$, whose components were x, y, z, and where we differentiate with respect to the time, to get the velocity vector $\mathbf{v}$, with components dx/dt, dy/dt, dz/dt. This type of derivative hardly requires further comment.

The next type of differentiation that we consider is the differentiation of a scalar with respect to x, y, and z, to give a vector, the gradient, which we encountered in Chap. III, Sec. 2, in discussing the relationship between the force vector and the potential energy. There, given a potential energy function V, a scalar function of position, we found it useful to introduce a vector, the gradient of V, whose components are $\partial V/\partial x$, $\partial V/\partial y$, $\partial V/\partial z$. We must in the first place check our right to call this quantity a vector at all. For we have seen in (15) and (16) that the components of a vector transform in a particular way when we rotate coordinates. We may denote a quantity with three components as a vector only if its components transform in this same way. That is, we may denote grad V as a vector only if relations of the form

$$\frac{\partial V}{\partial x'} = \alpha_{11}\frac{\partial V}{\partial x} + \alpha_{21}\frac{\partial V}{\partial y} + \alpha_{31}\frac{\partial V}{\partial z}, \text{ etc.,} \tag{17}$$

are satisfied. Let us prove that these relations are in fact fulfilled. Certainly from the fundamental theorem of partial differentiation we have

$$\frac{\partial V}{\partial x'} = \frac{\partial V}{\partial x}\frac{\partial x}{\partial x'} + \frac{\partial V}{\partial y}\frac{\partial y}{\partial x'} + \frac{\partial V}{\partial z}\frac{\partial z}{\partial x'}, \text{ etc.} \tag{18}$$

But $x = \mathbf{i} \cdot \mathbf{r}$, the component of the radius vector along the x axis, and $x' = \mathbf{i}' \cdot \mathbf{r}$, so that, using (6) and (8), we have

$$x = \alpha_{11}x' + \alpha_{12}y' + \alpha_{13}z', \text{ etc.}$$

We then have, differentiating,

$$\frac{\partial x}{\partial x'} = \alpha_{11}, \qquad \frac{\partial x}{\partial y'} = \alpha_{12}, \qquad \frac{\partial x}{\partial z'} = \alpha_{13}$$

$$\frac{\partial y}{\partial x'} = \alpha_{21}, \qquad \frac{\partial y}{\partial y'} = \alpha_{22}, \qquad \frac{\partial y}{\partial z'} = \alpha_{23}$$

$$\frac{\partial z}{\partial x'} = \alpha_{31}, \qquad \frac{\partial z}{\partial y'} = \alpha_{32}, \qquad \frac{\partial z}{\partial z'} = \alpha_{33}.$$

Using these relations, we then immediately show the identity of (17) and (18), and hence verify that grad V is in fact a vector.

We may write the gradient in a form that brings out an interesting property of the differential operators. We write

$$\text{grad } V = \left(\mathbf{i}\frac{\partial}{\partial x} + \mathbf{j}\frac{\partial}{\partial y} + \mathbf{k}\frac{\partial}{\partial z}\right)V.$$

Here we have written the gradient symbolically as the product of a vector operator, and the scalar V. This vector operator is ordinarily denoted by a special symbol ∇ (pronounced "del"), defined by

$$\nabla = \mathbf{i}\frac{\partial}{\partial x} + \mathbf{j}\frac{\partial}{\partial y} + \mathbf{k}\frac{\partial}{\partial z}. \tag{19}$$

We prove that this operator transforms like a vector when the axes are rotated, by a method just like that used in the preceding paragraph. Whenever we use the operator ∇, we understand that the differentiations are to operate on whatever appears to the right of the operator. With this definition, we see that we may write the identity

$$\text{grad } V \equiv \nabla V.$$

In some texts on vectors, the gradient is simply denoted by ∇V.

Having established the vector nature of the operator ∇, we see that we can define two types of derivatives of a vector: if we have a vector $\mathbf{F}$, we can define derivatives by taking the scalar or the vector product of ∇ with the vector, resulting in $\nabla \cdot \mathbf{F}$ and $\nabla \times \mathbf{F}$. These are the quantities defined as the divergence and the curl, which we have met in the equation of continuity in hydrodynamics, in Chap. XIII, and in the discussion of forces derivable from a potential, in Chap. III, respectively. From the definition (19), we have

$$\text{div } \mathbf{F} \equiv \nabla \cdot \mathbf{F} = \frac{\partial F_x}{\partial x} + \frac{\partial F_y}{\partial y} + \frac{\partial F_z}{\partial z}$$

and

$$\text{curl } \mathbf{F} \equiv \nabla \times \mathbf{F} = \mathbf{i}\left(\frac{\partial F_z}{\partial y} - \frac{\partial F_y}{\partial z}\right) + \mathbf{j}\left(\frac{\partial F_x}{\partial z} - \frac{\partial F_z}{\partial x}\right) + \mathbf{k}\left(\frac{\partial F_y}{\partial x} - \frac{\partial F_x}{\partial y}\right).$$

We can prove that these operations preserve their form when the axes are rotated, by methods that are analogous to those already used in similar cases.

Pursuing the vector nature of the operator ∇, we can introduce several other vector differential operations. One additional operation involving first derivatives is sometimes encountered. It is formed with the aid of a vector function of position, for instance, $\mathbf{v}$, and may be written

$$\mathbf{v} \cdot \nabla = \mathbf{v} \cdot \text{grad} = v_x \frac{\partial}{\partial x} + v_y \frac{\partial}{\partial y} + v_z \frac{\partial}{\partial z}.$$

Being a scalar operator, this can be applied either to a scalar function of position, resulting in a scalar, or to a vector function of position, resulting in a vector. We encounter this operation applied to a vector in Chap. XIII, Sec. 3, in discussing the Eulerian equations of motion for a fluid. Then there are several operations involving second derivatives. The most familiar ones involve the operator $\nabla \cdot \nabla = \nabla^2$, which written out is

$$\nabla^2 = \frac{\partial^2}{\partial x^2} + \frac{\partial^2}{\partial y^2} + \frac{\partial^2}{\partial z^2}. \tag{20}$$

This is the operator that we encounter often in the wave equation, Laplace's equation, etc., and that is often called the "Laplacian," for that reason. Being a scalar operator, it can be applied to either a scalar or a vector, and both forms frequently occur. Another second differential operator that is encountered often in electromagnetic theory, though not often in mechanics, is the vector operator curl curl, applied to a vector: curl curl $\mathbf{F} = \nabla \times (\nabla \times \mathbf{F})$. We prove in a problem the useful relation

$$\text{curl curl } \mathbf{F} = \text{grad div } \mathbf{F} - \nabla^2 \mathbf{F}$$

reducing this operator to the Laplacian, which we have already met, and to grad div $\mathbf{F} = \nabla(\nabla \cdot \mathbf{F})$. This completes the list of the vector operations that are often encountered.

The Divergence Theorem and Stokes's Theorem.—Two vector theorems involving integrals, somewhat similar in principle to the theorem regarding integration by parts in calculus, are of great importance in vector analysis. These are the divergence theorem, sometimes known as Gauss's theorem, and Stokes's theorem. We shall now prove these theorems. The divergence theorem relates to a closed volume V in space, and the surface S that bounds it. It is assumed that there is a vector function of position $\mathbf{F}$. The theorem then states that the surface integral of the normal component of $\mathbf{F}$, over the surface S, equals the volume integral of div $\mathbf{F}$, over the volume V. That is,

$$\iint_S F_n \, da = \iint_S \mathbf{F} \cdot \mathbf{n} \, da = \iiint_V \text{div } \mathbf{F} \, dv \qquad (21)$$

where $\mathbf{n}$ is unit vector along the outer normal, so that $\mathbf{F} \cdot \mathbf{n}$ is another way of writing F_n, the component of $\mathbf{F}$ along the outer normal. To

Fig. 41.—Construction for the divergence theorem.

prove our theorem, we start by dividing up the volume V into thin elements bounded by planes $y = $ constant, $z = $ constant, as in Fig. 41. The component F_x will be a function of x along such an element, and we have obviously

$$\int_{x_1}^{x_2} \frac{\partial F_x}{\partial x} \, dx = F_x \Big|_{x_1}^{x_2} \qquad (22)$$

where x_1, x_2 are the values of x at which the element cuts through the surface S. Let n_1, n_2 be the outer normals at these two ends of the element, and let da_1, da_2 be the corresponding areas of surface bounding the ends of the elements. We shall have

$$-da_1 \cos (n_1,x) = dy\, dz$$
$$da_2 \cos (n_2,x) = dy\, dz$$

where (n_1,x) and (n_2,x) refer to the angles between the vectors n_1 and n_2 and the x axis, where the negative sign in the first equation arises because the outer normal has a negative projection on the x axis at the end x_1, and where dy, dz represent the thickness of the element along the y and z directions. Multiplying both sides of (22) by $dy\, dz$, we then have

$$\int_{x_1}^{x_2} \frac{\partial F_x}{\partial x}\, dx\, dy\, dz = [F_{x_1} \cos (n_1,x)\, da_1 + F_{x_2} \cos (n_2,x)\, da_2].$$

Carrying out a summation over all elements of this type, the integral on the left will become a volume integral over V, the sum on the right will become a surface integral over S, and we have

$$\int\!\!\int_V\!\!\int \frac{\partial F_x}{\partial x}\, dv = \int\!\!\int_S F_x \cos (n,x)\, da. \tag{23}$$

We now proceed similarly with y and z, breaking up the volume into thin elements with their axes along y and z, and obtain two other equations similar to (23). Adding them, we have

$$\int\!\!\int_V\!\!\int \left(\frac{\partial F_x}{\partial x} + \frac{\partial F_y}{\partial y} + \frac{\partial F_z}{\partial z}\right) dv$$
$$= \int\!\!\int_S [F_x \cos (n,x) + F_y \cos (n,y) + F_z \cos (n,z)]\, da.$$

But the integrand on the right is just the scalar product $\mathbf{F} \cdot \mathbf{n}$, so that we have proved our theorem (21). This theorem, the divergence theorem, is met in the equation of continuity, as in Chap. XIII. It is also a fundamental theorem in other problems involving flux, such as heat flow, the flow of electric current, and the flux of electric and magnetic force. It is very important in electromagnetic theory, and a theorem derived from it, called " Green's theorem," is constantly met in electromagnetic and potential theory.

A simplified version of our proof, though not entirely satisfactory, is instructive. This comes from proving the theorem for a volume consisting of an infinitesimal rectangular parallelepiped, bounded by

$x, x + dx, y, y + dy, z, z + dz$. First we compute the surface integral of F_n over the six faces of the volume. For the face at x, F_n is $-F_x$, and the integral is $-F_x(x)\, dy\, dz$, where the value of F_x is to be computed at x. For the face at $x + dx$, F_n is F_x, and the integral is $F_x(x + dx)\, dy\, dz$. Thus the surface integral over these two faces is approximately $(\partial F_x/\partial x)\, dx\, dy\, dz$. Adding similar contributions from the faces normal to the y and z axes, we find for the total surface integral the amount div $\mathbf{F}\, dx\, dy\, dz$, which is what the divergence theorem would give. This treatment suggests a simple physical definition for the divergence of a vector: it is the total outward flux of the vector per unit volume. To get from this form of the theorem to that involving a finite volume, we may subdivide the finite volume into infinitesimal parallelepipeds. The total flux outward of the vector through the surface of the finite volume is just equal to the sum of the fluxes outward over the surfaces of the infinitesimal volumes; for at each interior surface of separation between infinitesimal volumes, the flux outward from one volume is just balanced by the flux into its neighbor, leaving only the contributions of the exterior surfaces. The weakness of this proof lies only in the fact that a real volume cannot be built up entirely of infinitesimal parallelepipeds; around the boundary there would have to be infinitesimal volumes with surfaces inclined to the coordinate planes, which this treatment does not consider. Our earlier treatment, however, removes this objection.

Next we consider Stokes's theorem. This theorem relates to a closed line L in space, and a surface S which is bounded by L. Again we have a vector function of position $\mathbf{F}$. Stokes's theorem states that the line integral of the tangential component of $\mathbf{F}$, around L, equals the surface integral of the normal component of curl $\mathbf{F}$, over S. That is,

$$\int_L \mathbf{F} \cdot \mathbf{ds} = \int\int_S (\text{curl } \mathbf{F}) \cdot \mathbf{n}\, da \qquad (24)$$

where $\mathbf{ds}$ is a vector element of distance around the boundary, and $\mathbf{n}$ is the normal to the surface, chosen to point up if the positive direction of traversing the boundary is chosen (that is, if we go around the boundary in a counterclockwise direction). We shall give a simplified discussion of this theorem, similar to the second method we used for handling the divergence theorem. Let us subdivide the surface S into a set of small approximately rectangular areas. We shall prove the theorem for each of the separate areas, and then combine them. As we see from Fig. 42, the contributions to the line integrals from the interior boundaries will cancel, so that the sum of all the line integrals will equal the line integral around the perimeter. The sum of the surface integrals over the separate rectangles will clearly equal the surface integral over the whole surface. Thus by adding the separate contributions we arrive at the theorem (24), which we wish to prove. The only reservation is that the line integral is computed for a saw-tooth type of curve approximating the actual boundary. It is not hard to show, though we shall omit it, that the line integral $\int \mathbf{F} \cdot \mathbf{ds}$ over a saw-tooth curve approximating the actual curve sufficiently smoothly differs by a negligible amount from the integral over the actual curve, so that we can construct a rigorous proof of the theorem without trouble.

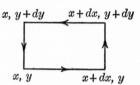

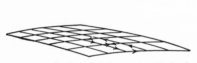

FIG. 42.—Surface for discussing Stokes's theorem.

FIG. 43.—Circuit for proving Stokes's theorem.

We must then prove our theorem (24) for a small rectangular area. Let us choose the x and y axes to point along the sides of the rectangle, the z axis along the normal $\mathbf{n}$; if we can prove the result in this coordinate system, it will have to hold as well in any coordinate system, on account of the way in which vector operations are unaffected by rotation of coordinates. The rectangle is considered to be bounded by the values x, $x + dx$, y, $y + dy$, as in Fig. 43. The surface integral on the right of (24) is then $(\partial F_y/\partial x - \partial F_x/\partial y)\, dx\, dy$. Let us next compute $\int \mathbf{F} \cdot \mathbf{ds}$ for the element of area. It is evidently

$$F_x(x,y)\, dx + F_y(x + dx, y)\, dy - F_x(x,y + dy)\, dx - F_y(x,y)\, dy$$
$$= \left(\frac{\partial F_y}{\partial x} - \frac{\partial F_x}{\partial y}\right) dx\, dy$$

if we go around so as always to keep the surface on the left. Thus the theorem (24) is true for the infinitesimal rectangular surface, and by the argument above it then holds for a finite surface as well.

Stokes's theorem, as we see in Chap. III, is useful in discussing the question of whether a given force field is conservative or not. In this volume, we have little reason to make use of fields that are not conservative, but in some branches of physics, as in electromagnetic theory, we often meet such fields, and the curl, and Stokes's theorem, are of great importance. A similar situation arises in hydrodynamics, as is discussed in Chap. XIII, where in the simple case of streamline flow the curl of the velocity is zero, but where in the case of vorticity there is a curl different from zero, and we are concerned with the line integral of the tangential component of velocity about a closed curve, a quantity that is known as the "circulation."

Problems

1. Find the angle between the diagonal of a cube and one of the edges. (*Hint:* Regard the diagonal as a vector $\mathbf{i} + \mathbf{j} + \mathbf{k}$.)

2. Given a vector $\mathbf{i} + 2\mathbf{j} + 3\mathbf{k}$, and a second $\mathbf{i} - 2\mathbf{j} + a\mathbf{k}$, find a so that the two vectors are at right angles to each other.

3. Prove that $lx + my + nz = k$, where l, m, n, k are constants, and $l^2 + m^2 + n^2 = 1$, is the equation of a plane whose normal has the direction cosines l, m, n, and whose shortest distance from the origin is k.

4. Prove that $\mathbf{A} \cdot (\mathbf{B} \times \mathbf{C}) = \mathbf{B} \cdot (\mathbf{C} \times \mathbf{A}) = \mathbf{C} \cdot (\mathbf{A} \times \mathbf{B})$, where $\mathbf{A}$, $\mathbf{B}$, $\mathbf{C}$ are any vectors. Show that these are equal to the determinant

$$\begin{vmatrix} A_x & A_y & A_z \\ B_x & B_y & B_z \\ C_x & C_y & C_z \end{vmatrix}.$$

5. Prove that $\mathbf{A} \times (\mathbf{B} \times \mathbf{C}) = \mathbf{B}(\mathbf{A} \cdot \mathbf{C}) - \mathbf{C}(\mathbf{A} \cdot \mathbf{B})$, where $\mathbf{A}$, $\mathbf{B}$, $\mathbf{C}$ are any vectors.

6. Prove that div $a\mathbf{F} = a$ div $\mathbf{F} + (\mathbf{F} \cdot \text{grad } a)$, where a is a scalar, $\mathbf{F}$ a vector.

7. Prove that curl $a\mathbf{F} = a$ curl $\mathbf{F} + [(\text{grad } a) \times \mathbf{F}]$, where a is a scalar, $\mathbf{F}$ a vector.

8. Prove that div $(\mathbf{F} \times \mathbf{G}) = (\mathbf{G} \cdot \text{curl } \mathbf{F}) - (\mathbf{F} \cdot \text{curl } \mathbf{G})$, where $\mathbf{F}$, $\mathbf{G}$ are vectors.

9. Prove that div curl $\mathbf{F} = 0$, where $\mathbf{F}$ is any vector.

10. Prove that curl curl $\mathbf{F} = \text{grad div } \mathbf{F} - \nabla^2\mathbf{F}$, where $\mathbf{F}$ is any vector.

11. Prove that the vector product is invariant under a rotation of axes.

12. Prove that the divergence, curl, and Laplacian are invariant under a rotation of axes; that is, that they have the same form in the new axes as in the old.

APPENDIX V

TENSORS

A tensor, for the purposes of the present volume, is a quantity like T_{ij}, having two indices, and furthermore characterized by the fact that, when we combine it with a vector of components F_j, by the rule

$$G_i = \sum_j T_{ij}F_j, \tag{1}$$

the resulting quantity of components G_i is likewise a vector. We have met several examples of tensors. First, in Chap. V, we met the moment of inertia tensor I_{ij}, which satisfied Eq. (2.6) of that chapter,

$$p_a = \sum_b I_{ab}\omega_b,$$

where p_a represents the components of the angular momentum vector, and ω_b the components of the angular velocity vector. Another example came in Chap. VII, where we had a tensor A_{ij} determining the interaction between a set of particles held together by linear restoring forces, satisfying the relation

$$F_i = -\sum_j A_{ij}x_j,$$

where F_i is the force on the ith particle, and x_j the vector displacement of the jth particle. In Chap. X, in discussing changes of variables in function space, we introduced a tensor A_{nk}, such that a characteristic function u_n (a generalized vector) could be expanded in terms of unperturbed functions u_k^0 (also a generalized vector) by the expression

$$u_n = \sum_k A_{nk}u_k^0.$$

In Chap. XII, we encountered the stress tensor T_{ij}, such that the force vector of components F_i exerted across unit area of a plane whose normal was a vector α_j was given by

$$F_i = \sum_j T_{ij}\alpha_j.$$

Again, in Chap. XII, and also in Appendix IV, we have been concerned with rotation of axes. These rotations were determined by quantities α_{ij}, such that the components F_i of a vector in original coordinates are related to the components F'_j in rotated coordinates by the relations

$$F_i = \sum_j \alpha_{ij} F'_j.$$

It is clear that all these cases have a formal relationship to each other. For our present purposes we do not need much more information about tensors than is given by these simple relations, but we shall go somewhat further in discussing their properties.

In many important cases we have met symmetric tensors, in which $T_{ij} = T_{ji}$; this was the case with the moment of inertia, the tensor of linear restoring forces, and the stress, though not the rotation tensor α_{ij}. There can also be antisymmetric tensors, in which $T_{ij} = -T_{ji}$, and in which as a corollary the diagonal terms, for $i = j$, must be zero. An example, which would not occur to one at first sight, is the vector product of two vectors. If we have two vectors, of components F_i, G_i, and form the tensor $T_{ij} = F_i G_j - F_j G_i$, we note at once that by the definition it is antisymmetric, so that it has only six nonvanishing components, of which three are equal and opposite to the other three, so that really there are only three independent components. Of these, letting the indices take on the values x, y, z, we find that

$$T_{yz} = F_y G_z - F_z G_y = (\mathbf{F} \times \mathbf{G})_x$$
$$T_{zx} = F_z G_x - F_x G_z = (\mathbf{F} \times \mathbf{G})_y$$
$$T_{xy} = F_x G_y - F_y G_x = (\mathbf{F} \times \mathbf{G})_z.$$

This interpretation of the vector product, and correspondingly of the curl of a vector, as an antisymmetric tensor instead of as a vector, is sometimes of considerable value, and is often used in advanced discussions of electromagnetic theory. We note at once that, although some tensors are symmetric, some antisymmetric, any arbitrary tensor may be written as the sum of a symmetric and an antisymmetric tensor, by the simple equation

$$T_{ij} = \tfrac{1}{2}(T_{ij} + T_{ji}) + \tfrac{1}{2}(T_{ij} - T_{ji})$$

in which it is clear that the first term is symmetric, the second antisymmetric.

When we consider algebraic operations involving tensors, we have already seen in (1) how we can multiply a tensor by a vector to get a vector.   Clearly we can multiply a tensor by two vectors to get a scalar:

$$(\mathbf{G} \cdot \mathbf{H}) = \sum_i G_i H_i = \sum_{ij} T_{ij} H_i F_j.$$

Examples of this process have been seen in Chap. V, Eq. (2.8), where we found the kinetic energy T by the equation

$$T = \tfrac{1}{2} \sum_{ab} I_{ab} \omega_a \omega_b$$

as well as in Chap. VII, where the potential energy was

$$V = \tfrac{1}{2} \sum_{ij} A_{ij} x_i x_j,$$

and in various other places.   There are various other types of products involving tensors, but we have not had occasion to use them.

In Chap. XII we encountered certain facts regarding the behavior of a tensor under a rotation of coordinates.   We have been interested in such a rotation that a given tensor is reduced to diagonal form; that is, a rotation to principal axes.   Using the stress tensor as an example, we find that $\sum_k T_{jk}\alpha_{ki}$ represents the x_j component of force per unit area across unit plane normal to x_i'; it is sort of a mixed tensor, referring half to the unprimed, half to the primed coordinates.   We demand that this force be parallel to x_i'; that is, that it be a constant, T_i', times the unit vector along x_i'.   Since this unit vector has a component α_{ji} along the x_j direction, this leads to the equation

$$\sum_k T_{jk}\alpha_{ki} = T_i'\alpha_{ji}, \qquad \sum_k (T_{jk} - T_i'\delta_{jk})\alpha_{ki} = 0, \qquad (2)$$

which is the same as Eq. (1.3), Chap. XII.   As we have pointed out several times, these equations form a set of n simultaneous equations (if n is the number of values over which the index k ranges, equal to three in the ordinary vector case) for n unknowns α_{ki}, where k goes from 1 to n.   But n such simultaneous homogeneous linear equations have in general no solution unless the determinant of their coefficients equals zero.   To see this, if the result is not familiar, we may take a set of equations

$$a_{11}x_1 + \cdots + a_{1n}x_n = b_1$$
$$a_{21}x_1 + \cdots + a_{2n}x_n = b_2$$
$$\cdot \; \cdot \; \cdot \; \cdot \; \cdot \; \cdot \; \cdot \; \cdot \; \cdot \; \cdot \; \cdot \; \cdot$$
$$a_{n1}x_1 + \cdots + a_{nn}x_n = b_n, \qquad (3)$$

in which the a's and b's are coefficients, the x's unknowns. The solution of these equations by determinants is

$$x_1 = \frac{\begin{vmatrix} b_1 & a_{12} & a_{13} & \ldots & a_{1n} \\ b_2 & a_{22} & a_{23} & \ldots & a_{2n} \\ \cdot & \cdot & \cdot & \cdot & \cdot \\ b_n & a_{n2} & a_{n3} & \ldots & a_{nn} \end{vmatrix}}{\begin{vmatrix} a_{11} & a_{12} & a_{13} & \ldots & a_{1n} \\ a_{21} & a_{22} & a_{23} & \ldots & a_{2n} \\ \cdot & \cdot & \cdot & \cdot & \cdot \\ a_{n1} & a_{n2} & a_{n3} & \ldots & a_{nn} \end{vmatrix}} \tag{4}$$

with similar solutions for the other x's. Our case (2) is the special case where the b's in (3) are all zero, the homogeneous equation. In this case, the determinant in the numerator of (4) is zero, and x_1, and all the x's, will be zero, except in the special case where the denominator is also zero, so that the ratio is indeterminate. It is for this reason that the determinant of coefficients in (2) must vanish, leading to the secular equation for the values T_i.

The secular equation, formed by setting the determinant of coefficients in Eq. (2) equal to zero, is an algebraic equation of the nth degree for T_i', and hence has n roots. We label these roots from 1 to n, for instance, in order of size, and call the first one T_1', the second T_2', and so on. Inserting any one of these roots, such as the ith, into Eq. (2), we now find that the equations have solutions for the α_{ki}'s. As we have pointed out in the text, the equations serve to determine only the ratios of the α_{ki}'s, not their absolute magnitudes, for we may divide Eqs. (2) by one of the α's, for instance, α_{1i}, and obtain n equations for the $n - 1$ variables α_{ki}/α_{1i}, $k = 2, 3, \cdots n$. These equations may be solved in the usual way for these ratios; any $n - 1$ of them will give a set of solutions, and these solutions will automatically satisfy the nth equation as well, because the secular equation is satisfied. We may if we choose determine the magnitudes of the α's by imposing the normalization condition $\sum_k \alpha_{ki}^2 = 1$.

Now that we have found the α_{ki}'s, we may show that the vectors so found are orthogonal, so that the principal axes form a set of orthogonal axes. To show this, we take Eq. (2), which we shall slightly generalize to the form $\sum_k T_{jk}\alpha_{ki} = T_i' c_j \alpha_{ji}$, so that we can take account of the case of normal modes of oscillation, as met in Eq. (2.1), Chap. VII, as well; in that case the T_{ij}'s are replaced by A_{ij}'s, and the c_j's become m_j's. We now multiply by α_{jn}, and sum over j, obtaining

$$\sum_{jk} T_{jk}\alpha_{jn}\alpha_{ki} = T'_i \sum_j c_j\alpha_{ji}\alpha_{jn}. \tag{5}$$

We may rewrite (2), using other symbols, in the form

$$\sum_k T_{jk}\alpha_{kn} = T'_n c_j\alpha_{jn}. \tag{6}$$

Multiplying (6) by α_{ji}, and summing over j, we have

$$\sum_{jk} T_{jk}\alpha_{kn}\alpha_{ji} = T'_n \sum_j c_j\alpha_{ji}\alpha_{jn}. \tag{7}$$

In the double summation on the left side of (7), we may interchange the names of the symbols j and k, and that summation becomes identical with $\sum_{jk} T_{kj}\alpha_{jn}\alpha_{ki}$. Subtracting (7), with this modification, from (5), we have

$$\sum_{jk} (T_{jk} - T_{ki})\alpha_{jn}\alpha_{ki} = (T'_i - T'_n) \sum_j c_j\alpha_{ji}\alpha_{jn}. \tag{8}$$

Now, if T_{ij} is a symmetric tensor, we shall have $T_{jk} = T_{kj}$, and the left side of (8) will vanish.

This is the only case in which the proof of orthogonality holds (so long as all the tensors concerned are real; we disregard the case of complex tensors). Then the right side of (8) must be zero. This leads to two possibilities: first, T'_i may be different from T'_n, and in this case $\sum_j c_j\alpha_{ji}\alpha_{jn} = 0$, proving the orthogonality that we wished to show; secondly, T'_i may equal T'_n, in which case our proof gives no new information. We may have $T'_i = T'_n$ for either of two reasons: i may equal n, in which case the summation is $\sum_j c_j\alpha_{ji}^2$, which is certainly not zero (since we have assumed it to be normalized to unity); or i may not equal n, and yet the T''s may be equal, in which case we have degeneracy. In a case of degeneracy, it is not necessary that the principal axes be orthogonal. For instance, in a symmetrical rigid body, we have seen that any axis in the plane normal to the axis of symmetry can act like a principal axis, in the sense of the present paragraph. It is always possible, however, in such a case to choose the principal axes to be orthogonal to each other, and we assume that

that has been done. Thus in every case the transformation to principal axes results in an orthogonal set of unit vectors, which define a rotation of axes.

We have seen that $\sum_k T_{lk}\alpha_{kj}$ represents the x_l component of force across unit plane normal to x_j', where we now disregard the c_j's. From this we can easily find the x_i' component of force across unit plane normal to x_j', which we may call T_{ij}'. We need merely use Eq. (15), Appendix IV, and find

$$T_{ij}' = \sum_{lk} T_{lk}\alpha_{li}\alpha_{kj}. \tag{9}$$

This is the general equation for the components of a tensor in rotated coordinates, analogous to the expressions (15) and (16) of Appendix IV for giving the components of a vector in rotated coordinates. As an illustration of this equation, let us verify the fact that the tensor becomes diagonal when the axes are rotated to the principal axes. That is, we assume that the α's are determined by Eq. (2). Inserting this in (9), we then have at once

$$T_{ij}' = \sum_l \alpha_{li} \sum_k T_{lk}\alpha_{kj} = \sum_l \alpha_{li} T_j' \alpha_{lj} = T_j' \delta_{ij}$$

which shows that T_{ij}' is diagonal, with its diagonal components given by T_j'.

We have now gained some insight into the nature of tensors, and their behavior when the coordinates are rotated. In addition, we need information regarding their derivatives. In this regard we have met only one differential operation, the tensor divergence, which we encountered in our discussion of elasticity, in Chap. XII, Sec. 4. This quantity was given by $\sum_j \partial T_{ij}/\partial x_j$, and represented the ith component of force per unit volume, a vector. Clearly it is the product of the vector ∇, and the tensor T_{ij}, formed according to the definition (1). Other more complicated differential operations can be set up, just as other types of products can be set up, using ∇ in various ways, but they need not concern us here.

This brief summary of some of the properties of tensors is merely sufficient to give the orientation necessary for the applications that we have had to make of tensor methods. As a matter of fact, tensor calculus is a widespread subject, with many uses. We may in the first place generalize to having tensors with any arbitrary number of indices, not merely two. In fact, a vector is regarded in this generalized sense as a tensor with one index; the type of tensor that we have considered in this appendix has two, but there can be tensors with any number of indices, a scalar being the particular case in which there are no indices at all. Naturally the types of products and of differential operations become very great under these circumstances. The further developments of tensor analysis mostly deal with the general behavior of tensors, not merely under a rotation of coordinates, but also under an arbitrary change of variables. We shall meet a small part of this theory in Appendix VII, where we consider vector operations in curvilinear coordinates. The most celebrated application of this generalized tensor theory is found in the theory of general relativity, where the laws of mathematical physics are expressed in a form that is preserved when any arbitrary change of variables is introduced.

The theory of the rotation of axes to the principal axes, which we have illustrated in this appendix, forms the basis of the matrix theory of quantum mechanics. Our Eq. (2) is identical with the fundamental equation of matrix mechanics, and our proof of orthogonality in (8) is substantially like the corresponding proof in quantum mechanics, except that there one deals with complex, rather than with real, quantities. In quantum mechanics, one also operates with Schrödinger's equation, a partial differential equation like the wave equation, whose solutions are orthogonal functions. One finds that the orthogonality properties of the solutions of Schrödinger's equation are closely connected with the orthogonality relations for the principal axes. The mathematics that one encounters in that field is closely analogous to what we have met in discussing the perturbation theory for the vibrating string, in Chap. X, Sec. 4, in which we started with orthogonal functions u_n^0, expanded the unknown solutions u_n of the problem in series of u_n^0's by the equation $u_n = \sum_k A_{nk} u_k^0$, and then determined the quantities A_{nk} by an equation like (2) of this appendix. From this example one sees the far-reaching analogy between orthogonal functions and the rotation of coordinates, and between the theory of partial differential equations and of the algebra of linear transformations.

Problem

With the help of the divergence theorem, give a general proof that the stress tensor is symmetric.

APPENDIX VI

FOURIER SERIES

Fourier's theorem may be stated as follows: Given an arbitrary function $\varphi(x)$. Then [unless $\varphi(x)$ contains an infinite number of discontinuities in a finite range, or similarly misbehaves itself] we can write

$$\varphi(x) = \frac{A_0}{2} + \sum_{n=1}^{\infty}\left(A_n \cos \frac{2\pi nx}{X} + B_n \sin \frac{2\pi nx}{X}\right) \qquad (1)$$

where

$$A_n = \frac{2}{X}\int_{-X/2}^{X/2} \varphi(x) \cos \frac{2\pi nx}{X}\, dx,$$

$$B_n = \frac{2}{X}\int_{-X/2}^{X/2} \varphi(x) \sin \frac{2\pi nx}{X}\, dx. \qquad (2)$$

This equation holds for values of x between $-X/2$ and $X/2$, but not in general outside this range. The series of sines and cosines is called "Fourier's series." There are two sides to the proof of Fourier's theorem. First, we may prove that, if a series of sines and cosines of this sort can represent the function, then it must have the coefficients we have given. This is simple, and we shall carry it through. But, second, we could show that the series we so set up actually represents the function. That is, we should investigate the convergence of the series, show that it does converge, and that its sum is the function $\varphi(x)$. This second part we shall omit, merely stating the results of the discussion.

Let us suppose that $\varphi(x)$ is represented by a series as in (1), and ask what values the A's and B's must have if the equation is to be true. Multiply both sides of the equation by $\cos(2\pi mx/X)$, where m is an integer, and integrate from $-X/2$ to $X/2$. We then have

$$\int_{-X/2}^{X/2} \varphi(x) \cos \frac{2\pi mx}{X}\, dx = \int_{-X/2}^{X/2} \left(\frac{A_0}{2} \cos \frac{2\pi mx}{X}\right.$$

$$\left. + \sum_n A_n \cos \frac{2\pi nx}{X} \cos \frac{2\pi mx}{X} + \sum_n B_n \sin \frac{2\pi nx}{X} \cos \frac{2\pi mx}{X}\right) dx. \qquad (3)$$

But we can easily show by direct integration that

$$\int_{-X/2}^{X/2} \cos \frac{2\pi nx}{X} \cos \frac{2\pi mx}{X} \, dx = 0$$

if n and m are integers, unless $n = m$, and that

$$\int_{-X/2}^{X/2} \sin \frac{2\pi nx}{X} \cos \frac{2\pi mx}{X} \, dx = 0$$

if n and m are integers. Thus all terms on the right of (3) are zero except one, for which $n = m$. The first term falls in with this rule, when we remember that $\cos 0 = 1$. This one term then gives us

$$A_m \int_{-X/2}^{X/2} \cos^2 \frac{2\pi mx}{X} \, dx = A_m \frac{X}{2},$$

as we can readily show. Hence

$$A_n = \frac{2}{X} \int_{-X/2}^{X/2} \varphi(x) \cos \frac{2\pi nx}{X} \, dx.$$

In a similar way, multiplying by $\sin (2\pi mx/X)$, we can prove the formula for B_n.

We have thus shown that, if a function $\varphi(x)$ is to be represented by a series (1), the coefficients must be given by (2). We shall next make a few remarks about the other part of the problem, the question whether the series so defined really converges to represent the function $\varphi(x)$. In the first place, the series cannot in general represent the function, except in the region between $-X/2$ and $X/2$; for the series is periodic, repeating itself in every period, whereas the function $\varphi(x)$ in general is not. Only periodic functions of this period can be represented in all their range by Fourier series. If we try to represent a nonperiodic function, the representation will be correct within the range from $-X/2$ to $X/2$, but the same thing will automatically repeat outside the range. Incidentally, we can easily change the range in which the series represents the function. If we merely change the range of integration so as to be from x_0 to $x_0 + X$, where x_0 is arbitrary, the series will represent the function within this range. The case we have used above corresponds to $x_0 = -X/2$; another choice frequently made is $x_0 = 0$. Then again, if we change the value of X, we can change the length of the range in which the series is correct. To represent a function through a large range of x, we may use a large value of X. In fact, as X becomes infinite, the quantities $2\pi n/X$ for successive

n's become arbitrarily close together, and the summations involved in (1) and (2) may be replaced by integrations. Thus, if we let $2\pi n/X$ equal ω, the interval $d\omega$ between successive values of this quantity will be $d\omega = 2\pi/X$. We may then replace (1) by the integration

$$\varphi(x) = \frac{X}{2\pi} \int_0^\infty (A_n \cos \omega x + B_n \sin \omega x) \, d\omega,$$

where

$$A_n = \frac{2}{X} \int_{-\infty}^\infty \varphi(\xi) \cos \omega\xi \, d\xi,$$

$$B_n = \frac{2}{X} \int_{-\infty}^\infty \varphi(\xi) \sin \omega\xi \, d\xi.$$

Here we have left out the term in A_0, which becomes negligible in the limit. Combining, we finally have

$$\varphi(x) = \frac{1}{\pi} \int_0^\infty d\omega \int_{-\infty}^\infty \varphi(\xi) \cos \omega(\xi - x) \, d\xi. \tag{4}$$

This theorem expresses Fourier's integral theorem, which as we see is merely the limiting form of Fourier's series for infinite value of the period X.

Although the range within which a Fourier series converges to the value of the function it is supposed to represent is limited, as we have seen, to the value X, there is a compensation, in that within this range a Fourier series can be used to represent much worse curves than a power series. Thus a Fourier series can still converge, even though the function has a finite number of discontinuities. It can consist, for example, of one function in one part of the region, another in another (in this case, to carry out the integrations, we must break up the integral into separate integrals over these parts, and add them). The less serious the discontinuities, however, the better the convergence. Thus, if the function itself has discontinuities, the coefficients will fall off as $1/n$, whereas if only the first derivative has discontinuities the coefficients will fall off as $1/n^2$, and so on. Differentiating a function makes the convergence of a series worse, as we can see, for example, if a function is continuous but its first derivative is discontinuous. Then the coefficients fall off as $1/n^2$, but, if we differentiate, the coefficients of the resulting series will fall off as $1/n$. There is an interesting point connected with the series for a discontinuous function. If the function jumps from one value u_1 to another u_2 at a given value of x, then the series at this point converges to the mean value, $(u_1 + u_2)/2$.

In the special problem of the vibrating string, the series we require is somewhat different from the general case, in that there are only sines, and not cosines. We are therefore led to investigate series of sines only, or of cosines only. Suppose we take the series

$$\frac{A_0}{2} + \sum_{n=1}^{\infty}{}' A_n \cos \frac{2\pi n x}{X},$$

the series formed by taking the cosine part of the general Fourier series. Now each one of the terms is even in x; that is, if we inter-

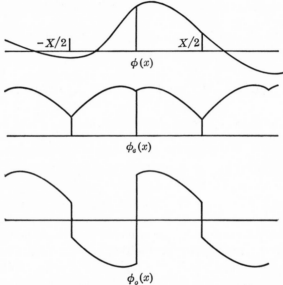

FIG. 44.—A function, with even and odd periodic functions made from it. The even and odd functions, $\varphi_e(x)$ and $\varphi_o(x)$, agree with the original function $\varphi(x)$ between 0 and $X/2$. Between 0 and $-X/2$, $\varphi_e(x)$ is the mirror image of $\varphi(x)$, while $\varphi_o(x)$ has the opposite sign. Outside the region from $-X/2$ to $X/2$, both functions repeat periodically.

change x with $-x$, the function is not changed. A cosine series represents therefore an even function. Similarly the series

$$\sum_{n=1}^{\infty} B_n \sin \frac{2\pi n x}{X},$$

of which each term is odd, represents an odd function (one for which, if x is interchanged with $-x$, the function changes its signs but not its magnitude). It is well known that any function $\varphi(x)$ can be written as the sum of an even and an odd function:

$$\varphi(x) = \tfrac{1}{2}[\varphi(x) + \varphi(-x)] + \tfrac{1}{2}[\varphi(x) - \varphi(-x)],$$

of which the first term is even, the second odd. Thus the cosine part of a Fourier series represents the even part of the function, the sine series the odd part. As a corollary, any even function can be represented by a cosine series alone, any odd function by a sine series.

Now suppose we are really interested in a function only between 0 and $X/2$, and that we do not care what the series does outside that region. Then we may define an even function $\varphi_e(x)$ as follows: it equals the given function $\varphi(x)$ between 0 and $X/2$, but has just the same value for $-x$ that it has for x (as in Fig. 44). Outside the range from $-X/2$ to $X/2$, it repeats itself. The Fourier representation of φ_e will be a cosine series, but it will represent the given function φ correctly between 0 and $X/2$. Evidently it is the series

$$\frac{A_0}{2} + \sum_{n=1}^{\infty} A_n \cos \frac{2\pi n x}{X},$$

where we write the coefficients as the sum of two integrals,

$$
\begin{aligned}
A_n &= \frac{2}{X} \int_{-X/2}^{X/2} \varphi_e(x) \cos \frac{2\pi n x}{X} \, dx \\
&= \frac{2}{X} \left[\int_{-X/2}^{0} \varphi(-x) \cos \frac{2\pi n x}{X} \, dx + \int_{0}^{X/2} \varphi(x) \cos \frac{2\pi n x}{X} \, dx \right] \\
&= \frac{4}{X} \int_{0}^{X/2} \varphi(x) \cos \frac{2\pi n x}{X} \, dx.
\end{aligned}
$$

Similarly we may define an odd function $\varphi_0(x)$, which equals $\varphi(x)$ between 0 and $X/2$, but at $-x$ has the negative of its value at $+x$. This function is represented by a sine series $\sum_{n=1}^{\infty} B_n \sin \frac{2\pi n x}{X}$, where we readily see that

$$B_n = \frac{4}{X} \int_{0}^{X/2} \varphi(x) \sin \frac{2\pi n x}{X} \, dx.$$

Hence, between 0 and $X/2$, the same function can be represented by either a cosine or a sine series. But outside this range, the series represent quite different functions.

An alternative form of Fourier's theorem (1) and (2), expressed in terms of exponential rather than trigonometric functions, is simpler to write, and for many purposes is more convenient.   To derive it, we express the sines and cosines in (1) and (2) in complex exponential form.   Grouping together the terms in $e^{j2\pi nx/X}$, and the terms in $e^{-j2\pi nx/X}$, we find without trouble that an equivalent statement of the theorem is

$$\varphi(x) = \sum_{n=-\infty}^{\infty} C_n e^{j2\pi nx/X}$$

where

$$C_n = \frac{1}{X} \int_{-X/2}^{X/2} \varphi(x) e^{-j2\pi nx/X} \, dx.$$

The terms for equal positive and negative values of n combine to give the sines and cosines correctly, and the term for $n = 0$ gives the term in A_0 in (1).   Though the C_n's, from their definition, are complex, it is easily shown that, if $\varphi(x)$ is real, C_n and C_{-n} are complex conjugates, and the series itself is real.   We can easily write an expression of Fourier's integral theorem, equivalent to (4), but in exponential language, similar to (5) and (6).

Problems

1. Expand in Fourier series the function that is equal to $-x$ for x between $-X/2$ and 0, and equal to x for x between 0 and $X/2$.

2. Expand in Fourier series the function that is equal to -1 for x between $-X/2$ and 0, and equal to 1 for x between 0 and $X/2$.   See if this series can be found by differentiating the series of Prob. 1 term by term.   Consider the convergence of these two series, with reference to their continuity.   What happens if we try to differentiate again term by term?

3. Expand in Fourier series the function that is equal to x^2 for x between $-X/2$ and $X/2$.   Compute the sum of the first four terms of this series, and see how good an approximation to the function you have.

4. Expand in Fourier series the function that is equal to zero except for x between $-\xi/2$ and $\xi/2$, where $\xi \ll X$, while in this region it equals unity.   Discuss the behavior of this function in the limit as ξ becomes zero.

5. Expand in Fourier integral the function that is zero up to $x = 0$, is sinusoidal until $x = A$, and then is zero for larger values of x.   (*Note:* If we use t instead of x, an expansion in Fourier integral furnishes essentially a mathematical description of the spectrum of the disturbance.   Thus you have found the spectrum of a wave train of finite length.)   Discuss the behavior of the spectrum as the wave train becomes a shorter and shorter number of wave lengths; a longer and longer number of wave lengths.

6. Find the spectrum of a disturbance that starts at $t = 0$, and is a sinusoidal damped wave after that.   Show that the curve for intensity as a function of frequency has the same form as a resonance curve, in general, and that its breadth is connected with the rate of damping in the same way.   This illustrates an important principle: the emission and absorption spectrum of the same resonator are essentially equivalent.

APPENDIX VII

VECTOR OPERATIONS IN CURVILINEAR COORDINATES

Let us assume three orthogonal coordinates q_1, q_2, q_3, so that the three sets of coordinate surfaces, $q_1 =$ constant, $q_2 =$ constant, $q_3 =$ constant, intersect at right angles, though in general the surfaces will be curved. Now let us move a distance ds_1 normal to a surface $q_1 =$ constant. By doing so, q_2 and q_3 do not change, but we reach another surface on which q_1 has increased by dq_1, which in general is different from ds_1. Thus, with polar coordinates, if the displacement is along the radius, so that r is changing, $ds = dr$; but, if it is along a tangent to a circle, so that θ is changing, $ds = r\, d\theta$. In general, we have

$$ds_1 = h_1\, dq_1, \qquad ds_2 = h_2\, dq_2, \qquad ds_3 = h_3\, dq_3, \qquad (1)$$

where in polar coordinates the h connected with r is unity, but that connected with θ is r. The first step in setting up vector operations in any set of coordinates is to derive these h's, which can be done by elementary geometrical methods. Thus in cylindrical coordinates, where the coordinates are r, θ, z, we have $ds_1 = dr$, $ds_2 = r\, d\theta$, $ds_3 = dz$, so that $h_1 = 1$, $h_2 = r$, $h_3 = 1$. In spherical polar coordinates, r, θ, φ, we have $ds_1 = dr$, $ds_2 = r\, d\theta$, $ds_3 = r \sin \theta\, d\varphi$, so that $h_1 = 1$, $h_2 = r$, $h_3 = r \sin \theta$.

Gradient.—The component of the gradient of a scalar S in any direction is its rate of change in that direction. Thus the component in the direction 1 (normal to the surface $q_1 =$ constant) is

$$\frac{dS}{ds_1} = \left(\frac{1}{h_1}\right)\left(\frac{\partial S}{\partial q_1}\right),$$

with similar formulas for the other components. Thus in cylindrical coordinates we have

$$\operatorname{grad}_r S = \frac{\partial S}{\partial r}, \qquad \operatorname{grad}_\theta S = \frac{1}{r}\frac{\partial S}{\partial \theta}, \qquad \operatorname{grad}_z S = \frac{\partial S}{\partial z}, \qquad (2)$$

and in spherical coordinates we have

$$\operatorname{grad}_r S = \frac{\partial S}{\partial r}, \qquad \operatorname{grad}_\theta S = \frac{1}{r}\frac{\partial S}{\partial \theta}, \qquad \operatorname{grad}_\varphi S = \frac{1}{r \sin \theta}\frac{\partial S}{\partial \varphi}. \qquad (3)$$

Divergence.—Let us apply the divergence theorem to a small volume element $dv = ds_1\, ds_2\, ds_3$, bounded by coordinate surfaces at q_1, $q_1 + dq_1$, etc. If we have a vector **A**, with components A_1, A_2, A_3 along the three curvilinear axes, the flux into the volume over the face at q_1, whose area is $ds_2\, ds_3$, is $(A_1\, ds_2\, ds_3)_{q_1}$, and the corresponding flux out over the opposite face is $(A_1\, ds_2\, ds_3)_{q_1+dq_1}$, where we note that the area $ds_2\, ds_3$ changes with q_1 as well as the flux density A_1. Thus the flux out over these two faces is

$$\frac{\partial}{\partial q_1}(A_1\, ds_2\, ds_3)\, dq_1 = \frac{\partial}{\partial q_1}(A_1 h_2 h_3)\, dq_1\, dq_2\, dq_3$$

$$= \frac{1}{h_1 h_2 h_3}\frac{\partial}{\partial q_1}(A_1 h_2 h_3)\, dv.$$

Proceeding similarly with the other pairs of faces, and setting the whole outward flux equal to div **A** dv, we have

$$\operatorname{div}\mathbf{A} = \frac{1}{h_1 h_2 h_3}\left[\frac{\partial}{\partial q_1}(A_1 h_2 h_3) + \frac{\partial}{\partial q_2}(A_2 h_3 h_1) + \frac{\partial}{\partial q_3}(A_3 h_1 h_2)\right]. \quad (4)$$

Thus in cylindrical coordinates we have

$$\operatorname{div}\mathbf{A} = \frac{1}{r}\frac{\partial}{\partial r}(rA_r) + \frac{1}{r}\frac{\partial A_\theta}{\partial \theta} + \frac{\partial A_z}{\partial z} \quad (5)$$

and in spherical coordinates

$$\operatorname{div}\mathbf{A} = \frac{1}{r^2}\frac{\partial}{\partial r}(r^2 A_r) + \frac{1}{r\sin\theta}\frac{\partial}{\partial \theta}(\sin\theta A_\theta) + \frac{1}{r\sin\theta}\frac{\partial A_\varphi}{\partial \varphi}. \quad (6)$$

Laplacian.—Writing the Laplacian of a scalar S as div grad S, and placing $A_1 = \operatorname{grad}_1 S$, etc., in the expression for div **A**, we have

$$\nabla^2 S = \frac{1}{h_1 h_2 h_3}\left[\frac{\partial}{\partial q_1}\left(\frac{h_2 h_3}{h_1}\frac{\partial S}{\partial q_1}\right) + \frac{\partial}{\partial q_2}\left(\frac{h_3 h_1}{h_2}\frac{\partial S}{\partial q_2}\right) + \frac{\partial}{\partial q_3}\left(\frac{h_1 h_2}{h_3}\frac{\partial S}{\partial q_3}\right)\right]. \quad (7)$$

Thus in cylindrical coordinates we have

$$\nabla^2 S = \frac{1}{r}\frac{\partial}{\partial r}\left(r\frac{\partial S}{\partial r}\right) + \frac{1}{r^2}\frac{\partial^2 S}{\partial \theta^2} + \frac{\partial^2 S}{\partial z^2} \quad (8)$$

and in spherical coordinates

$$\nabla^2 S = \frac{1}{r^2}\frac{\partial}{\partial r}\left(r^2\frac{\partial S}{\partial r}\right) + \frac{1}{r^2\sin\theta}\frac{\partial}{\partial \theta}\left(\sin\theta\frac{\partial S}{\partial \theta}\right) + \frac{1}{r^2\sin^2\theta}\frac{\partial^2 S}{\partial \varphi^2}. \quad (9)$$

Curl.—We apply Stokes's theorem to an approximately rectangular area bounded by q_1, $q_1 + dq_1$, q_2, $q_2 + dq_2$. The line integral of a vector **A** about the circuit is

$$A_1(q_1,q_2) \, ds_1 + A_2(q_1 + dq_1,q_2) \, ds_2$$
$$- A_1(q_1,q_2 + dq_2) \, ds_1 - A_2(q_1,q_2) \, ds_2.$$

This is approximately equal to

$$\left[\frac{\partial}{\partial q_1}(h_2 A_2) - \frac{\partial}{\partial q_2}(h_1 A_1)\right] dq_1 \, dq_2. \tag{10}$$

Since this must be curl$_3$ **A** $ds_1 \, ds_2$, we have

$$\text{curl}_3 \, \mathbf{A} = \frac{1}{h_1 h_2}\left[\frac{\partial}{\partial q_1}(h_2 A_2) - \frac{\partial}{\partial q_2}(h_1 A_1)\right]. \tag{11}$$

Thus in cylindrical coordinates we have

$$\text{curl}_r \, \mathbf{A} = \frac{1}{r}\frac{\partial A_z}{\partial \theta} - \frac{\partial A_\theta}{\partial z}$$

$$\text{curl}_\theta \, \mathbf{A} = \frac{\partial A_r}{\partial z} - \frac{\partial A_z}{\partial r}$$

$$\text{curl}_z \, \mathbf{A} = \frac{1}{r}\frac{\partial}{\partial r}(r A_\theta) - \frac{1}{r}\frac{\partial A_r}{\partial \theta} \tag{12}$$

and in spherical coordinates

$$\text{curl}_r \, \mathbf{A} = \frac{1}{r \sin\theta}\frac{\partial}{\partial \theta}(\sin\theta \, A_\varphi) - \frac{1}{r \sin\theta}\frac{\partial A_\theta}{\partial \varphi}$$

$$\text{curl}_\theta \, \mathbf{A} = \frac{1}{r \sin\theta}\frac{\partial A_r}{\partial \varphi} - \frac{1}{r}\frac{\partial}{\partial r}(r A_\varphi)$$

$$\text{curl}_\varphi \, \mathbf{A} = \frac{1}{r}\frac{\partial}{\partial r}(r A_\theta) - \frac{1}{r}\frac{\partial A_r}{\partial \theta}. \tag{13}$$

Problems

1. Verify directly, from our general formulas, that the divergence of a curl is zero, and the curl of a gradient is zero, in general curvilinear coordinates.

2. Find the formula for the Laplacian of a vector, in general curvilinear coordinates, using the relation curl curl **A** = grad div **A** − ∇^2**A**. Note that the 1, 2, and 3 components of the Laplacian of a vector **A** are not simply the scalar Laplacians, as computed in Eq. (7), of the 1, 2, and 3 components of **A**, respectively.

APPENDIX VIII

PROPERTIES OF BESSEL'S FUNCTIONS

Bessel's equation is

$$\frac{1}{z}\frac{d}{dz}\left(z\frac{dZ}{dz}\right) + \left(1 - \frac{m^2}{z^2}\right)Z = 0$$

and its solutions are $Z = J_m(z)$, $Z = N_m(z)$. By the power-series method, as described in Appendix II, we may show that

$$J_m(z) = \frac{1}{m!}\left(\frac{z}{2}\right)^m - \frac{1}{(m+1)!}\left(\frac{z}{2}\right)^{m+2} + \frac{1}{2!(m+2)!}\left(\frac{z}{2}\right)^{m+4} \cdots$$

where the coefficient of the first term is chosen according to an arbitrary convention. There is no similarly simple expansion for the Neumann function $N_m(z)$; it requires not only terms in positive and negative powers of z, but also logarithmic terms. For $N_0(z)$, the leading term for small values of z is the logarithmic term:

$$\lim_{z\to 0} N_0(z) = \frac{2}{\pi}(\ln z - 0.11593).$$

For the higher values of m, the term in inverse powers of z is the leading term for small z:

$$\lim_{z\to 0} N_m(z) = -\frac{(m-1)!}{\pi}\left(\frac{2}{z}\right)^m, \qquad m > 0.$$

For large values of z, the Bessel and Neumann functions have approximations derived essentially by the W-K-B method, as discussed in Chap. X, Sec. 2. These asymptotic expressions are

$$\lim_{z\to\infty} J_m(z) = \sqrt{\frac{2}{\pi z}}\cos\left(z - \frac{2m+1}{4}\pi\right)$$

$$\lim_{z\to\infty} N_m(z) = \sqrt{\frac{2}{\pi z}}\sin\left(z - \frac{2m+1}{4}\pi\right).$$

An important relation connecting the Bessel and Neumann functions is

$$N_{m-1}(z)J_m(z) - N_m(z)J_{m-1}(z) = \frac{2}{\pi z}.$$

An important relation gives $J_m(z)$ as an integral:

$$J_m(z) = \frac{1}{2\pi j^m} \int_0^{2\pi} e^{jz\cos w} \cos(mw)\, dw,$$

where $j = \sqrt{-1}$.

In addition to these relations, there is a group of important relations which hold equally well for either the Bessel or Neumann functions, and which we shall therefore state in terms of $Z_m(z)$, meaning by this either $J_m(z)$ or $N_m(z)$. For the Bessel functions, most of these relations can be proved without difficulty from the series representation. The relations are more general, however, in that they apply to the Neumann functions as well, and can be proved directly from the properties of the differential equation. They are the following:

$$Z_{m-1}(z) + Z_{m+1}(z) = \frac{2m}{z} Z_m(z)$$

$$Z_{-m}(z) = (-1)^m Z_m(z)$$

$$\frac{d}{dz} Z_m(z) = \frac{1}{2}[Z_{m-1}(z) - Z_{m+1}(z)]$$

$$\frac{d}{dz}[z^m Z_m(z)] = z^m Z_{m-1}(z), \qquad \frac{d}{dz}[z^{-m} Z_m(z)] = -z^{-m} Z_{m+1}(z)$$

$$\int Z_1(z)\, dz = -Z_0(z), \qquad \int z Z_0(z)\, dz = z Z_1(z)$$

$$\int Z_0^2(z) z\, dz = \frac{z^2}{2}[Z_0^2(z) + Z_1^2(z)]$$

$$\int Z_m^2(z) z\, dz = \frac{z^2}{2}[Z_m^2(z) - Z_{m-1}(z) Z_{m+1}(z)].$$

For further information regarding Bessel and Neumann functions, the reader is referred to Jahnke and Emde, *Tables of Functions* (B.G. Teubner, Leipzig, 1933, or Dover Publications, New York, 1943), and to Watson, *Theory of Bessel Functions* (Cambridge University Press). It should be noted that, although all the relations of this appendix hold for integral m, some of them hold for nonintegral m as well.

SUGGESTED REFERENCES

In a single volume like the present one, it is impossible to do justice to the whole of mechanics, and its mathematical foundations. The references that we give in the present section are far from a complete list, but it seems worth while to suggest a few texts to which the student who is familiar with the present book can refer, without too great difficulty.

In the first place, the reader of inadequate preparation may wish to review his elementary mechanics, using for instance *Introduction to Mechanics and Heat*, by N.H. Frank (McGraw-Hill). For general mathematical training and background, the student will first want texts on advanced calculus, such as *Treatise on Advanced Calculus*, by P. Franklin (Wiley), or *Advanced Calculus*, by E.B. Wilson (Ginn). More advanced texts on analysis will be helpful, such as *Mathematical Analysis*, by Goursat and Hedrick (Ginn), *Partielle Differential-gleichungen der Physik*, by Riemann and Weber (Rosenberg), or *Higher Mathematics*, by R.S. Burington and C.C. Torrance (McGraw-Hill). Several texts on mathematics for special purposes are valuable: *Applied Mathematics for Engineers and Physicists*, by L.A. Pipes (McGraw-Hill); *The Mathematics of Physics and Chemistry*, by H. Margenau and G.M. Murphy (Van Nostrand); and *Mathematical Methods for Engineering*, by T. von Kármán and M.A. Biot (McGraw-Hill).

Among more specialized mathematical texts in the fields of particular importance to mechanics are *Introduction to Higher Algebra*, by M. Bôcher (Macmillan); *Ordinary Differential Equations*, by E.L. Ince (Dover); *Fourier Series and Spherical Harmonics*, by W.E. Byerly (Ginn); *Newtonian Potential Function*, by B.O. Peirce (Ginn); *Fourier Series and Boundary Value Problems*, by R.V. Churchill (McGraw-Hill); *Vector Analysis*, by H.B. Phillips (Wiley); and *Vector and Tensor Analysis*, by H.V. Craig (McGraw-Hill). The standard volumes of tables, *A Short Table of Integrals*, by B.O. Peirce (Ginn), and *Funktionentafeln*, by Jahnke and Emde (Dover), will be found invaluable for detailed assistance in calculation. For definite integrals that are not given in these books, *Nouvelles Tables d'Intégrales Définies*, by Bierens de Haan (Stechert), will be found a source of much information.

A number of general texts on theoretical physics cover mechanics among other topics. Among these we may mention *Introduction to Theoretical Physics*, by L. Page (Van Nostrand); *Theoretical Physics*, by G. Joos (Stechert); *Introduction to Theoretical Physics*, by A. Haas (Constable); *Introduction to Mathematical Physics*, by R.A. Houstoun (Longmans); and *Principles of Mathematical Physics*, by W.V. Houston (McGraw-Hill). Two longer treatises on theoretical physics, in several volumes, may also be mentioned: *Introduction to Theoretical Physics*, by M. Planck (Macmillan), an English translation of a well-known German text, and *Einführung in die theoretische Physik*, by C. Schaefer (De Gruyter). The last two works go a good deal more into detail than is possible in the present book.

Next we come to a number of references on the various branches of mechanics. On dynamics, we may enumerate *Dynamics*, by A.G. Webster (Stechert); *A Treatise on Analytical Dynamics*, by E.T. Whittaker (Cambridge); *Dynamics*, by A.S. Ramsey (Cambridge); and *Principles of Mechanics*, by J.L. Synge and B.A. Griffith (McGraw-Hill). Particularly useful for rigid bodies are *Theoretical Mechanics*, by W.D. MacMillan (McGraw-Hill); *Gyrostatics and Rotational Motion*, by A. Gray (Macmillan); and *Elementare Mechanik*, by G. Hamel (B.G. Teubner). For vibrations and sound, a number of references are *Theory of Sound*, by Lord Rayleigh (Dover), a treatise on such a broad basis that it forms practically an introduction to theoretical physics; *The Dynamical Theory of Sound*, by H. Lamb (E. Arnold); *Vibration and Sound*, by P.M. Morse (McGraw-Hill); and *Wave Propagation in Periodic Structures*, by L. Brillouin (McGraw-Hill). Static elasticity is handled in *Mathematical Theory of Elasticity*, by A.E.H. Love (Dover), and *Theory of Elasticity*, by S. Timoshenko (McGraw-Hill). Finally, treatments of hydrodynamics are given in *Hydrodynamics*, by H. Lamb (Cambridge); *Hydromechanics*, by W.H. Besant and A.S. Ramsey (G. Bell); *Physics of Solids and Fluids*, by Ewald, Pöschl, and Prandtl (Blackie); and *Theoretical Hydrodynamics*, by L.M. Milne-Thomson (Macmillan).

INDEX

A

Admittance, 31, 33
Alpha particle, scattering of, 65
Angles, Euler's, 104, 107–120
Angular momentum, 56, 73
 of rotating rigid body, 92–120
Angular rotation, lack of vector character of, 102–104
Anharmonic oscillator, 40, 42
Approximate solution for nonuniform string, 183–186
Archimedes' principle, 230, 236
Aristotle, 1
Artificial electric line, analogy to weighted string, 151, 178
Associated Legendre polynomials, or associated spherical harmonics, 205
Atwood's machine, 86
Axis of rotation, instantaneous, 95–96

B

Beats, 35, 168
Bent beam, 222
Bernoulli's equation, 232–233
Bessel's equation and function, 181, 200–204, 240–241, 251–252, 288–289
Body forces, in elasticity, 206
 in hydrodynamics, 230
Boundary conditions, for circular membrane, 200–204
 for rectangular membrane, 197
 for string, 148, 175, 185–186

C

Center of mass, 91
Central field, motion in, 52–68
Centrifugal force, 57
Circular membrane, 199–204

Coefficients, of Fourier series, 150, 279–284
 of viscosity, 233
Combination tones, 42
Complex exponentials and complex numbers, 26, 255–257
Compressibility of elastic solid, 214–217
Conductance, 31
Conservation of energy, 13–16, 46–52, 77
Conservative system, condition for, 13, 46–52
Constraints, 70, 79
Continuity, equation of, 226–227
Continuous medium, 206–237
Convergence, of Fourier series, 281
 of power series, 244–250
Coordinates, curvilinear, vector operations in, 285–287
Copernicus, 1
Coriolis force, 56
Coulomb's law, 53–54
Coupled systems, 122–140
Curl, in curvilinear coordinates, 286
 of a vector, 148, 231–232, 266
Curvilinear coordinates, 285–287

D

Damping, critical, 25
 logarithmic, 27
 of vibrating string, 160–161
Decrement, logarithmic, 27, 29
Deformation of elastic solid, 211–215
Degeneracy, in circular membrane, 202
 in coupled oscillators, 135–136
 in square membrane, 204
Degrees of freedom, 70
Determinant, 127, 275
Difference equations, 239–242
Differential analyzer, 8